GCSE
Biology

Complete Revision
and Practice

198367

570 CGP

Contents

Contents

Published by Coordination Group Publications Ltd

Editors:
Ellen Bowness, Tim Burne, Tom Cain, Katherine Craig, Mary Falkner, Gemma Hallam,
Sarah Hilton, Kate Houghton, Sharon Keeley, Andy Park, Rose Parkin, Kate Redmond,
Alan Rix, Rachel Selway, Ami Snelling, Claire Thompson, Jane Towle, Julie Wakeling.

Contributors:
James Foster, Sandy Gardner, Julian Hardwick, Derek Harvey, Richard Parsons,
Steven Phillips, Claire Reed, Philip Rushworth, Adrian Schmit, Claire Stebbing.

*Data used to construct graph on page 98 taken from Etheridge et al, 1998.
Historical CO_2 records from the Law Dome DE08, DE08-2, and DSS ice cores.*

With thanks to Sue Hocking for the proofreading.

With thanks to Laura Phillips for the copyright research.

ISBN: 978 1 84146 656 9

Groovy website: www.cgpbooks.co.uk

Printed by Elanders Hindson Ltd, Newcastle upon Tyne.
Jolly bits of clipart from CorelDRAW®

Theories Come, Theories Go

SCIENTISTS ARE ALWAYS RIGHT — OR ARE THEY?

Well it'd be nice if that were so, but it just ain't — never has been and never will be. Increasing scientific knowledge involves making mistakes along the way. Let me explain...

Scientists come up with **hypotheses** — then **test** them

1) Scientists try and <u>explain</u> things. Everything.

2) They start by <u>observing</u> or <u>thinking about</u> something they don't understand — it could be anything, e.g. planets in the sky, a person suffering from an illness, what matter is made of... anything.

3) Then, using what they already know (plus a bit of insight), they come up with a <u>hypothesis</u> (a <u>theory</u>) that could <u>explain</u> what they've observed.

Hundreds of years ago, we thought demons caused illness.

> Remember, a hypothesis is just a <u>theory</u>, a <u>belief</u>. And <u>believing</u> something is true doesn't <u>make</u> it true — not even if you're a scientist.

4) So the next step is to try and convince other scientists that the hypothesis is right — which involves using <u>evidence</u>. First, the hypothesis has to fit the <u>evidence</u> already available — if it doesn't, it'll convince <u>no one</u>.

5) Next, the scientist might use the hypothesis to make a <u>prediction</u> — a crucial step. If the hypothesis predicts something, and then <u>evidence</u> from <u>experiments</u> backs that up, that's pretty convincing.

> This <u>doesn't</u> mean the hypothesis is <u>true</u> (the 2nd prediction, or the 3rd, 4th or 25th one might turn out to be <u>wrong</u>) — but a hypothesis that correctly predicts something in the <u>future</u> deserves respect.

A hypothesis is a good place to start

You might have thought that science was all about facts... well, it's not as cut and dried as that — you also need to know about the process that theories go through to become accepted, and how those theories change over time. Remember, nothing is set in stone...

Theories Come, Theories Go

Other scientists will **test** the hypotheses too

1) Now then... <u>other</u> scientists will want to use the hypothesis to make their <u>own predictions</u>, and they'll carry out their <u>own experiments</u>. (They'll also try to <u>reproduce</u> earlier results.) And if all the experiments in all the world back up the hypothesis, then scientists start to have a lot of <u>faith</u> in it.

2) However, if a scientist somewhere in the world does an experiment that <u>doesn't</u> fit with the hypothesis (and other scientists can <u>reproduce</u> these results), then the hypothesis is in trouble. When this happens, scientists have to come up with a new hypothesis (maybe a <u>modification</u> of the old theory, or maybe a completely <u>new</u> one).

3) This process of testing a hypothesis to destruction is a vital part of the scientific process. Without the '<u>healthy scepticism</u>' of scientists everywhere, we'd still believe the first theories that people came up with — like thunder being the belchings of an angered god (or whatever).

Then we thought it was caused by 'bad blood' (and treated it with leeches).

If **evidence** supports a hypothesis, it's **accepted** — for now

1) If pretty much every scientist in the world believes a hypothesis to be true because experiments back it up, then it usually goes in the <u>textbooks</u> for students to learn.

Now we know most illnesses are due to microorganisms.

2) Our <u>currently accepted</u> theories are the ones that have survived this 'trial by evidence' — they've been tested many, many times over the years and survived (while the less good ones have been ditched).

3) However... they never, <u>never</u> become hard and fast, totally indisputable <u>fact</u>.

> You can never know... it'd only take <u>one</u> odd, totally inexplicable result, and the hypothesising and testing would start all over again.

You expect me to believe that — then show me the evidence

If scientists think something is true, they need to produce evidence to convince others — it's all part of <u>testing a hypothesis</u>. One hypothesis might survive these tests, while others won't — it's how things progress. And along the way some hypotheses will be disproved — i.e. shown not to be true. So, you see... not everything scientists say is true. <u>It's how science works</u>.

Your Data's Got to Be Good

Evidence is the key to science — but not all evidence is equally good.
The way that evidence is gathered can have a big effect on how trustworthy it is.

Lab experiments are better than rumour or small samples

1) Results from controlled experiments in laboratories are great. A lab is the easiest place to control variables so that they're all kept constant (except for the one you're investigating).

   This makes it easier to carry out a fair test.

   It's also the easiest way for different scientists around the world to carry out the same experiments. (There are things you can't study in a lab though, like climate.)

2) Old wives' tales, rumours, hearsay, 'what someone said', and so on, should be taken with a pinch of salt. They'd need to be tested in controlled conditions to be genuinely scientific.

3) Data based on samples that are too small don't have much more credibility that rumours do.

   A sample should be representative of the whole population (i.e. it should share as many of the various characteristics in the whole population as possible) — a small sample just can't do that.

Evidence is only reliable if other people can repeat it

Scientific evidence needs to be reliable (or reproducible). If it isn't, then it doesn't really help.

RELIABLE means that the data can be reproduced by others.

Example: Cold fusion

In 1989, two scientists claimed that they'd produced 'cold fusion' (the energy source of the Sun — but without the enormous temperatures).

It was huge news — if true, this could have meant energy from sea water — the ideal energy solution for the world... forever.

However, other scientists just couldn't get the same results — i.e. the results weren't reliable. And until they are, 'cold fusion' isn't going to be generally accepted as fact.

Reliability is really important in science
The scientific community won't accept someone's data if it can't be repeated by anyone else. It may sound like a really fantastic new theory, but if there's no other support for it, it just isn't reliable.

Your Data's Got to Be Good

Evidence also needs to be *valid*

To answer scientific questions scientists often try to <u>link</u> changes in <u>one</u> variable with changes in <u>another</u>. This is useful evidence, as long as it's <u>valid</u>.

VALID means that the data is <u>reliable</u> AND <u>answers the original question</u>.

Example: Do power lines cause cancer?

Some studies have found that children who live near <u>overhead power lines</u> are more likely to develop <u>cancer</u>. What they'd actually found was a correlation between the variables "<u>presence of power lines</u>" and "<u>incidence of cancer</u>" — they found that as one changed, so did the other.

But this evidence is <u>not enough</u> to say that the power lines <u>cause</u> cancer, as other explanations might be possible.

For example, power lines are often near <u>busy roads</u>, so the areas tested could contain <u>different levels</u> of <u>pollution</u> from traffic. Also, you need to look at types of neighbourhoods and <u>lifestyles</u> of people living in the tested areas (could diet be a factor... or something else you hadn't thought of...).

So these studies don't show a definite link and so don't <u>answer the original question</u>.

Controlling all the variables is *really hard*

In reality, it's <u>very hard</u> to control <u>all the variables</u> that might (just might) be having an effect.

You can do things to help — e.g. <u>choose</u> two <u>groups</u> of people (those near power lines and those far away) who are <u>as similar as possible</u> (same mix of ages, same mix of diets etc.). But you can't easily rule out every possibility.

If you could do a <u>properly controlled lab experiment</u>, that'd be better — but you just can't do it without cloning people and exposing them to things that might cause cancer... <u>hardly ethical</u>.

Does the data really say that?

If it's so hard to be <u>definite</u> about anything, how does anybody <u>ever</u> get convinced about anything? Well, what usually happens is that you get a <u>load</u> of evidence that all points the same way. If one study can't rule out a particular possibility, then maybe another one can. So you gradually build up a whole <u>body of evidence</u>, and it's this (rather than any single study) that <u>convinces people</u>.

Bias and How to Spot it

Scientific results are often used to make a point, but results are sometimes presented in a biased way.

You don't need to *lie* to make things **biased**

1) For something to be misleading, it doesn't have to be untrue. We tend to read scientific facts and assume that they're the 'truth', but there are many different sides to the truth. Look at this headline...

> **1 in 2 people are of above average weight** ⇐ *Sounds like we're a nation of fatties.*

2) But an average is a kind of 'middle value' of all your data. Some readings are higher than average (about half of them, usually). Others will be lower than average (the other half).

So the above headline could just as accurately say: ⇒ **1 in 2 people are of below average weight**

3) The point is... both headlines sound quite worrying, even though they're not. That's the thing... you can easily make something sound really good or really bad — even if it isn't. You can...

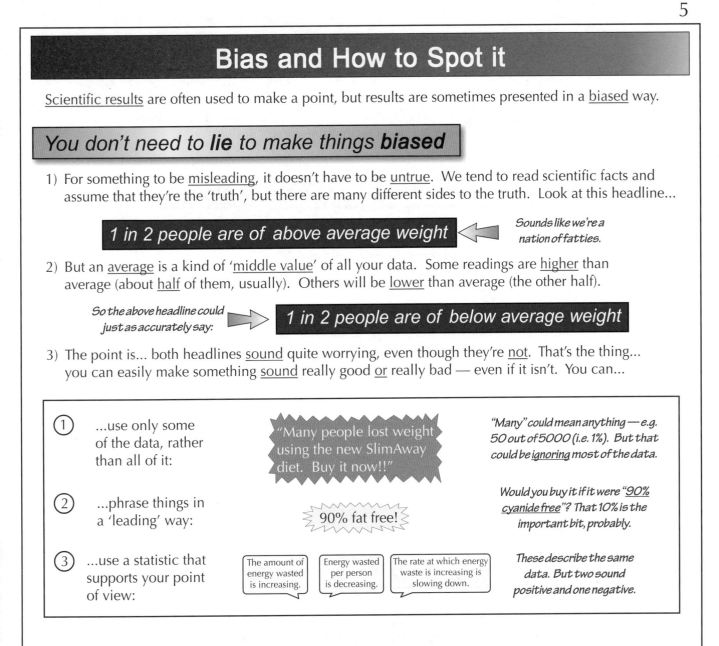

① ...use only some of the data, rather than all of it:

"Many people lost weight using the new SlimAway diet. Buy it now!!"

"Many" could mean anything — e.g. 50 out of 5000 (i.e. 1%). But that could be ignoring most of the data.

② ...phrase things in a 'leading' way:

90% fat free!

Would you buy it if it were "90% cyanide free"? That 10% is the important bit, probably.

③ ...use a statistic that supports your point of view:

The amount of energy wasted is increasing.

Energy wasted per person is decreasing.

The rate at which energy waste is increasing is slowing down.

These describe the same data. But two sound positive and one negative.

Think about *why* things *might* be **biased**

1) People who want to make a point can sometimes present data in a biased way to suit their own purposes (sometimes without knowing they're doing it).

2) And there are all sorts of reasons why people might want to do this — for example...

- Governments might want to persuade voters, other governments, journalists, etc. Evidence might be ignored if it could create political problems, or emphasised if it helps their cause.
- Companies might want to 'big up' their products. Or make impressive safety claims, maybe.
- Environmental campaigners might want to persuade people to behave differently.

3) People do it all the time. This is why any scientific evidence has to be looked at carefully. Are there any reasons for thinking the evidence is biased in some way?

- Does the experimenter (or the person writing about it) stand to gain (or lose) anything?
- Might someone have ignored some of the data for political or commercial reasons?
- Is someone using their reputation rather than evidence to help make their case?

Scientific data's not always misleading, you just need to be careful. The most credible argument will be the one that describes all the data that was found, and gives the most balanced view of it.

Science Has Limits

Science can give us amazing things —cures for diseases, space travel, heated toilet seats...
But science has its limitations — there are questions that it just can't answer.

Some questions are **unanswered** by science — so far

1) We don't understand everything. And we never will. We'll find out more, for sure — as more
hypotheses are suggested, and more experiments are done.
But there'll always be stuff we don't know.

> For example, today we don't know as much as we'd like about
> climate change (global warming). Is climate change definitely
> happening? And to what extent is it caused by humans?

2) These are complicated questions, and at the moment scientists don't all agree on the answers.
But eventually, we probably will be able to answer these questions once and for all.

3) But by then there'll be loads of new questions to answer.

Other questions are **unanswerable** by science

1) Then there's the other type... questions that all the experiments in the world won't
help us to answer — the "Should we be doing this at all?" type questions.
There are always two sides...

> The question of whether something is morally or ethically right
> or wrong can't be answered by more experiments — there is
> no "right" or "wrong" answer.

2) The best we can do is get a consensus from society — a judgement that most people are
more or less happy to live by. Science can provide more information to help people
make this judgement, and the judgement might change over time. But in the end it's up
to people and their conscience.

To answer or not to answer, that is the question
It's official — no one knows everything. Your teacher/mum/annoying older sister (delete as applicable)
might think and act as if they know it all, but sadly they don't. So in reality you know one thing they
don't — which clearly makes you more intelligent and generally far superior in every way. Possibly.

Science Has Limits

People have **different opinions** about **ethical questions**

1) Take embryo screening (which allows you to choose an embryo with particular characteristics). It's possible to do it — but does that mean we should?

2) Different people have different opinions. For example...

- Some people say it's good... couples whose existing child needs a bone marrow transplant, but who can't find a donor, will be able to have another child selected for its matching bone marrow. This would save the life of their first child — and if they want another child anyway... where's the harm?

- Other people say it's bad... they say it could have serious effects on the child. In the above example the new child might feel unwanted — thinking they were only brought into the world to help someone else. And would they have the right to refuse to donate their bone marrow (as anyone else would)?

Loads of other **factors** can **influence decisions** too

Here are some other factors that can influence decisions about science, and the way science is used:

Economic factors

- Companies very often won't pay for research unless there's likely to be a profit in it.

- Society can't always afford to do things scientists recommend without cutting back elsewhere (e.g. investing heavily in alternative energy sources).

Social factors

- Decisions based on scientific evidence affect people — e.g. should fossil fuels be taxed more highly (to invest in alternative energy)? Should alcohol be banned (to prevent health problems)? Would the effect on people's lifestyles be acceptable...

Environmental factors

- Genetically modified crops may help us produce more food — but some people say they could cause environmental problems (see page 88).

Science is a "real-world" subject

Science isn't just done by people in white coats in labs who have no effect on the outside world. Science has a massive effect on the real world every day, and so real-life things like money, morals and how people might react need to be considered. It's why a lot of issues are so difficult to solve.

The Nervous System

The nervous system is what lets you react to what goes on around you, so you'd find life tough without it.

Sense organs detect *stimuli*

A stimulus is a change in your environment which you may need to react to (e.g. a recently pounced tiger). You need to be constantly monitoring what's going on so you can respond if you need to.

1) You have five different sense organs — eyes, ears, nose, tongue and skin.

2) They all contain different receptors. Receptors are groups of cells which are sensitive to a stimulus. They change stimulus energy (e.g. light energy) into electrical impulses.

3) A stimulus can be light, sound, touch, pressure, pain, chemical, or a change in position or temperature.

Sense organs and receptors
Don't get them mixed up:

The eye is a sense organ — it contains light receptors.
The ear is a sense organ — it contains sound receptors.

The five sense organs and the receptors that each contains:

1) Eyes　Light receptors.

2) Ears　Sound and "balance" receptors.

3) Nose　Smell receptors — sensitive to chemical stimuli.

4) Tongue　Taste receptors: — sensitive to bitter, salt, sweet and sour, plus the taste of savoury things like monosodium glutamate (MSG) — chemical stimuli.

5) Skin
Sensitive to touch, pressure and temperature change.

Sensory neurones
The nerve cells that carry signals as electrical impulses from the receptors in the sense organs to the central nervous system.

Motor neurones
The nerve cells that carry signals to the effector muscles or glands.

The *central nervous system* coordinates a *response*

1) The central nervous system (CNS) is where all the information from the sense organs is sent, and where reflexes and actions are coordinated.

The central nervous system consists of the brain and spinal cord only.

2) Neurones (nerve cells) transmit the information (as electrical impulses) very quickly to and from the CNS.

3) 'Instructions' from the CNS are sent to the effectors (muscles and glands), which respond accordingly.

Effectors
Muscles and glands are known as effectors. They respond in different ways — muscles contract in response to a nervous impulse, whereas glands secrete hormones.

Nervous System = 5 sense organs + neurones + brain + spinal cord

In the exam, you might have to take what you know about a human and apply it to a horse (easy... sound receptors in its ears, light receptors in its eyes, etc.), or to a snake (so if you're told that certain types of snakes have heat receptors in nostril-like pits on their head, you should know what type of stimulus those pits are sensitive to).

Reflexes

Your brain can <u>decide</u> how to respond to a stimulus <u>pretty quickly</u>.
But sometimes waiting for your brain to make a decision is just <u>too slow</u>. That's why you have <u>reflexes</u>.

Reflexes help prevent *injury*

1) <u>Reflexes</u> are <u>automatic</u> responses to certain stimuli — they can reduce the chances of being injured.

2) For example, if someone shines a <u>bright light</u> in your eyes, your <u>pupils</u> automatically get smaller so that less light gets into the eye — this stops it getting <u>damaged</u>.

3) Or if you get a shock, your body releases the <u>hormone</u> adrenaline automatically — it doesn't wait for you to <u>decide</u> that you're shocked.

4) The route taken by the information in a reflex (from receptor to effector) is called a <u>reflex arc</u>.

The **reflex arc** goes through the **central nervous system**

1) The neurones in reflex arcs go through the <u>spinal cord</u> or through an <u>unconscious part of the brain</u>.

2) When a <u>stimulus</u> (e.g. a painful bee sting) is detected by receptors, an impulse is sent along a <u>sensory neurone</u> to the CNS.

3) In the CNS the sensory neurone passes on the message to another type of neurone — a <u>relay neurone</u>.

4) The relay neurone <u>relays</u> the impulse to a <u>motor neurone</u>.

5) The impulse then travels along the motor neurone to the <u>effector</u> (in the example below it's a muscle).

6) The muscle responds by <u>contracting</u>. A gland responds by <u>secreting</u>.

7) Because you don't have to think about the response (which takes time) it's <u>quicker</u> than normal responses.

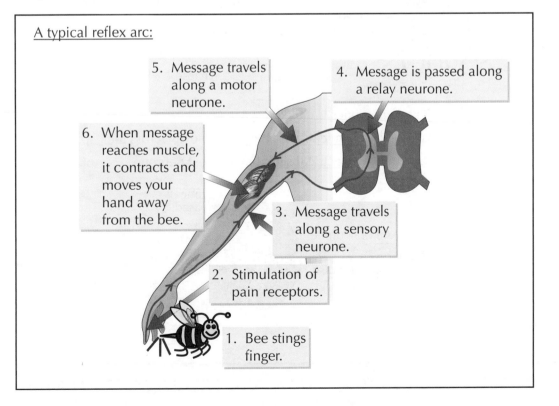

A typical reflex arc:

5. Message travels along a motor neurone.

4. Message is passed along a relay neurone.

6. When message reaches muscle, it contracts and moves your hand away from the bee.

3. Message travels along a sensory neurone.

2. Stimulation of pain receptors.

1. Bee stings finger.

Reflexes

Make sure you've learnt the order of a reflex arc.

Stimulus, receptor, neurones, effector, response

Here's a block diagram of a reflex arc — it shows what happens, from stimulus to response.

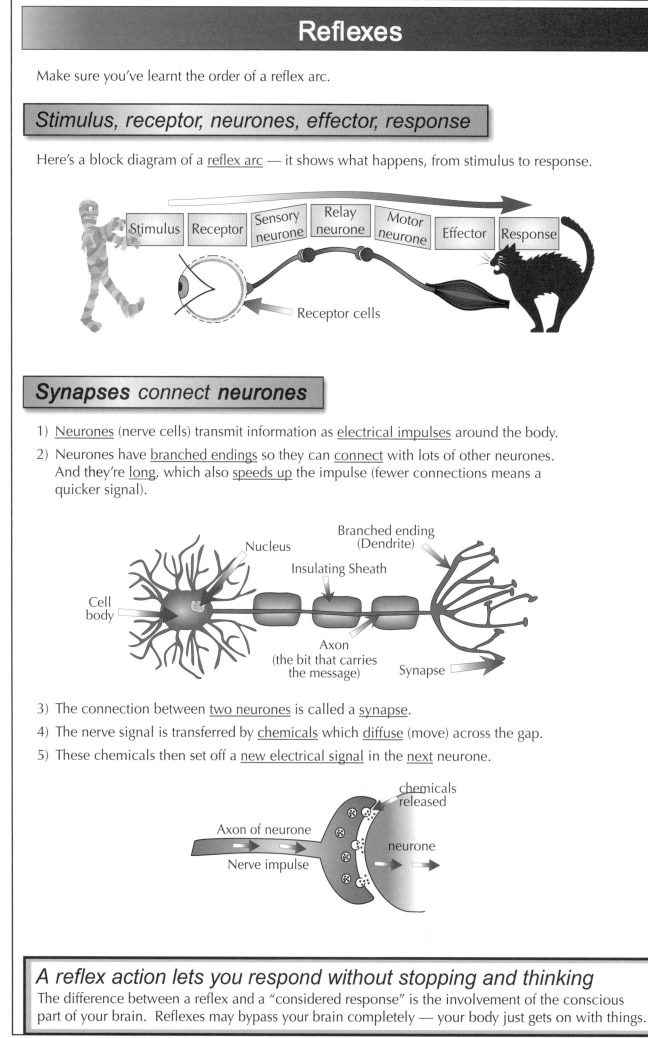

Stimulus | Receptor | Sensory neurone | Relay neurone | Motor neurone | Effector | Response

Receptor cells

Synapses connect neurones

1) Neurones (nerve cells) transmit information as electrical impulses around the body.

2) Neurones have branched endings so they can connect with lots of other neurones. And they're long, which also speeds up the impulse (fewer connections means a quicker signal).

Nucleus

Branched ending (Dendrite)

Insulating Sheath

Cell body

Axon (the bit that carries the message)

Synapse

3) The connection between two neurones is called a synapse.

4) The nerve signal is transferred by chemicals which diffuse (move) across the gap.

5) These chemicals then set off a new electrical signal in the next neurone.

chemicals released

Axon of neurone

Nerve impulse

neurone

A reflex action lets you respond without stopping and thinking

The difference between a reflex and a "considered response" is the involvement of the conscious part of your brain. Reflexes may bypass your brain completely — your body just gets on with things.

The Eye

The eye's a good example of a sense organ...

Learn **the eye** with all its labels:

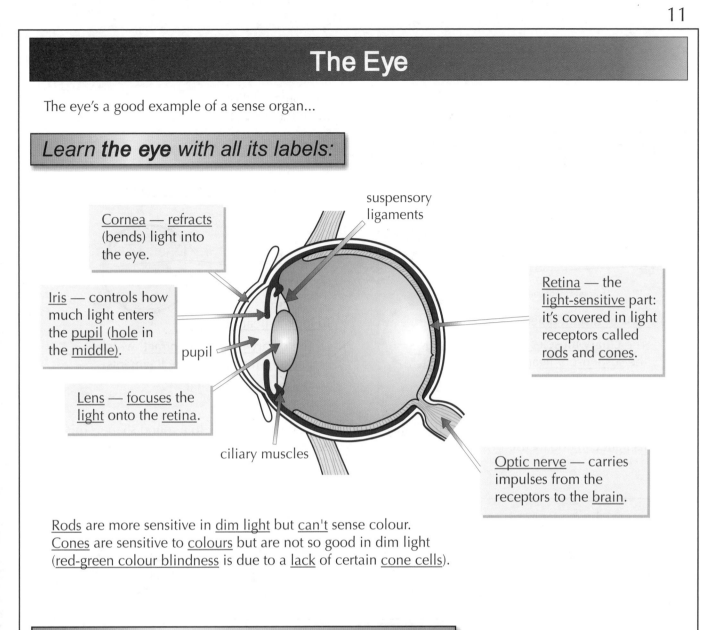

Cornea — refracts (bends) light into the eye.

Iris — controls how much light enters the pupil (hole in the middle).

pupil

Lens — focuses the light onto the retina.

ciliary muscles

suspensory ligaments

Retina — the light-sensitive part: it's covered in light receptors called rods and cones.

Optic nerve — carries impulses from the receptors to the brain.

Rods are more sensitive in dim light but can't sense colour.
Cones are sensitive to colours but are not so good in dim light
(red-green colour blindness is due to a lack of certain cone cells).

The **iris reflex** — adjusting for **bright light**

Very bright light can damage the retina — so you have a reflex to protect it.

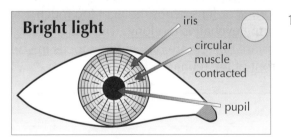

Bright light

iris

circular muscle contracted

pupil

1) Very bright light triggers a reflex that makes the pupil smaller, allowing less light in. (See p.9 for more about reflexes... but basically, light receptors detect the bright light, send a message to an unconscious part of the brain along a sensory neurone, and then the brain sends a message straight back along a motor neurone telling the circular muscles in the iris to contract, which makes the pupil smaller.)

2) The opposite process happens in dim light. This time, the brain tells the radial muscles to contract, which makes the pupil bigger.

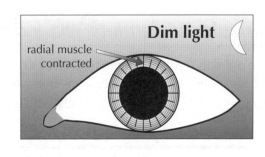

Dim light

radial muscle contracted

The Eye

This page is all about the ciliary muscles and their role in accommodation.
Not to be confused with the circular muscles and their role in the iris reflex...

Focusing on near and distant objects — another reflex

The eye focuses light by changing the <u>shape</u> of the <u>lens</u> — this is known as <u>accommodation</u>.

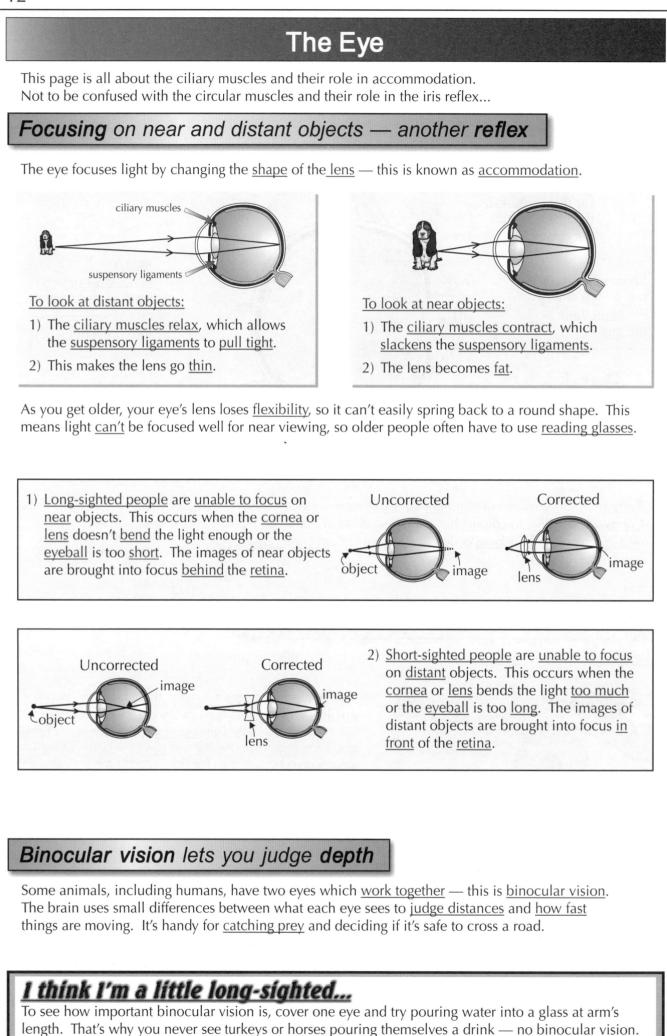

To look at distant objects:

1) The <u>ciliary muscles relax</u>, which allows the <u>suspensory ligaments</u> to <u>pull tight</u>.

2) This makes the lens go <u>thin</u>.

To look at near objects:

1) The <u>ciliary muscles contract</u>, which <u>slackens</u> the <u>suspensory ligaments</u>.

2) The lens becomes <u>fat</u>.

As you get older, your eye's lens loses <u>flexibility</u>, so it can't easily spring back to a round shape. This means light <u>can't</u> be focused well for near viewing, so older people often have to use <u>reading glasses</u>.

1) <u>Long-sighted people</u> are <u>unable to focus</u> on <u>near</u> objects. This occurs when the <u>cornea</u> or <u>lens</u> doesn't <u>bend</u> the light enough or the <u>eyeball</u> is too <u>short</u>. The images of near objects are brought into focus <u>behind</u> the <u>retina</u>.

Uncorrected   Corrected

2) <u>Short-sighted people</u> are <u>unable to focus</u> on <u>distant</u> objects. This occurs when the <u>cornea</u> or <u>lens</u> bends the light <u>too much</u> or the <u>eyeball</u> is too <u>long</u>. The images of distant objects are brought into focus <u>in front</u> of the <u>retina</u>.

Uncorrected   Corrected

Binocular vision lets you judge depth

Some animals, including humans, have two eyes which <u>work together</u> — this is <u>binocular vision</u>. The brain uses small differences between what each eye sees to <u>judge distances</u> and <u>how fast</u> things are moving. It's handy for <u>catching prey</u> and deciding if it's safe to cross a road.

I think I'm a little long-sighted...

To see how important binocular vision is, cover one eye and try pouring water into a glass at arm's length. That's why you never see turkeys or horses pouring themselves a drink — no binocular vision.

Warm-Up and Exam Questions

Welcome to the first page of questions. I reckon you'll realise pretty soon how important these are.

Warm-Up Questions

1) What are the five sense organs in the human body?
2) What is the role of the central nervous system (CNS)?
3) In what form is information transmitted along nerve cells?
4) What name is given to the gap between two nerve cells?
5) The eye can focus on near objects and on distant objects by changing the shape of the lens. What is this known as?
6) Why is it an advantage to have binocular vision?

Exam Questions

1   Gordon accidentally touches a hot object, causing his hand to immediately move away from it. The diagram below shows some of the parts involved in this response.

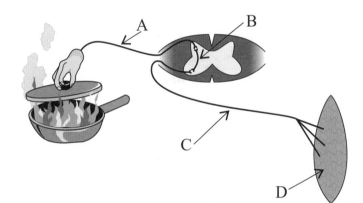

(a) What is the name of this type of automatic response?

(1 mark)

(b) On the diagram:

   (i) Which letter points to a relay neurone?

(1 mark)

   (ii) Which letter points to an effector?

(1 mark)

(c) Explain how an electrical impulse in one neurone is able to pass to the next neurone.

(2 marks)

(d) Give one physiological advantage, to the body, of these automatic responses.

(1 mark)

2   (a) Explain how the iris reflex can reduce the amount of light entering the eye.

(4 marks)

(b) What is the advantage of this reflex?

(1 mark)

Hormones

The other way to send information around the body (apart from along nerves) is by using hormones.

Hormones are chemical messengers sent in the blood

1) Hormones are chemicals released directly into the blood. They're carried in the blood plasma to other parts of the body, but only affect particular cells (called target cells) in particular places. Hormones control things in organs and cells that need constant adjustment.

2) Hormones are produced in various glands, as shown on the diagram. They travel through your body at "the speed of blood".

3) Hormones tend to have relatively long-lasting effects.

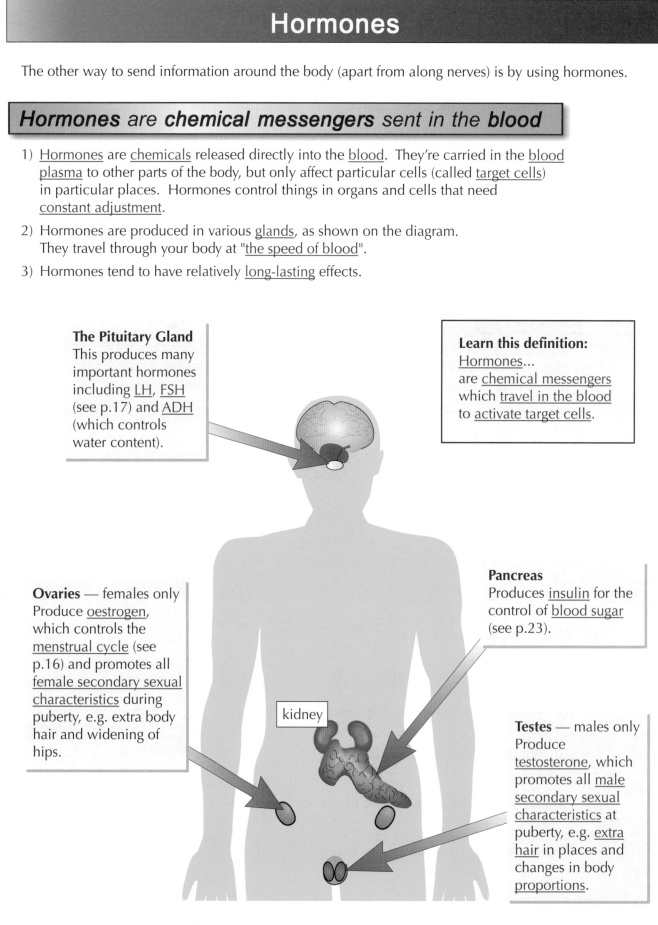

The Pituitary Gland
This produces many important hormones including LH, FSH (see p.17) and ADH (which controls water content).

Learn this definition:
Hormones...
are chemical messengers which travel in the blood to activate target cells.

Ovaries — females only
Produce oestrogen, which controls the menstrual cycle (see p.16) and promotes all female secondary sexual characteristics during puberty, e.g. extra body hair and widening of hips.

Pancreas
Produces insulin for the control of blood sugar (see p.23).

kidney

Testes — males only
Produce testosterone, which promotes all male secondary sexual characteristics at puberty, e.g. extra hair in places and changes in body proportions.

These are just examples — there are loads more, each doing its own thing.

Hormonal and Nervous Responses

You'll be expected to be able to compare nervous responses with hormonal ones, so have a look at this...

Hormones and *nerves* do similar jobs, but there are *differences*

Nerves

1) Very <u>fast</u> message.

2) Act for a very <u>short time</u>.

3) Act on a very <u>precise</u> area.

4) <u>Electrical</u> message.

Hormones

1) <u>Slower</u> message.

2) Act for a <u>long time</u>.

3) Act in a more <u>general</u> way.

4) <u>Chemical</u> message.

If you're not sure whether a response is nervous or hormonal, have a think about the <u>speed</u>, <u>longevity</u> and <u>affected area</u>...

If the response is really quick, it's probably nervous

Some information needs to be passed to effectors <u>really quickly</u> (e.g. <u>pain</u> signals, or information from your <u>eyes</u> telling you about the <u>lion</u> heading your way), so it's no good using hormones to carry the message — they're <u>too slow</u>.

But if a response lasts for a long time, it's probably hormonal

For example, when you get a <u>shock</u>, a hormone called <u>adrenaline</u> is released into the bloodstream (causing the fight-or-flight response, where your body is hyped up ready for action). You can tell it's a hormonal response (even though it kicks in pretty quickly) because you feel a bit <u>wobbly</u> for a while <u>afterwards</u>.

Learn the differences between nervous and hormonal responses

Hormones control various organs and cells in the body, though they tend to control things that aren't immediately life-threatening. For example, they take care of most things to do with sexual development, pregnancy, birth, breast-feeding, blood sugar levels, water content... and so on.

Puberty and the Menstrual Cycle

Hormones control almost everything to do with <u>sex</u> and <u>reproduction</u>.

Hormones promote *sexual characteristics* at *puberty*

At puberty your body starts releasing <u>sex hormones</u> — <u>testosterone</u> in men and <u>oestrogen</u> in women. These trigger off the <u>secondary sexual characteristics</u>:

In men

1) <u>Extra hair</u> on face and body.
2) <u>Muscles develop</u>.
3) <u>Penis and testicles</u> enlarge.
4) <u>Sperm</u> production.
5) <u>Deepening</u> of <u>voice</u>.

In women

1) <u>Extra hair</u> on underarms and pubic area.
2) <u>Hips widen</u>.
3) Development of <u>breasts</u>.
4) <u>Egg release</u> and <u>periods start</u>.

The *menstrual cycle* has *four stages*

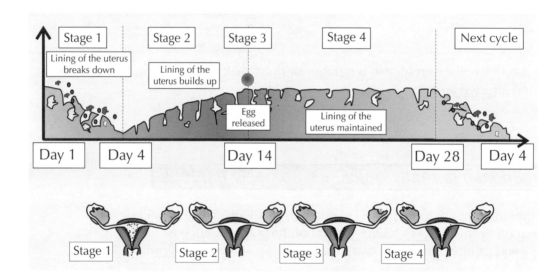

Stage 1

<u>Day 1 is when the bleeding starts</u>.
The uterus lining breaks down for about four days.

Stage 2

<u>The lining of the uterus builds up again</u>, from day 4 to day 14, into a thick spongy layer full of blood vessels, ready to receive a fertilised egg.

Stage 3

<u>An egg is developed and then released</u> from the ovary at day 14.

Stage 4

<u>The wall is then maintained</u> for about 14 days, until day 28. If no fertilised egg has landed on the uterus wall by day 28, the spongy lining starts to break down and the whole cycle starts again.

Puberty and the Menstrual Cycle

There are only a few hormones you need to know about in this section,
and apart from insulin, they're all on this page...

The *menstrual cycle's* controlled by *four hormones*

1. FSH (follicle-stimulating hormone)

1) Causes an <u>egg to develop</u> in one of the ovaries.
2) Stimulates the <u>ovaries</u> to produce <u>oestrogen</u>.

Produced in the <u>pituitary gland</u>.

2. LH (luteinising hormone)

Stimulates the <u>release of an
egg</u> at day 14.

Produced in the <u>pituitary gland</u>.

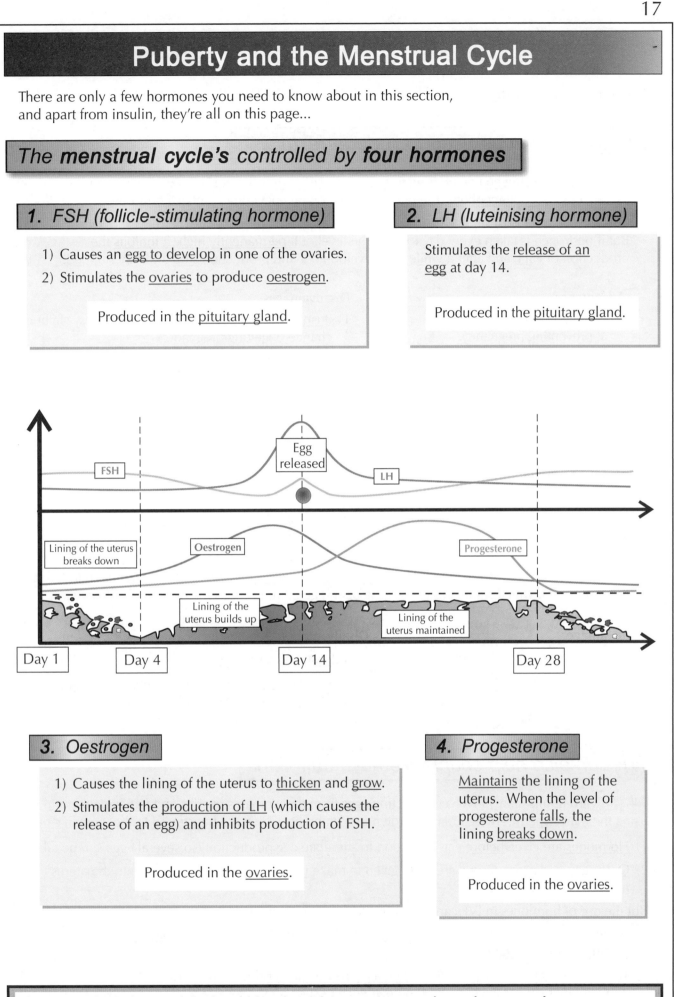

3. Oestrogen

1) Causes the lining of the uterus to <u>thicken</u> and <u>grow</u>.
2) Stimulates the <u>production of LH</u> (which causes the release of an egg) and inhibits production of FSH.

Produced in the <u>ovaries</u>.

4. Progesterone

<u>Maintains</u> the lining of the uterus. When the level of progesterone <u>falls</u>, the lining <u>breaks down</u>.

Produced in the <u>ovaries</u>.

OK, I admit it — this is quite hard to get your head around

In the exam, you might have to explain what hormone causes what in the menstrual cycle. It's tough, because they're all interlinked... but if you know your stuff, it should be quite straight forward.

Controlling Fertility

The hormones <u>FSH</u>, <u>oestrogen</u> and <u>LH</u> can be used to change artificially <u>how fertile</u> a woman is.

Hormones *can be used to* reduce fertility*...*

1) The hormone <u>oestrogen</u> can be used to <u>prevent</u> the <u>release</u> of an <u>egg</u> — so oestrogen can be used as a method of <u>contraception</u>. <u>The pill</u> is an oral contraceptive that contains oestrogen.

2) This may seem kind of strange (since naturally oestrogen helps stimulate the release of eggs). But if oestrogen is taken <u>every day</u> to keep the level of it <u>permanently high</u>, it <u>inhibits</u> the production of <u>FSH</u>, and <u>after a while</u> egg development and production <u>stop</u> and stay stopped.

Advantages

1) The pill's <u>over 99% effective</u> at preventing pregnancy.

2) It <u>reduces</u> the <u>risk</u> of getting some types of <u>cancer</u>.

Disadvantages

1) It <u>isn't 100% effective</u> — there's still a very slight chance of getting pregnant.

2) It can cause <u>side effects</u> like headaches, nausea, irregular menstrual bleeding, and fluid retention.

3) It <u>doesn't protect</u> against <u>sexually transmitted infections</u> (STIs).

...or increase it

1) Some women have levels of <u>FSH</u> that are <u>too low</u> to cause their <u>eggs to mature</u>. This means that <u>no eggs are released</u> and the women <u>can't get pregnant</u>.

2) The hormone FSH can be taken by these women to stimulate <u>egg production</u> in their <u>ovaries</u>. (Well, in reality... FSH stimulates the <u>ovaries</u> to produce <u>oestrogen</u>, which stimulates the pituitary gland to produce LH, which stimulates the <u>release of an egg</u>... but FSH has the desired effect anyway.)

Advantage

It helps a lot of women to <u>get pregnant</u> when previously they couldn't... pretty obvious.

Disadvantages

1) It <u>doesn't always work</u>.

2) <u>Too many eggs</u> could be stimulated, resulting in unexpected <u>multiple pregnancies</u> (twins, triplets etc.).

IVF *can also help couples to have* children

IVF ("in vitro fertilisation") involves collecting <u>eggs</u> from the woman's <u>ovaries</u> and <u>fertilising</u> them in a <u>lab</u> using the man's <u>sperm</u>. These are then grown into <u>embryos</u>, which are <u>transferred</u> to the woman's uterus.

1) <u>Hormones</u> are given <u>before</u> egg collection to stimulate egg production (so <u>several</u> eggs can be taken).

2) <u>Oestrogen</u> and <u>progesterone</u> are often given to make <u>implantation</u> of the embryo into the uterus more likely to succeed.

But the use of hormones in IVF can cause problems for some women...

1) Some women have a very strong <u>reaction</u> to the hormones — including <u>abdominal pain</u>, <u>vomiting</u> and <u>dehydration</u>.

2) There have been some reports of an <u>increased risk of cancer</u> due to the hormonal treatment (though other studies have reported no evidence of such a risk).

Warm-Up and Exam Questions

You could skim through this page in a few minutes, but there's no point unless you check over any bits you don't know and make sure you understand everything. It's not quick but it's the only way.

Warm-Up Questions

1) Define the term hormone.
2) Which organ in the human body produces insulin?
3) Give three differences between nervous and hormonal responses.
4) List four male secondary sexual characteristics.
5) Briefly describe the process of in vitro fertilisation.

Exam Questions

1 Which of the following statements about the oestrogen-containing contraceptive pill is **not** true?

   A   It does not protect against sexually transmitted diseases.

   B   It is over 99% effective at preventing pregnancy.

   C   It is free from side effects.

   D   It reduces the risk of developing some forms of cancer.

(1 mark)

2 Which of the following is controlled by the hormone FSH?

   A   Development of secondary sexual characteristics.

   B   Production of oestrogen by the ovaries.

   C   Release of LH from the pituitary.

   D   Release of an egg from the ovary.

(1 mark)

3 The menstrual cycle is controlled by several different hormones.

   (a) What effect does oestrogen have on the uterus lining?

(1 mark)

   (b) What is the effect of progesterone on the uterus lining?

(1 mark)

   (c) On what day of the menstrual cycle is the egg released?

(1 mark)

4 Give **two** potential side-effects associated with IVF.

(2 marks)

Homeostasis

Homeostasis involves balancing body functions to maintain a "constant internal environment". Hormones are sometimes (but not always) involved.

Homeostasis is maintaining a constant internal environment

Conditions in your body need to be kept steady so that cells can function properly. This involves balancing inputs (stuff going into your body) with outputs (stuff leaving). For example...

1) Levels of CO_2 — respiration in cells (p.124) constantly produces CO_2, which you need to get rid of.

2) Levels of oxygen — you need to replace the oxygen that your cells use up in respiration.

3) Water content — you need to keep a balance between the water you gain (in drink and food, and from respiration) and the water you pee, sweat and breathe out.

4) Body temperature — you need to get rid of excess body heat when you're hot, but retain heat when the environment is cold.

Negative feedback helps keep all these things steady

Changes in the environment trigger a response that counteracts the changes — e.g. a rise in body temperature causes a response that lowers body temperature.

This means that the internal environment tends to stay around a norm, the level at which the cells work best.

This only works within certain limits — if the environment changes too much then it might not be possible to counteract it (see the bit about heatstroke at the bottom of page 21).

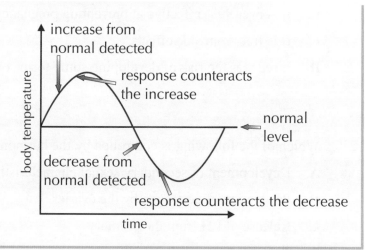

Water is lost from the body in various ways

Water is taken into the body as food and drink and is lost from the body in these ways:

1) through the skin as sweat...
2) via the lungs in breath...
3) via the kidneys as urine.

Some water is also lost in faeces.

The balance between sweat and urine can depend on what you're doing, or what the weather's like...

On a cold day, or when you're not exercising, you don't sweat much, so you'll produce more urine, which will be pale (since the waste carried in the urine is more diluted).

On a hot day, or when you're exercising, you sweat a lot, and so you will produce less urine, but this will be more concentrated (and hence a deeper colour). You will also lose more water through your breath when you exercise because you breathe faster.

Homeostasis

Body temperature is kept at about 37 °C

1) All enzymes work best at a certain temperature. The enzymes in the human body work best at about 37 °C — and so this is the temperature your body tries to maintain.

2) A part of the brain acts as your own personal thermostat. It's sensitive to the blood temperature in the brain, and it receives messages from the skin that provide information about skin temperature.

3) To keep you at this temperature your body does these things:

When you're **too hot**:

1) Hairs lie flat.

2) Lots of sweat is produced — when it evaporates it transfers heat from you to the environment, cooling you down.

3) Blood vessels close to the surface of the skin widen (vasodilation). This allows more blood to flow near the surface, so it can radiate more heat into the surroundings.

4) You can take off layers of clothing to help you cool down.

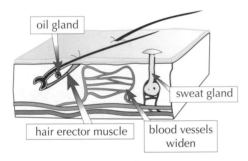

If you're exposed to high temperatures you can get dehydrated and you could get heat stroke. This can kill you (see below).

When you're **too cold**:

1) Hairs stand on end to trap an insulating layer of air which helps keep you warm.

2) Very little sweat is produced.

3) Blood vessels near the surface constrict (vasoconstriction) so that less heat can be transferred from the blood to the surroundings.

4) You shiver, and the movement generates heat in the muscles. Exercise does the same.

5) You can put on more clothes, to trap the heat in.

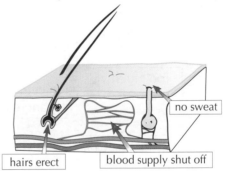

Your body temperature can drop to dangerous levels if you're exposed to very low temperatures for a long time — this is called hypothermia. If you don't get help quickly you can die.

Ion content is regulated by the kidneys

1) Ions (e.g. sodium, Na^+) are taken into the body in food, then absorbed into the blood.

2) If the food contains too much of any kind of ion then the excess ions need to be removed. E.g. a salty meal will contain far too much Na^+.

3) Some ions are lost in sweat (which tastes salty, you'll have noticed).

4) The kidneys will remove the excess from the blood — this is then got rid of in urine.

5) Sports drinks (which usually contain electrolytes and carbohydrates) can help your body keep things in order. The electrolytes (e.g. sodium) replace those lost in sweat, while the carbohydrates can give a bit of an energy boost. But claims about sports drinks need to be looked at carefully.

Heat stroke is no laughing matter

If you're in really high temperatures for a long time you can get heat stroke — sweating stops, since you get so dehydrated, and there's a big rise in your body temperature. If you don't cool down you can die.

Insulin

Blood sugar is controlled as part of homeostasis, using the hormone insulin. Learn how it works.

Insulin controls blood sugar levels

1) Eating foods containing <u>carbohydrate</u> puts <u>glucose</u> into the blood from the <u>gut</u>.

2) Normal <u>respiration</u> in cells <u>removes</u> glucose from the blood.

3) Vigorous <u>exercise</u> also removes a lot of glucose from the blood.

4) Levels of glucose in the blood must be kept <u>steady</u>. <u>Changes</u> in blood glucose are monitored and controlled by the <u>pancreas</u>, using <u>insulin</u>...

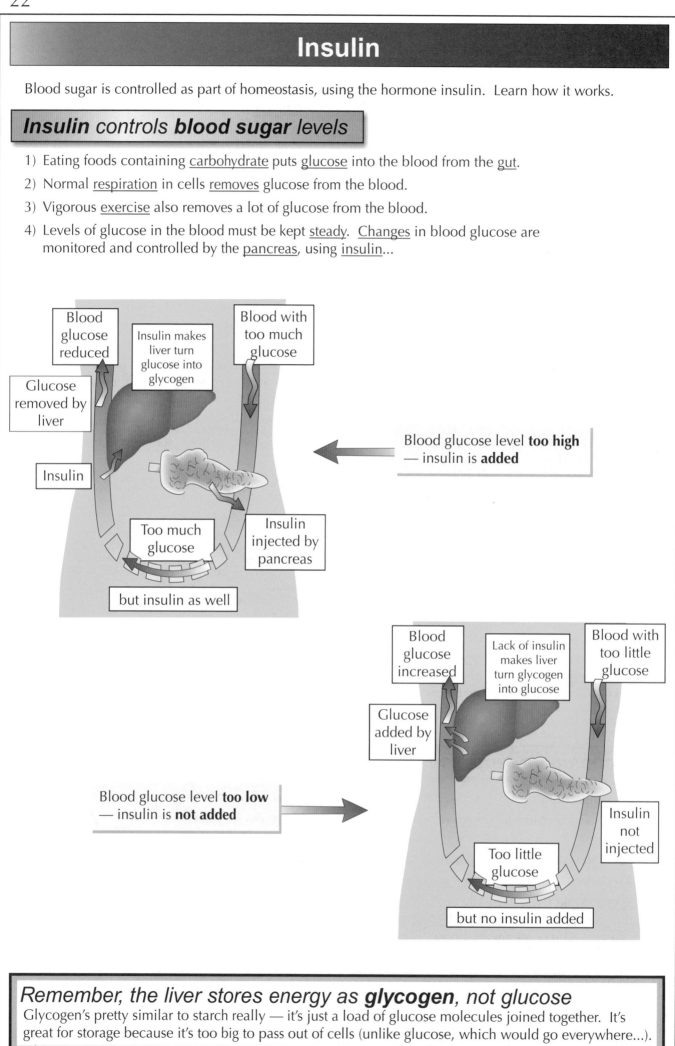

Remember, the liver stores energy as glycogen, not glucose

Glycogen's pretty similar to starch really — it's just a load of glucose molecules joined together. It's great for storage because it's too big to pass out of cells (unlike glucose, which would go everywhere...).

Insulin and Diabetes

The system described on the last page shows how insulin controls blood glucose levels.
In people who suffer from diabetes this system does not function properly.

Diabetes — the **pancreas** stops making enough **insulin**

1) <u>Diabetes</u> (type 1) is a condition where the <u>pancreas</u> doesn't produce enough <u>insulin</u>.

2) The result is that a person's blood sugar can rise to a level that can <u>kill them</u>.

3) The problem can be <u>controlled</u> in <u>two ways</u>:

Method 1: <u>Avoiding foods</u> rich in simple carbohydrates
(i.e. sugars)

The digestion of simple carbohydrates causes
<u>glucose levels</u> to <u>rise rapidly</u>.

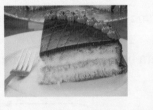

It can also be helpful to take <u>exercise</u> after eating
carbohydrates to try and <u>use up</u> the <u>extra glucose</u>,
but this isn't usually very practical.

Method 2: <u>Injecting insulin</u> into the blood at mealtimes
(especially if the meal is high in simple carbohydrates).

Injecting insulin makes the liver <u>remove</u> the <u>glucose</u> from
the blood as soon as it enters it from the gut.

This stops the level of glucose in the blood from
<u>getting too high</u> and is a very <u>effective</u> treatment.
However, diabetics must make sure they <u>eat sensibly</u> after
injecting insulin, or their blood sugar could <u>drop dangerously</u>.

4) The amount of insulin that needs to be injected depends on the person's <u>diet</u>
and how <u>active</u> they are.

5) Diabetics can <u>check</u> their blood sugar using a <u>glucose-monitoring device</u>.
This is a little hand-held machine. They prick their finger to get a drop of <u>blood</u>
for the machine to check.

It's important to learn how to control diabetes

Hormones control a lot of your body's functions. So if one of these functions isn't being done
quite right, it might be possible to fix it by injecting suitable hormones — just like with diabetes.

Warm-Up and Exam Questions

Warm-Up Questions

1) What is meant by the term homeostasis?
2) List six things that need to be kept constant within the body.
3) List four ways in which water is lost from the body.
4) Why is it important that human body temperature is kept at about 37 °C?
5) How can diabetics check their blood sugar levels?

Exam Questions

1   Describe the four ways in which the body responds to a drop in temperature.

(4 marks)

2   Which organ is responsible for regulating the ion content of the blood?

(1 mark)

3   The diagram below shows how blood sugar levels are regulated in humans.

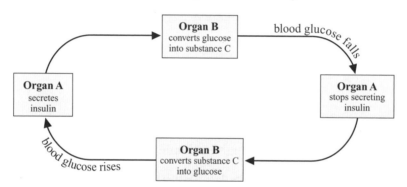

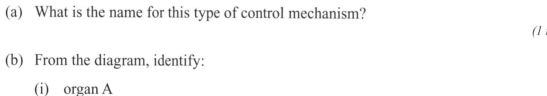

(a)   What is the name for this type of control mechanism?

(1 mark)

(b)   From the diagram, identify:

(i)   organ A

(1 mark)

(ii)   organ B

(1 mark)

(iii)   substance C

(1 mark)

(c)   (i)   Suggest a reason why blood glucose might rise.

(1 mark)

(ii)   What process constantly removes glucose from the blood?

(1 mark)

(iii)   What would cause blood glucose levels to fall rapidly?

(1 mark)

(d)   Give two ways in which type 1 diabetes can be controlled.

(2 marks)

Revision Summary for Section One

Congratulations, you've made it to the end of the first section. I reckon that section wasn't too bad, there's some pretty interesting stuff there — nerves, hormones, homeostasis... what more could you want? Actually, I know what more you could want... some questions to make sure you know it all.

1) Where would you find the following receptors in a dog?
   a) smell   b) taste   c) light   d) pressure   e) sound.

2) What is the purpose of a reflex action?

3) Describe the pathway of a reflex arc from stimulus to response.

4) Draw a diagram of a typical neurone, labelling all its parts.

5) What's a synapse? How are signals passed across a synapse?

6) Describe the iris reflex. Why is this needed?

7) How does accommodation of the eye work? Is the lens fat or thin to look at distant objects?

8) Give two examples of hormones, saying where they're made and what they do.

9)* Here's a table of data about response times.

Response	Reaction time (s)	Response duration (s)
A	0.005	0.05
B	2	10

   a) Which response (if any) is carried by nerves?
   b) Which (if any) is carried by hormones?

10) What secondary sexual characteristics does testosterone trigger in males?
    And oestrogen in females?

11) Sketch a timeline of the 28-day menstrual cycle.
    Label the four stages of the cycle and show when the egg is released.

12) What roles do oestrogen, progesterone, FSH and LH play in the menstrual cycle?

13) State two advantages and two disadvantages of using the contraceptive pill.

14) Which hormone is used to stimulate egg production in fertility treatment?

15) Describe how IVF is carried out. Describe some of the main issues in the IVF debate.

16) Explain how negative feedback helps to maintain a constant internal environment.

17) Describe how the amount and concentration of urine you produce varies depending on how much exercise you do and how hot it is.

18) Describe how body temperature is reduced when you're too hot. What happens if you're cold?

19) Explain how insulin controls blood sugar levels.

20) Define diabetes and describe two ways in which it can be controlled.

*Answers on page 284.

Eating Healthily

You might not think it but you don't just eat to stop you feeling <u>hungry</u> — you need a <u>balanced diet</u> to make sure that everything keeps working as it's supposed to.

*A **balanced diet** supplies all your **essential nutrients***

A balanced diet gives you all the <u>essential nutrients</u> you need.

The six essential nutrients are <u>carbohydrates</u>, <u>proteins</u>, <u>fats</u>, <u>vitamins</u>, <u>minerals</u> and <u>water</u>. You also need <u>fibre</u> (to keep the gut in good working order).

Different nutrients are required for different functions in the body:

NUTRIENTS	FUNCTIONS
Carbohydrates	Carbohydrates (e.g. glucose) provide energy.
Fats	Fats provide energy, act as an energy store and provide insulation.
Proteins	Proteins are needed for growth and repair of tissue, and to provide energy in emergencies.
Vitamins	Various functions: e.g. vitamin C is needed to prevent scurvy.
Minerals	Various functions: e.g. iron is needed to make haemoglobin for healthy blood.
Water	We need a constant supply to replace water lost through urinating, breathing and sweating.

Carbohydrates**, **fats** and **proteins** are made up of **simpler molecules

1) <u>Carbohydrates</u> are made up of <u>simple sugars</u> like <u>glucose</u>.

2) <u>Fats</u> are made up of <u>fatty acids</u> and <u>glycerol</u>.

3) <u>Proteins</u> are made up of <u>amino acids</u>.

Some amino acids can't be made by the body, so you have to get them from your <u>diet</u> — these are called <u>essential amino acids</u>.

You can get all the essential amino acids by eating protein that comes from <u>animals</u> (in other words, meat). These animal proteins are called <u>first class proteins</u>.

<u>Vegetarians</u> have to eat a <u>varied diet</u> to get all the essential amino acids they need.

Eating Healthily

Having a balanced diet isn't as simple as making sure that you get all of the essential nutrients. The amount of each nutrient that you require will depend on your body's individual needs.

Energy and nutrient needs vary in different people

A balanced diet isn't a set thing — it's different for everyone. The balance of the different nutrients a person needs depends on things like their age, gender and activity level.

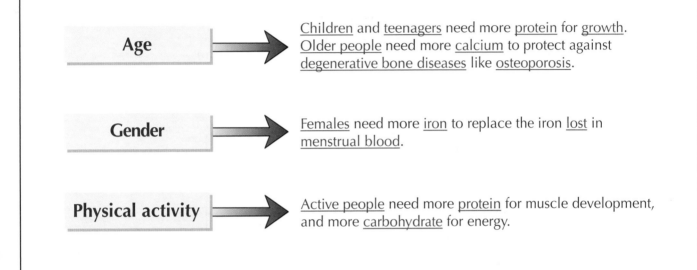

Age → Children and teenagers need more protein for growth. Older people need more calcium to protect against degenerative bone diseases like osteoporosis.

Gender → Females need more iron to replace the iron lost in menstrual blood.

Physical activity → Active people need more protein for muscle development, and more carbohydrate for energy.

Your metabolic rate is the speed you consume energy at

The amount of energy you need from your food also depends on your resting metabolic rate.

1) You need energy to fuel the chemical reactions in the body that keep you alive. These reactions are called your metabolism, and the speed at which they occur is your metabolic rate.

2) There are slight variations in the resting metabolic rate of different people.

   For example, muscle needs more energy than fatty tissue, which means (all other things being equal) people with a higher proportion of muscle to fat in their bodies will have a higher metabolic rate.

3) Men tend to have a slightly higher rate than women — they're generally slightly bigger and have a larger proportion of muscle. Other genetic factors may also have some effect.

4) And regular exercise can boost your resting metabolic rate because it builds muscle.

Getting the right intake of nutrients is vital to health

Exercise is important too — people who exercise regularly are usually fitter. But being fit isn't the same as being healthy — you can be fit and slim, but still unhealthy because your diet isn't balanced.

Diet Problems

Having <u>too much</u> or <u>too little</u> of any type of food in your diet can cause <u>health problems</u>.

Body mass index indicates if you're under- or overweight

The <u>body mass index</u> (BMI) is used as a guide to help decide whether someone is <u>underweight</u>, <u>normal</u>, <u>overweight</u> or <u>obese</u>. It's calculated from their <u>height</u> and <u>weight</u>:

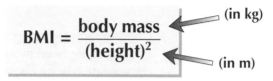

$$BMI = \frac{\text{body mass}}{(\text{height})^2}$$

(in kg)

(in m)

This table shows how BMI is used to <u>classify</u> people's weight.

Body Mass Index	Weight Description
below 18.5	underweight
18.5 - 24.9	normal
25 - 29.9	overweight
30 - 40	moderately obese
above 40	severely obese

BMI isn't always reliable. <u>Athletes</u> have lots of muscle, which weighs more than fat, so they can come out with a high BMI even though they're not overweight.

An alternative to BMI is measuring <u>% body fat</u>.

In developed countries the problem is often too much food

In <u>developed</u> countries, obesity is becoming a serious problem. In the UK, 1 in 5 adults are obese, with obesity contributing to the deaths of over 30 000 people each year in England alone.

1) <u>Obesity</u> is defined as being <u>20% (or more) over your recommended body weight</u>.

2) <u>Too much sugary or fatty food</u> and <u>too little exercise</u> are the main causes of obesity.

3) People can also be obese due to an <u>underactive thyroid gland</u>, but this problem isn't common.

4) Obesity can increase the risk of <u>diabetes</u>, <u>arthritis</u>, <u>high blood pressure</u>, <u>coronary heart disease (CHD)</u> and even some forms of <u>cancer</u>, e.g. breast cancer.

Diet Problems

In **developing** countries there may be **too little food**

1) This can be a lack of one or more <u>specific types</u> of food, or not enough food <u>of any sort</u> (<u>starvation</u>).

   Young children, the elderly and women tend to suffer most and the effects vary depending on what foods are missing from the diet.

   Common problems include <u>slow growth</u> (in children), <u>fatigue</u> and poor <u>resistance</u> to <u>infection</u>.

2) Eating too little <u>protein</u> can cause a condition called <u>kwashiorkor</u>.

   A common symptom is a <u>swollen stomach</u>.

   Kwashiorkor is especially common in <u>poorer developing countries</u> — protein-rich foods are often <u>too expensive</u> to buy.

   <u>Children</u> need a <u>greater proportion</u> of protein than adults (for <u>growth</u>), so they may be more likely to suffer.

You can calculate the <u>recommended daily allowance</u> (RDA) of <u>protein</u> using this formula:

$$\text{RDA (g)} = 0.75 \times \text{body mass (kg)}$$

Malnutrition can be the result of an **eating disorder**

Even in developed countries, some <u>psychological disorders</u> can cause under-nutrition, e.g. <u>anorexia nervosa</u> and <u>bulimia nervosa</u>.

1) Anorexia nervosa leads to <u>self-starvation</u>.

2) Bulimia nervosa involves bouts of <u>binge eating</u>, followed by <u>self-induced vomiting</u>.

3) They're both usually caused by <u>low self-esteem</u> and <u>anxiety about body fat</u> — sufferers have a <u>poor self-image</u>.

These disorders can cause a host of <u>other illnesses</u>, e.g. liver failure, kidney failure, heart attacks, muscle wastage, low blood pressure and mineral deficiencies. Both disorders can be <u>fatal</u>.

Too much or too little — it's a fine line to tread

Studying problems like obesity and starvation is hard because accurate data can be <u>difficult</u> to collect. For example, starving people in developing countries may <u>not reach</u> medical aid. And with obesity the health problems tend to be more <u>long-term</u>, and people don't necessarily seek medical assistance.

Cholesterol and Salt

You need some cholesterol in your body, but too much can put your health at risk. It's all a matter of eating the right amount and the right type of fat.

A *high cholesterol level* is a risk factor for *heart disease*

1) Cholesterol is a fatty substance that's essential for good health. It's found in every cell in the body.

2) But you don't want too much of it because a high cholesterol level in the blood causes an increased risk of various problems — like coronary heart disease.

3) This is due to blood vessels getting clogged with fatty cholesterol deposits. This reduces blood flow to the heart, which can lead to angina (chest pain), or a heart attack (if the vessel is blocked completely).

4) The liver is really important in controlling the amount of cholesterol in the body. It makes new cholesterol and removes it from the blood so that it can be eliminated from the body.

5) The amount the liver makes depends on your diet (see below) and inherited factors.

Cholesterol is *carried* around the body by *HDLs* and *LDLs*

1) Cholesterol is transported around the body in the blood by lipoproteins (i.e. fat attached to protein). These can be high density lipoproteins (HDLs), or low density lipoproteins (LDLs).

2) LDLs carry fat to the cells — they're called 'bad cholesterol' as excess LDLs can cause a build up of cholesterol in the arteries.

3) HDLs carry cholesterol to the liver for removal from the body — they're called 'good cholesterol'.

4) The LDL/HDL balance is important. Ideally, you want more HDLs than LDLs in the blood.

5) The level of cholesterol in the body is affected by fat in the diet. But it's not just the amount of fat — the types of fat you eat are even more crucial.

- SATURATED FATS raise blood cholesterol levels, so you should only eat them in moderation.

- POLYUNSATURATED FATS tend to lower blood cholesterol by increasing its removal from the body.

- MONOUNSATURATED FATS used to be considered 'neutral' for health.

  But recent evidence suggests they may help to lower blood cholesterol.

  People who have a diet high in monounsaturates tend to have lower levels of heart disease.

Cholesterol and Salt

Eating too much <u>salt</u> is another potential cause of <u>health problems</u>.
Most people have <u>more salt</u> than they need in their diet.

Too much **salt** can cause **high blood pressure**

1) Another <u>risk factor</u> (i.e. something that <u>increases the risk</u>) of heart
disease is <u>high blood pressure</u> (<u>hypertension</u>).

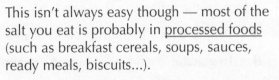

2) Eating too much <u>salt</u> may cause high blood pressure (hypertension).
This is a particular problem for about 30% of the UK population,
who are '<u>salt sensitive</u>' and need to carefully monitor <u>how much salt</u>
<u>they eat</u>.

This isn't always easy though — most of the
salt you eat is probably in <u>processed foods</u>
(such as breakfast cereals, soups, sauces,
ready meals, biscuits...).

The salt you <u>sprinkle</u> on food makes up quite
a small proportion.

And as if things weren't complicated enough,
on food labels, <u>salt</u> is usually listed as <u>sodium</u>.

High blood pressure causes serious health problems

There are <u>other</u> risk factors for <u>high blood pressure</u> too —
e.g. you're more likely to suffer from it as you get <u>older</u>,
if you're <u>overweight</u>, if you drink too much <u>alcohol</u> or
if you're <u>stressed</u>.

High blood pressure can lead to blood vessels <u>bursting</u>,
which can cause all kinds of different problems depending
on where in the body it happens — as well as heart attacks
it can lead to <u>strokes</u>, <u>brain damage</u> and <u>kidney damage</u>.

So it's a good idea to sort your lifestyle out.

Too much salt and cholesterol can damage your health

The more risk factors in your life, the <u>more likely</u> you are to suffer from a disease, but it doesn't mean
you <u>definitely</u> will. A smoker with high cholesterol and high blood pressure is <u>30 times more likely</u> to
develop heart disease than someone without these risk factors. But it's not guaranteed...

Warm-Up and Exam Questions

By the time the big day comes you need to know all the facts in these warm-up questions and exam questions like the back of your hand. It's not a barrel of laughs, but it's the only way to get good marks.

Warm-Up Questions

1) List three possible causes of obesity.
2) Why is it important to eat enough fibre as part of a balanced diet?
3) Which organ is responsible for controlling the amount of cholesterol in the body?
4) Why does high blood cholesterol increase the risk of heart disease?
5) Give three risk factors for high blood pressure.

Exam Questions

1   Which of the following statements about metabolic rate is **not** true?

    A   People with a high proportion of muscle to fat tend to have a high metabolic rate.

    B   In general, men have a higher metabolic rate than women.

    C   Two people of the same size and weight will have the same metabolic rate.

    D   Regular exercise increases resting metabolic rate.

(1 mark)

2   (a) (i) James is 185 cm tall and weighs 81 kg. Calculate his BMI.
              BMI = body mass (kg) ÷ height^2 (m)

(1 mark)

        (ii) Use the table to give his weight description.

(1 mark)

BMI	Weight description
below 18.5	underweight
18.5 - 24.9	normal
25.0 - 29.9	overweight
30.0 - 40.0	obese
over 40.0	severely obese

    (b) Obesity increases the risk of various health problems. Name one such problem.

(1 mark)

3   (a) What would be the likely effect on your blood cholesterol levels of eating:

        (i) saturated fats?

(1 mark)

        (ii) polyunsaturated fats?

(1 mark)

    (b) Explain how a high intake of salt in your diet can increase your risk of suffering a stroke.

(2 marks)

Health Claims

It's sometimes hard to figure out if <u>health claims</u> or <u>adverts</u> are <u>true</u> or not.

New day, new food claim — *it can't all be true*

1) To get you to buy a product, advertisers aren't allowed to make claims that are <u>untrue</u> — that's <u>illegal</u>.

2) But they do sometimes make claims that could be <u>misleading</u> or difficult to <u>prove</u> (or <u>disprove</u>).

   For example, some claims are just <u>vague</u> (calling a product "light" for instance — does that mean low calorie, low fat, something else...).

   Alternatively, they might call a breakfast cereal "low fat", and that'd be <u>true</u>. But that could suggest that <u>other</u> breakfast cereals are high in fat — when in fact they're not.

3) And every day there's a new <u>food scare</u> in the papers (eeek — we're all doomed). Or a new <u>miracle food</u> (phew — we're all saved).

4) It's not easy to decide what to <u>believe</u> and what to <u>ignore</u>. But these things are worth looking for:

   > a) Is the report a <u>scientific study</u>, published in a <u>reputable journal</u>?
   >
   > b) Was it written by a <u>qualified person</u> (not connected with the food producers)?
   >
   > c) Was the <u>sample</u> of people asked/tested <u>large enough</u> to give reliable results?
   >
   > d) Have there been <u>other studies</u> which found <u>similar results</u>?

5) A "yes" to one or more of these is a good sign.

Not all diets are *scientifically proven*

With each new day comes a new celebrity-endorsed diet.

1) A common way to promote a new <u>diet</u> is to say, "Celebrity A has lost x pounds using it".

2) But effectiveness in <u>one person</u> doesn't mean much. Only a <u>large survey</u> can tell if a diet is more or less effective than just <u>eating less</u> and <u>exercising more</u> — and these aren't done often.

Example: The Atkins diet

The <u>Atkins diet</u> was high profile, and controversial — so it got investigated. People on the diet certainly lost weight. But the diet's effect on general health (especially <u>long-term</u> health) has been questioned. The jury's still out.

3) Weight loss is a <u>complex</u> process. But just like with food claims, the best thing to do is look at the evidence in a scientific way.

Health Claims

The same rules apply when looking into claims about drugs — look at all the evidence in a scientific way.

It's the same when you look at claims about **drugs**

Claims about the effects of <u>drugs</u> (both medical and illegal ones) also need to be looked at <u>critically</u>. But at least here the evidence is usually based on <u>scientific</u> research.

Statins

1) There's evidence that drugs called <u>statins</u> lower <u>blood cholesterol</u> and significantly lower the risk of <u>heart disease</u> in diabetic patients.

2) The original research was done by <u>government</u> scientists with <u>no connection</u> to the manufacturers. And the <u>sample</u> was <u>big</u> — 6000 patients.

So control groups were used. And the results were reproducible.

3) It compared <u>two groups</u> of patients — those who <u>had</u> taken statins and those who <u>hadn't</u>. Other studies have since <u>backed up</u> these findings.

But research findings are not always so clear cut...

Cannabis

1) Many scientists have looked at whether <u>cannabis</u> use causes brain damage and mental health problems or leads to further drug taking. The results <u>vary</u>, and are sometimes open to different <u>interpretations</u>.

2) Basically, until more definite scientific evidence is found, no one's <u>sure</u>.

Evidence must be looked at in a scientific way

Learn what to look out for before you put too much faith in what you read. Think about who's making a claim, how much evidence there is to support it, and whether that evidence is reliable. And always remember to look at any health claim, whether it's to do with diets or drugs, in a scientific way.

Drugs

Drugs alter what goes on in your body. Your body's essentially a seething mass of <u>chemical reactions</u> — drugs can <u>interfere</u> with these reactions, sometimes for the better, sometimes not.

Drugs can be **beneficial** or **harmful**, **legal** or **illegal**

1) Drugs are substances which <u>alter the chemical reactions in the body</u>. Some drugs are <u>medically useful</u>, such as <u>antibiotics</u> (e.g. <u>penicillin</u>).

2) But many drugs are <u>dangerous</u> if misused (this goes for both illegal drugs <u>and</u> legal ones). That could mean problems with either your <u>physical</u> or <u>mental</u> health.

3) This is why you can buy some drugs <u>over the counter</u> at a pharmacy, others are restricted so you can only get them on <u>prescription</u> (your <u>doctor decides</u> if you should have them), and others are <u>illegal</u>.

4) Some people get <u>addicted</u> to some drugs — this means they have a physical need for that drug, and if they don't get it they experience <u>withdrawal symptoms</u>.

5) It's not just illegal drugs that are addictive — many legal ones are too, e.g. <u>caffeine</u>. Caffeine withdrawal symptoms include irritability and shaky hands.

6) <u>Tolerance</u> develops with some drugs — the body gets <u>used to having it</u> and so you need a <u>higher dose</u> to give the <u>same effect</u>. This can happen with legal drugs (e.g. alcohol), and illegal drugs (e.g. heroin).

Illegal drugs are classified into **three** main categories

1) Some drugs are <u>illegal</u> — usually because they're considered to be dangerous.

2) In the UK, they either belong to <u>Class A, B or C</u>. Which class a drug is in depends on how <u>dangerous</u> it is thought to be — Class A drugs are the most dangerous.

Class A drugs

    heroin, LSD, ecstasy and cocaine

Class B drugs

    amphetamines (speed) and cannabis

    (Amphetamines are class A if prepared for injection.)

Class C drugs

    anabolic steroids and tranquillisers

Drugs change the body's chemical reactions — for better or worse

There's been a lot of debate recently about how useful the illegal drug classification system is. A lot of people argue that it isn't based on scientific evidence, and that it should be redesigned. Luckily for you, that's not going to be in the exams — just learn the current system and you'll be fine.

Drugs

So far you've looked at how drugs can be <u>classified</u> depending on how <u>dangerous</u> they're thought to be, but this page is all about what they actually <u>do</u>.

Drugs can affect your **behaviour**

1) A lot of drugs affect your <u>nervous system</u>. Drugs can interfere with the way <u>signals</u> are sent around your body from <u>receptors</u> to the <u>brain</u>, and from the <u>brain</u> to <u>muscles</u> (see page 8).

2) The effects of drugs on the nervous system can alter <u>behaviour</u> (which has the potential to cause <u>danger</u> — either for the person who took the drug, or for others).

3) For example, <u>driving</u> and operating <u>machinery</u> aren't safe if you've taken certain drugs — e.g. alcohol, tranquillisers or cannabis (see page 41 for more info about alcohol).

4) Some drugs (e.g. alcohol) can also affect people's <u>judgement</u>. This could mean someone just '<u>losing their inhibitions</u>' — relaxing a bit at a party, for instance.

5) But it could mean they take more <u>risks</u> — e.g. <u>sharing needles</u> and having <u>unprotected sex</u> are more likely to happen under the influence of drink or drugs, increasing the risk of viral infections like <u>HIV</u>.

6) Drug abuse can also affect your <u>immune system</u> — making infections more <u>likely</u>.

Sedatives slow you down

These are also called <u>depressants</u>.

— e.g. alcohol, barbiturates, solvents, temazepam.

These <u>decrease</u> the <u>activity of the brain</u>. This slows down the <u>responses</u> of the <u>nervous system</u>, causing <u>slow reactions</u> and <u>poor judgement</u> of speed and distances.

Stimulants speed you up

— e.g. nicotine, ecstasy, caffeine.

These do the opposite of depressants — they <u>increase</u> the <u>activity of the brain</u>. This makes you feel more <u>alert</u> and <u>awake</u>.

Learn all the grim facts

Many people regularly have <u>sedatives</u> and <u>stimulants</u>, the most common ones being alcohol and caffeine. Those two don't seem to be too bad for you in small doses — it's <u>misuse</u> that can get you into trouble (e.g. having 25 coffees and 17 pints a day is likely to put you in hospital).

Drug Testing

Drugs have medical uses too, obviously. But before they can be used, they have to be tested...

Medical drugs have to be thoroughly tested

New drugs are constantly being <u>developed</u>. But before they can be given to the general public, they have to go through a <u>thorough</u> testing procedure. This is what usually happens...

<u>Computer models</u> are often used in the early stages — these simulate a human's response to a drug.

This can identify promising drugs to be tested in the next stage (but sometimes it's not as accurate as actually seeing the effect on a <u>live organism</u>).

Drugs are then developed further by testing on <u>human tissues</u> in the lab.

However, you can't use human tissue to test drugs that affect <u>whole</u> or <u>multiple</u> body systems, e.g. testing a drug for blood pressure must be done on a whole animal because it has an intact circulatory system.

The next step is to develop and test the drug using <u>live animals</u>. The law in Britain states that any new drug must be tested on <u>two</u> different <u>live mammals</u>.

Some people think it's <u>cruel</u> to test on animals, but others believe this is the <u>safest</u> way to make sure a drug isn't dangerous before it's given to humans.

But some people think that animals are so different from humans that testing on animals is pointless.

After the drug has been tested on animals it's tested on <u>human volunteers</u> in a <u>clinical trial</u> — this should determine whether there are any <u>side effects</u>.

There's more about clinical trials on the next page.

Try to be as open minded as you can with this one

Most people have an opinion of some kind when it comes to testing drugs on animals. Whatever yours is, you need to be able to give both sides of the story. So make sure you learn how animal testing fits in with the other tests new drugs are put through — learn the whole page.

Drug Testing

So, new drugs have to go through fairly <u>thorough</u> testing before they get anywhere near <u>humans</u>. And even when they do get to the clinical trial stage, you can't always test <u>everything</u>.

Clinical trials involve two groups of patients

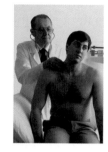

1) One group is given the <u>new drug</u>, the other is given a <u>placebo</u> (a 'dummy treatment' that looks like the real drug but doesn't do anything). This is done so scientists can see the actual difference the drug makes — it allows for the <u>placebo effect</u> (when the patient expects the treatment to work and so <u>feels better</u>, even though the treatment isn't doing anything).

2) Clinical trials are <u>blind</u> — the patient in the study <u>doesn't know</u> whether they're getting the drug or the placebo. In fact, they're often <u>double blind</u> — neither the <u>patient</u> nor the <u>scientist</u> knows until all the results have been gathered.

Things have gone wrong in the past

An example of what can happen when drugs are not thoroughly tested is the case of <u>thalidomide</u> — a drug developed in the 1950s.

1) Thalidomide was intended as a <u>sleeping pill</u>, and was tested for that use. But later it was also found to be effective in relieving <u>morning sickness</u> in pregnant women.

2) Unfortunately, thalidomide <u>hadn't</u> been <u>tested</u> for this use, and so it wasn't known that it could pass through the placenta and affect the <u>foetus</u>, causing <u>stunted growth</u> of the foetus's arms and legs. In some cases, babies were born with no arms or legs at all.

3) About <u>10 000</u> babies were affected by thalidomide, and only about <u>half</u> of them survived.

4) The drug was <u>banned</u>, and more <u>rigorous</u> testing procedures were introduced.

5) Thalidomide has recently been reintroduced — as a treatment for <u>leprosy</u>, <u>AIDS</u> and certain <u>cancers</u>. But it can't be used on pregnant women.

Developing new drugs is expensive

1) New drugs are often very sophisticated, and it can take <u>many years</u> to <u>develop</u> and <u>test</u> a drug to the stage where it can be put into use.

2) Also, most potential drugs are <u>rejected</u> during the trials.

3) All of this adds to the <u>cost</u> of coming up with a drug that can be used <u>safely</u> on humans.

A little learning is a dangerous thing

Thalidomide was an attempt to <u>improve</u> people's lives which then caused some pretty tragic knock-on effects. Could the same thing happen <u>today</u>? Well, maybe not the exact same thing, but there's no such thing as <u>perfect</u> knowledge — you can never eliminate risk <u>completely</u>.

Warm-Up and Exam Questions

There's no point in whizzing through the section and glancing over the questions. Do the warm-up questions and go back over any bits you don't know. Then practise and practise the exam questions.

Warm-Up Questions

1) What is a drug?
2) List four things that should be considered when deciding if a health claim is reliable.
3) Name one legal drug to which people may become addicted.
4) What is a placebo?
5) Why is developing new drugs an expensive process?

Exam Questions

1   (a)   Which of these drugs is a sedative?

   A   nicotine

   B   alcohol

   C   caffeine

   D   ecstasy

   (1 mark)

   (b)   What effect do sedatives have on the nervous system?

   (1 mark)

2   (a)   Give four stages of testing that a new drug will usually go through before it can be sold to the general public.

   (4 marks)

   (b)   Describe how a typical double blind clinical trial works.

   (2 marks)

3   (a)   It is possible to build up a tolerance and/or become addicted to both illegal and legal drugs. Explain what is meant by:

   (i)   addiction

   (1 mark)

   (ii)   tolerance

   (1 mark)

   (b)   Illegal drugs in the UK are placed into three main categories.

   (i)   Which class of drugs is the most dangerous?

   (1 mark)

   (ii)   Give an example of a drug in this class.

   (1 mark)

   (c)   Why are people who abuse drugs at greater risk of picking up infections?

   (1 mark)

Smoking and Alcohol

Drugs are also used <u>recreationally</u>. Some of these are legal, others illegal. And some are more <u>harmful</u> than others. But two drugs that have a massive impact on people and society are both <u>legal</u>.

Smoking **tobacco** can cause quite a few **problems**

1) Tobacco smoke contains <u>carbon monoxide</u> — this <u>combines</u> irreversibly with <u>haemoglobin</u> in blood cells, meaning the blood can carry <u>less oxygen</u>. In pregnant women, this can deprive the <u>foetus</u> of oxygen, leading to the baby being born <u>underweight</u>.

2) Tobacco smoke also contains carcinogens — chemicals that can lead to <u>cancer</u>. Lung cancer is way more common among smokers than nonsmokers.

3) Disturbingly, the <u>incidence rate</u> (the number of people who get lung cancer) and the <u>mortality rate</u> (the number who die from it) aren't massively different — lung cancer kills <u>most</u> of the people who get it.

4) Smoking also causes <u>disease</u> of the <u>heart</u> and <u>blood vessels</u> (leading to <u>heart attacks</u> and <u>strokes</u>), and damage to the <u>lungs</u> (leading to diseases like <u>emphysema</u> and <u>bronchitis</u>).

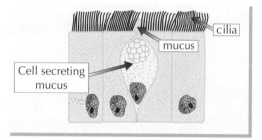

5) And the <u>tar</u> in cigarettes damages the <u>cilia</u> (little hairs) in your lungs and windpipe (see p.197). These hairs, along with <u>mucus</u>, catch a load of <u>dust</u> and <u>bacteria</u> before they reach the lungs. When these cilia are damaged, <u>chest infections</u> are more likely.

6) And to top it all off, smoking tobacco is <u>addictive</u> — due to the <u>nicotine</u> in tobacco smoke.

Smoking and lung cancer are now **known** to be linked

1) In the first half of the 20th century it was noticed that <u>lung cancer</u> and the popularity of <u>smoking</u> increased <u>together</u>. And studies found that far more <u>smokers</u> than <u>nonsmokers</u> got lung cancer.

2) But it was just a <u>statistical correlation</u> at that time (see p.283) — it didn't <u>prove</u> that smoking <u>caused</u> lung cancer. Some people (especially in the tobacco industry) argued that there was some <u>other</u> factor (e.g. a person's <u>genes</u>) which both caused lung cancer, and also made people more likely to smoke.

3) Later research eventually <u>disproved</u> these claims. Now even the tobacco industry has had to admit that smoking does <u>increase</u> the <u>risk</u> of lung cancer.

If that wasn't enough, it also gives you yellow teeth

This page might make you think 'yeah yeah yeah heard it before', but there's no way you can make an <u>informed decision</u> about drug use without being informed. Whatever your take on this kind of thing, you need to know about it for your <u>exam</u>. So make sure you learn all the details.

Smoking and Alcohol

Many people see drinking alcohol as more acceptable than smoking tobacco, but excessive drinking seems to be on the increase, and so are drink-related crimes and injuries.

Drinking alcohol can do its share of damage too

1) The main effect of alcohol is to <u>reduce the activity</u> of the <u>nervous system</u> — slowing your reactions. It can also make you feel <u>less inhibited</u> — which can help people to socialise and relax with each other.

2) However, too much leads to <u>impaired judgement</u>, <u>poor balance</u> and <u>coordination</u>, <u>lack of self-control</u>, <u>unconsciousness</u> and even <u>coma</u>.

Alcohol in excess also causes <u>dehydration</u>, which can damage <u>brain cells</u>, causing a noticeable <u>drop</u> in <u>brain function</u>. And too much drinking causes <u>severe damage</u> to the <u>liver</u>, leading to <u>liver disease</u>.

3) There are <u>social</u> costs too. Alcohol is linked with loads of murders, stabbings and domestic assaults.

These two legal drugs have a massive impact

<u>Alcohol</u> and <u>tobacco</u> have a bigger impact in the UK than illegal drugs, as <u>so many</u> people take them.

1) Tobacco

The National Health Service spends loads on treating people with <u>lung diseases</u> caused by <u>smoking</u> (or passive smoking). Add to this the cost to businesses of people missing days from work, and the figures get pretty scary.

2) Alcohol

The same goes for <u>alcohol</u>. The costs to the NHS are huge, but are pretty small compared to the costs related to <u>crime</u> (police time, damage to people/property) and the <u>economy</u> (lost working days etc.).

Learn all this stuff — not just for the exam

So it's legal drugs that have the most impact on the country as a <u>whole</u> — when you take everything into consideration. Should the <u>Government</u> do more to reduce the number of people who smoke — or is it up to individual <u>people</u> what they do with their lives... there's no easy answer to that one.

Solvents and Painkillers

Two other groups of drugs you need to know about are solvents and painkillers. There's not too much you need to know, just remember a few examples of each and what both the groups do.

Solvents affect the lungs and neurones

1) Solvents are found in lighter fuel, spray paints, aerosols, thinners and dry cleaning fluids. They're useful chemicals, but can be misused as <u>drugs</u> (by <u>inhaling</u> the fumes).

2) Solvents act on the <u>nervous system</u>. Like alcohol, they're <u>depressants</u> — they slow down messages as they're passed along <u>neurones</u> (and can cause all sorts of other damage as well).

3) Solvent abuse often causes <u>brain damage</u> in the long term — this could show up as a personality change, sleeplessness or short-term memory loss, for example.

4) Most solvents also irritate the <u>lungs</u> and the <u>breathing passages</u>.

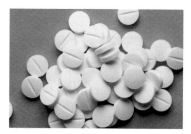

Paracetamol is a painkiller

1) <u>Paracetamol</u> is a medicine that can <u>relieve</u> mild to moderate <u>pain</u>, and reduce <u>fever</u>.

2) Paracetamol is generally pretty <u>safe</u>, but an <u>overdose</u> can be <u>deadly</u>. <u>Paracetamol overdose</u> causes horrendous liver damage. If it isn't treated quickly (and I mean really quickly) it's <u>very</u> dangerous. And paracetamol's especially dangerous after alcohol, so it's not a good idea for hangovers.

3) A paracetamol overdose is <u>particularly dangerous</u> because the damage sometimes isn't apparent for <u>4-6 days</u> after the drug's been taken. By that time, it's <u>too late</u> — there's nothing doctors can do to repair the damage. Dying from liver failure takes several days, and involves <u>heavy-duty pain</u>.

4) Paracetamol in <u>normal doses</u> won't damage the liver (though <u>accidental</u> overdoses are quite common).

Drugs can kill you or cure you (or anything in between)

Paracetamol's a drug that most people come across fairly regularly, and as long as you read the label and make sure you don't take too many, it's perfectly safe. The same can be said for a lot of drugs, but when it comes to solvents, you really are better off just steering well clear (assuming you value your lungs and/or brain). Unless of course you're doing some spray painting, which is fine. As long as you don't spend all day inhaling paint fumes, or paint your eyes shut or something.

Solvents and Painkillers

There's a good chance you'll know most of the things on this page already, but read through it thoroughly anyway to get an idea of what you need for the exams.

Opiates *and* **cannabinoids** *are used as* **painkillers**

Some types of painkillers can only be used under <u>medical supervision</u>.

Opiates

- Opiates include <u>opium</u>, <u>morphine</u> and <u>codeine</u>. They're all found in the opium poppy.

- Opiates are all <u>painkillers</u>. <u>Morphine</u>'s used by doctors — it's very effective. But just like heroin, morphine's very <u>addictive</u>, and so it's <u>illegal</u> without a prescription.

Cannabis

- Cannabis has been used as a medicine for centuries, but it's now <u>illegal</u>.

- For years, no one really <u>knew</u> what cannabis did inside the body — this was because research on <u>cannabinoids</u> (the active ingredients in cannabis) was tricky (due to <u>legal restrictions</u>).

- The situation changed when scientists discovered <u>receptors</u> in the body for cannabinoids. Recent research seems to suggest that cannabinoids do provide <u>benefit</u> for <u>some</u> patients (though for <u>most</u> people, there's probably something <u>better</u> available).

Different painkillers work in *different ways*

1) <u>Aspirin</u> and <u>ibuprofen</u> work by inhibiting the formation of <u>prostaglandins</u> (chemicals which cause <u>swelling</u>, and sensitise the endings of nerves that register pain).

2) <u>Paracetamol</u> seems to work in a <u>similar way</u> to aspirin and ibuprofen, but scientists <u>aren't really sure</u>.

3) <u>Opiates</u>, like morphine and codeine, are <u>very strong</u> painkillers. They work by interfering with the <u>mechanism</u> by which 'pain-sensing' nerve cells transmit messages. They also act on the <u>brain</u> to stop it sensing the pain.

You can learn this — take the pain, take the pain

Isn't it amazing that we're still not sure how paracetamol works... Apparently the pain-reducing effects of paracetamol were just discovered by accident. That's science for you — a series of accidents which add together to make amazing discoveries. Learn all the stuff, test yourself, and learn it again if need be.

Warm-Up and Exam Questions

Without a good warm-up you're likely to strain a brain cell or two. So take the time to run through these simple questions and get the basic facts straight before plunging into the exam questions.

Warm-Up Questions

1) Name two organs that can be damaged by solvent abuse.
2) To which class of painkillers does morphine belong?
3) Name two lung diseases, other than cancer, caused by smoking.
4) What are carcinogens?
5) Suggest why there has been so little research into the medicinal use of cannabinoids.

Exam Questions

1   The following chemicals are all found in cigarette smoke.
    Explain what effect each has on the body.

  (a) Tar

(1 mark)

  (b) Carbon monoxide

(1 mark)

  (c) Nicotine

(1 mark)

2   (a) Describe how the following painkillers work on the body:

  (i)   Aspirin

(1 mark)

  (ii) Morphine

(1 mark)

  (b) Explain why it is important not to take more than the recommended daily
       dose of paracetamol.

(1 mark)

3   In the UK it is illegal to drive if your blood alcohol concentration exceeds 80 mg of
    alcohol per 100 ml of blood.

  (a) Explain the effect alcohol has on the body, that increases the risk of having a car
       accident when drink driving.

(2 marks)

  (b) Give two long term health effects of excessive alcohol consumption.

(2 marks)

  (c) Other than drink-related driving accidents, give two ways in which excessive
       alcohol consumption has a negative effect on society.

(2 marks)

Causes of Disease

An <u>infectious</u> disease is a disease that can be <u>transmitted</u> from one person to another — either <u>directly</u> (person to person), or <u>indirectly</u> (where some kind of <u>carrier</u> is involved, e.g. mosquitoes spread malaria, and certain bacteria are passed on in food or water).

Infectious diseases are caused by pathogens

1) <u>Pathogens</u> are <u>microorganisms</u> (<u>microbes</u>) that cause <u>disease</u>.

2) They include some <u>bacteria</u>, <u>protozoa</u> (certain single-celled creatures), <u>fungi</u> and <u>viruses</u>.

3) All pathogens are <u>parasites</u> — they live off their host and give nothing in return.

4) Microorganisms can <u>reproduce very fast</u> inside a host organism.

Bacteria and viruses are very different

...but they can both multiply quickly inside your body — they love the warm conditions.

Bacteria are very small living cells

1) Bacteria are <u>very small cells</u> (about 1/100th the size of your body cells), which can reproduce rapidly inside your body.

2) They make you <u>feel ill</u> by doing <u>two</u> things — <u>damaging your cells</u> and <u>producing toxins</u> (poisons).

3) But... some bacteria are <u>useful</u> if they're in the <u>right place</u>, like in your digestive system.

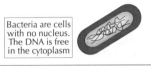

Bacteria are cells with no nucleus. The DNA is free in the cytoplasm

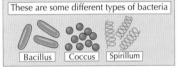

These are some different types of bacteria

Bacillus   Coccus   Spirillum

Viruses are not cells — they're much smaller

1) Viruses are <u>not cells</u>. They're <u>tiny</u>, about 1/100th the size of a bacterium. They're usually no more than a <u>coat of protein</u> around some <u>genetic material</u>.

2) They <u>replicate themselves</u> by <u>invading your cells</u> and using the <u>cell machinery</u> to produce <u>many copies</u> of themselves. Then they cause the cell to <u>break open</u>, releasing the new viruses into your body.

3) This <u>cell damage</u> is what makes you feel ill.

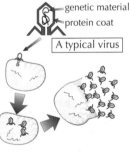

genetic material
protein coat

A typical virus

Other health disorders can be caused in various ways

1) <u>Vitamin deficiency</u>, e.g. you can get <u>scurvy</u> if you don't get enough <u>vitamin C</u>.

2) <u>Mineral deficiency</u>, e.g. a lack of <u>iron</u> in the diet can lead to <u>anaemia</u>. Iron is needed to make the protein <u>haemoglobin</u> (which carries <u>oxygen</u> in the red blood cells).

3) <u>Genetic inheritance</u> of disorders (see p.80), e.g. <u>red-green colour blindness</u> (sufferers find it hard to distinguish between red and green) and <u>haemophilia</u> (a blood clotting disorder).

4) <u>Body disorders</u> are caused by body cells not working properly, e.g. <u>diabetes</u> (see p.23) and <u>cancer</u>.

Cancer is caused by body cells growing <u>out of control</u>. This forms a <u>tumour</u> (a mass of cells). Tumours can either be <u>benign</u> or <u>malignant</u>:

1) <u>Benign</u> — This is where the tumour grows until there's no more room. The cells <u>stay</u> where they are. This type <u>isn't</u> normally dangerous.

2) <u>Malignant</u> — This is where the tumour grows and can <u>spread</u> to other sites in the body. Malignant tumours are <u>dangerous</u> and can be fatal.

The Body's Defence Systems

Your body is constantly fighting off attack from all sorts of nasties — yep, things really are out to get you. The body has <u>three</u> lines of defence to stop things causing disease.

The *first line of defence* stops pathogens *entering* the body

The first line of defence consists mostly of <u>physical barriers</u> — they stop <u>foreign bodies</u> getting in.

1) The <u>Skin</u>

<u>Undamaged skin</u> is a very effective barrier against microorganisms. And if it gets <u>damaged</u>, blood <u>clots</u> quickly to <u>seal cuts</u> and keep microorganisms <u>out</u>.

3) The <u>Respiratory System</u>

The nasal passage and trachea are lined with <u>mucus</u> and <u>cilia</u> which catch <u>dust</u> and <u>bacteria</u> before they reach the lungs.

2) The <u>Eyes</u>

<u>Eyes</u> produce (in <u>tears</u>) a chemical called <u>lysozyme</u> which <u>kills bacteria</u> on the surface of the eye. This is a <u>chemical barrier</u> — not a physical one.

The *second line of defence* is *non-specific white blood cells*

1) Anything that gets through the first line of defence and into the body should be picked up by white blood cells called <u>phagocytes</u> (a <u>chemical</u> barrier).

2) Phagocytes detect things that are '<u>foreign</u>' to the body, e.g. microbes. They <u>engulf microbes</u> and <u>digest them</u>.

3) Phagocytes are <u>non-specific</u> — they attack anything that's not meant to be there.

4) The white blood cells also trigger an <u>inflammatory response</u>. <u>Blood flow</u> to the infected area is <u>increased</u> (making the area <u>red</u> and <u>hot</u>), and <u>plasma</u> leaks into the damaged tissue (which makes the area <u>swell up</u>) — this is all so that the right cells can get to the area to <u>fight</u> the infection.

The *third line of defence* is *specific white blood cells*

Some produce *antibodies*

1) Every invading cell has unique molecules (called <u>antigens</u>) on its surface.

2) When certain white blood cells come across a <u>foreign antigen</u> (i.e. one it doesn't recognise), they will start to produce <u>proteins</u> called <u>antibodies</u> to lock on to the invading cells and mark them out for destruction by other white blood cells. The antibodies produced are specific to that type of antigen — they won't lock on to any others.

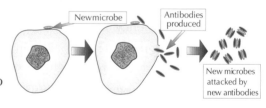

3) Antibodies are then produced <u>rapidly</u> and flow round the body to mark all similar bacteria or viruses.

4) Some of these white blood cells stay around in the blood after the original infection has been fought. They can reproduce very fast if the <u>same</u> antigen enters the body for a <u>second</u> time. That's why you're immune to <u>most</u> diseases if you've already had them — the body carries a "<u>memory</u>" of what the antigen was like, and can quickly produce loads of antibodies if you get infected again.

Some produce *antitoxins*

These counter the toxins produced by <u>invading microbes</u>.

Immunisation

Immunisation changed the way we deal with disease. Not bad for a little jab.

Immunisation — protects from future infections

1) When you're infected with a new <u>microorganism</u>, it takes your white blood cells a few days to <u>learn</u> how to deal with it. But by that time, you can be pretty <u>ill</u>.

2) <u>Immunisation</u> involves injecting <u>dead</u> or <u>inactive</u> microorganisms. These carry <u>antigens</u>, which cause your body to produce <u>antibodies</u> to attack them — even though the microorganism is <u>harmless</u> (since it's dead or inactive). For example, the MMR vaccine contains <u>weakened</u> versions of the viruses that cause <u>measles</u>, <u>mumps</u> and <u>rubella</u> (German measles) stuck together.

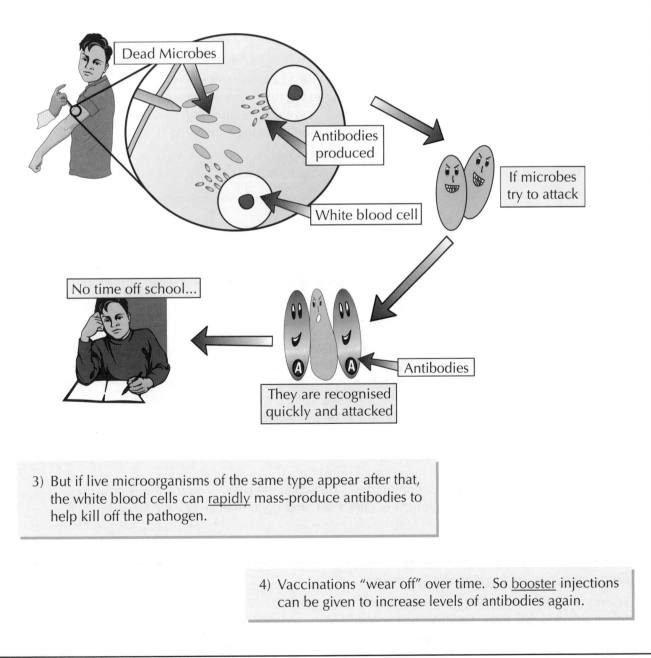

Dead Microbes

Antibodies produced

White blood cell

If microbes try to attack

Antibodies

No time off school...

They are recognised quickly and attacked

3) But if live microorganisms of the same type appear after that, the white blood cells can <u>rapidly</u> mass-produce antibodies to help kill off the pathogen.

4) Vaccinations "wear off" over time. So <u>booster</u> injections can be given to increase levels of antibodies again.

Immunisation

Immunisation provides huge benefits to society.
Having said that, there are a few risks that you should be aware of.

Immunisation is classed as **active immunity**

1) <u>Active immunity</u> is where the immune system makes <u>its own antibodies</u> after being stimulated by a <u>pathogen</u>. It includes becoming <u>naturally immune</u> (see page 46) and <u>artificially immune</u> (immunisation). Active immunity is usually <u>permanent</u>.

2) <u>Passive immunity</u> is where you use antibodies <u>made by another organism</u>, e.g. antibodies are passed from mother to baby through <u>breast milk</u>. Passive immunity is only <u>temporary</u>.

There are **benefits** and **risks** associated with **immunisation**

Benefits

1) Immunisation <u>stops you from getting ill</u>... a pretty obvious benefit.

2) Vaccinations mean we don't have to deal with a problem once it's happened — we can <u>prevent</u> it happening in the first place. Vaccines have helped <u>control</u> lots of infectious diseases that were once <u>common</u> in the UK (e.g. polio, measles, whooping cough, rubella, mumps, tetanus, TB...).

3) If an outbreak does occur, vaccines can <u>slow down</u> or <u>stop</u> the spread (if people don't catch the disease, they won't pass it on).

Risks

1) There can be <u>short-term side effects</u>, e.g. <u>swelling</u> and <u>redness</u> at the site of injection and feeling a bit <u>under the weather</u> for a week or two afterwards.

2) You can't have some vaccines if you're <u>already ill</u>, especially if your immune system is weakened.

3) Some people think that immunisation can <u>cause other disorders</u>, e.g. one study <u>suggested</u> a link between the <u>MMR</u> (measles, mumps and rubella) vaccine and <u>autism</u>. Most scientists say the MMR jab is perfectly safe, but a lot of parents aren't willing to take the risk. This has led to a big rise in the number of children catching measles, and some people are now worried about an epidemic.

All in all, the <u>benefits</u> of immunisation normally outweigh the <u>risks</u>. Vaccination is now used all over the world. <u>Smallpox</u> no longer occurs at all, and <u>polio</u> infections have fallen by 99%.

Prevention is better than cure

Science isn't just about doing an experiment, finding the answer and telling everyone about it — scientists often disagree. Not that long ago, scientists had different opinions on the MMR vaccine — and argued about its safety. Many different studies were done before they concluded that it was safe.

Treating Disease — Past and Future

The way we fight disease has changed loads over the last few decades. Thankfully.

Semmelweiss *cut deaths by using* antiseptics

1) While <u>Ignaz Semmelweiss</u> was working in Vienna General Hospital in the 1840s, he saw that women were dying in huge numbers after childbirth from a disease called puerperal fever.

2) He believed that <u>doctors</u> were spreading the disease on their <u>unwashed</u> hands. By telling doctors entering his ward to wash their hands in an <u>antiseptic solution</u>, he cut the death rate from 12% to 2%.

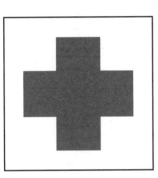

3) The antiseptic solution killed <u>bacteria</u> on doctors' hands, though Semmelweiss didn't know this (the <u>existence</u> of bacteria and their part in causing <u>disease</u> wasn't discovered for another 20 years). So Semmelweiss couldn't <u>prove</u> why his idea worked, and his methods were <u>dropped</u> when he left the hospital (allowing death rates to <u>rise</u> once again — d'oh).

4) Nowadays we know that <u>basic hygiene</u> is essential in controlling disease (though recent reports have found that a lack of it in some <u>modern</u> hospitals has helped the disease <u>MRSA</u> to spread — see below).

Antibiotics *changed the way we* fight infections

1) <u>Antibiotics</u> were an incredibly important (but accidental) discovery. Some killer diseases (e.g. pneumonia and tuberculosis) suddenly became much easier to treat. The 1940s are sometimes called the era of the <u>antibiotics revolution</u> — it was that big a deal.

2) Unfortunately, bacteria <u>evolve</u> (adapt to their environment). If antibiotics are taken to deal with an infection but not all the bacteria are killed, those that survive may be resistant to the antibiotic and go on to flourish. This process (an example of <u>natural selection</u>) leaves you with an <u>antibiotic-resistant strain</u> of bacteria — not ideal.

3) A good example of antibiotic-resistant bacteria is <u>MRSA</u> (methicillin-resistant *Staphylococcus aureus*) — it's resistant to methicillin, which is one of the most powerful antibiotics around. This is why it's important for patients to always <u>finish</u> a course of antibiotics, and for doctors to avoid <u>over-prescribing</u> them.

Antibiotic resistance is inevitable

Antibiotic resistance is a scary prospect. Bacteria reproduce quickly, and so are pretty fast at evolving to deal with threats (e.g. antibiotics). If we were back in the situation where we had no way to treat bacterial infections, we'd have a nightmare. That's why 'superbugs' like MRSA have been in the news so much. So do your bit, and finish your courses of antibiotics.

Treating Disease — Past and Future

When it comes to treating diseases, viruses are normally a bit more problematic than bacteria...

You *can't* use *antibiotics* to treat *viral* infections

Antibiotics <u>don't</u> destroy viruses.

1) Viruses reproduce <u>using your own body cells</u>, which makes it very difficult to develop drugs that destroy just the virus without killing the body's cells.

2) <u>Flu</u> and <u>colds</u> are caused by <u>viruses</u>. Usually you just have to wait for your body to deal with the virus, and relieve the <u>symptoms</u> if you start to feel really grotty.

3) There are some <u>antiviral</u> drugs available, but they're usually <u>reserved</u> for very <u>serious</u> viral illnesses (such as AIDS and hepatitis).

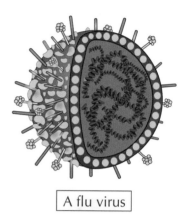

A flu virus

We face *new* and *scary dangers* all the time

1) For the last few decades, humans have been able to deal with <u>bacterial infections</u> pretty easily using <u>antibiotics</u>.

2) But there'd be a real problem if a <u>virus</u> or a strain of bacterium evolved so that it was both <u>deadly</u> and could easily pass from <u>person</u> to <u>person</u>. (<u>Flu</u> viruses, for example, evolve quickly so this is quite possible.)

3) If this happened, <u>precautions</u> could be taken to stop the virus spreading in the first place (though this is hard nowadays — millions of people travel by plane every day). And <u>vaccines</u> and <u>antiviral</u> drugs could be developed (though these take <u>time</u> to mass produce).

4) But in the worst-case scenario, a flu <u>pandemic</u> (e.g. one evolved from bird flu) could kill billions of people all over the world.

A pandemic is when a disease spreads all over the world.

Remember — antibiotics DO NOT kill viruses

The recent scare over 'bird flu' shows how vulnerable we are to viral infections. If one came along that was really dangerous and could spread easily, then it'd be a real problem. That's what happened in 1918 when a flu pandemic killed at least 50 million people — that's more than World War 1. Fortunately, nearly all the recent human cases of 'bird flu' have come from direct contact with birds — the virus has rarely passed from person to person.

Warm-Up and Exam Questions

It's easy to think you've learnt everything in the section until you try the warm-up questions.
Don't panic if there's a bit you've forgotten, just go back over that bit until it's firmly fixed in your brain.

Warm-Up Questions

1) What is a pathogen?
2) Explain how viruses replicate within your body.
3) Give three functions of white blood cells.
4) All pathogens are parasites. What does this mean?
5) What are antigens?

Exam Questions

1   Immunity can be both active and passive. Describe what is meant by:

   (a) active immunity

(1 mark)

   (b) passive immunity

(1 mark)

2   The table below describes some of the ways the body defends itself against invading
     microbes. Match the following defences, **A**, **B**, **C** and **D** with the way they protect the
     body against invading microbes **1 - 4** in the table.

   A   Mucus and cilia in the trachea

   B   Antibodies

   C   Phagocytes

   D   Tears

1	Contain the enzyme lysozyme to kill bacteria
2	Engulf and digest foreign molecules
3	Trap bacteria and dust
4	Lock onto invading microbes and mark them out for ingestion by other white blood cells.

(4 marks)

3   (a) Why would a course of antibiotics not be suitable for treatment of flu?

(2 marks)

   (b) What might the inappropriate use of antibiotics lead to?

(1 mark)

Exam Questions

4   Read the following passage.

> Typhoid is an infectious bacterial disease. The typhoid bacterium is often found in food and water where there is poor sanitation. The bacterium causes fever and severe diarrhoea. Typhoid can be fatal but can be treated using antibiotics. Fortunately, the spread of the disease can be reduced by vaccination.

(a)   Explain how vaccinating against typhoid helps reduce the spread of the disease.

(2 marks)

(b)   Put the following stages in order to describe how the typhoid vaccine works.

1.   Antibodies attack the typhoid bacteria even though it is harmless.

2.   When live typhoid bacteria infect the body, white blood cells rapidly mass produce antibodies to kill off the pathogen.

3.   Antigens on the dead/inactive bacteria stimulate the production of antibodies by white blood cells.

4.   Dead/inactive typhoid bacteria are injected.

5.   White blood cells remain in the body to provide a memory.

(1 mark)

(c)   Give one short-term side effect that might result from a vaccination.

(1 mark)

5   Some health disorders are listed below. Match the disorders **A**, **B**, **C** and **D** with their causes **1 - 4** in the table.

A   Scurvy

B   Haemophilia

C   Anaemia

D   Diabetes

Disorder	Cause
1	Lack of insulin
2	Lack of iron
3	Lack of vitamin C
4	Inheritance of a faulty gene

(4 marks)

Revision Summary for Section Two

That was a long(ish) section, but kind of interesting, I reckon. These questions will show what you know and what you don't... if you get stuck, have a look back to remind yourself. But before the exam, make sure you can do all of them without any help — if you can't, you know you're definitely <u>not ready</u>.

1) Name the six essential nutrients the body needs and say what each is used for.
2)* Put these people in order of how much energy they are likely to need from their food (from highest to lowest): a) builder, b) professional runner, c) waitress, d) secretary.
3) Define obesity and name three conditions obese people are at an increased risk of getting.
4) Explain what kwashiorkor is. Why is this condition more common in developing countries?
5) Explain what is meant by 'good cholesterol' and 'bad cholesterol'.
6) Why is it dangerous to have high levels of cholesterol?
7) Why is it bad for some people to eat too much salt?
8) If you don't add extra salt to your food, why will you not necessarily be safe from having too much salt in your diet?
10) Explain the terms prescription drug and drug addiction.
11) How does a stimulant drug work? Give two examples.
12) Describe the four stages of drug testing.
13) What is a double blind clinical trial?
14) Name a drug that was not tested thoroughly enough and describe the consequences of its use.
15) Describe four different illnesses that smoking can cause.
16) How do carbon monoxide, carcinogens and tar in tobacco smoke each affect the body?
17) Alcohol is a depressant drug. Describe the symptoms of too much alcohol. What effect does alcohol have on the nervous system?
18)*Here is a graph of Mark's blood alcohol concentration against time.
   a) When did Mark have his first alcoholic drink?
   b) When did Mark have his second alcoholic drink?
   c) The legal driving limit is 80 mg of alcohol per 100 ml of blood. Would Mark have been legally allowed to drive at 9pm?
19) Describe some of the effects that inhaling solvents can cause.
20) Why shouldn't you exceed the recommended dose of paracetamol?
21) Name two types of painkiller that can only be used under medical supervision.
22) How do aspirin and ibuprofen work? What about opiates?
23) Name the four types of microorganism that cause disease.
24) Explain the difference between benign and malignant tumours.
25) Name the three parts of the body which make up the first line of defence against pathogens.
26) What is the body's second line of defence against pathogens?
27) Explain how immunisation stops you getting infections.
28) Why shouldn't your doctor give you antibiotics for the flu?

*Answers on page 285.

Adaptation

Animals and plants survive in many different <u>environments</u> — from <u>hot deserts</u> to <u>cold polar regions</u>, and just about everywhere in between. They can do this because they've <u>adapted</u> to their environment.

Desert animals have adapted to *save water*

Animals that live in <u>hot</u>, <u>dry</u> conditions need to <u>keep cool</u> and use <u>water</u> efficiently.

Large surface area compared to *volume*

This lets desert animals <u>lose more body heat</u> — which helps to stop them overheating.

Efficient with water

1) Desert animals <u>lose less water</u> by producing small amounts of <u>concentrated urine</u>.

2) They also make very little <u>sweat</u>. Camels are able to do this by tolerating <u>big changes</u> in <u>body temperature</u>, while kangaroo rats live in <u>burrows</u> underground where it's <u>cool</u>.

Good in hot, sandy conditions

1) Desert animals have very thin layers of <u>body fat</u> to help them <u>lose</u> body heat. Camels keep nearly all their fat in their <u>humps</u>.

2) <u>Large feet</u> spread their <u>weight</u> across soft sand — making getting about easier.

3) A <u>sandy colour</u> gives good <u>camouflage</u> — so they're not as easy for their <u>predators</u> to spot.

Arctic animals have adapted to *reduce heat loss*

Animals that live in <u>really cold</u> conditions need to <u>keep warm</u>.

Small surface area compared to *volume*

Animals living in <u>cold</u> conditions have a <u>compact</u> (rounded) shape to keep their <u>surface area</u> to a minimum — this <u>reduces heat loss</u>.

Well insulated

1) They have a thick layer of <u>blubber</u> for <u>insulation</u> — this also acts as an <u>energy store</u> when food is scarce.

2) <u>Thick hairy coats</u> keep body heat in, and <u>greasy fur</u> sheds water (this <u>prevents cooling</u> due to evaporation).

Good in snowy conditions

1) Arctic animals have <u>white fur</u> to match their surroundings — for <u>camouflage</u>.

2) <u>Big feet</u> help by <u>spreading weight</u> — which stops animals sinking into the snow or breaking thin ice.

Adaptation

Whether you're an animal or a plant, you have to adapt to your environment — and that includes adapting to deal with other plants and animals...

Some **plants** have adapted to living in a **desert**

Desert-dwelling plants make best use of what little water is available.

Minimising water **loss**

1) Cacti have <u>spines instead of leaves</u> — to <u>reduce water loss</u>.
2) They also have a <u>small surface area</u> compared to their size (about 1000 times smaller than normal plants), which also <u>reduces water loss</u>.
3) A cactus <u>stores water</u> in its thick stem.

Maximising water **absorption**

Some cacti have <u>shallow</u> but <u>extensive roots</u> to <u>absorb</u> water quickly over a large area. Others have <u>deep roots</u> to access <u>underground water</u>.

Some **plants and animals** are adapted to **deter predators**

There are various <u>special features</u> used by animals and plants to help <u>protect</u> them against being <u>eaten</u>.

1) Some plants and animals have <u>armour</u> — like brambles (with <u>thorns</u>), cacti (with <u>sharp spines</u>) and tortoises (with <u>hard shells</u>).

2) Others produce <u>poisons</u> — like bees and poison ivy.

3) And some have amazing <u>warning colours</u> to scare off predators — like wasps and some caterpillars.

In a nutshell, it's horses for courses

It's <u>no accident</u> that animals and plants look like they do. So by looking at an animal's <u>characteristics</u>, you should be able to have a pretty good guess at the kind of <u>environment</u> it lives in — or vice versa. Why does it have a large/small surface area... what are those spines for... why is it white... and so on.

Classification

Scientists <u>classify</u> species so that anyone who reads their research knows exactly <u>which organism</u> it is that they're talking about.

Classification *is organising* **living organisms** *into groups*

1) Nowadays scientists classify organisms into groups based on <u>genetic similarities</u>.

   For example, bats, whales and humans might <u>seem</u> quite different, but they have a similar bone pattern in their forelimbs, and they're all <u>genetically</u> related.
   The classification system reflects these <u>similarities</u> (they're all mammals).

2) Living things are divided into <u>kingdoms</u> (e.g. the animal kingdom, the plant kingdom, etc.).

   Kingdoms are then <u>subdivided</u> into smaller and smaller groups.

   An example of one of these smaller groups is a <u>genus</u>.

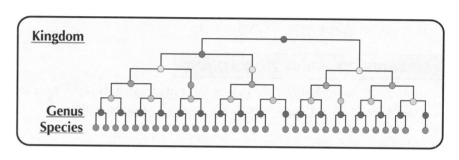

3) A <u>genus</u> is a group of closely-related <u>species</u> — and a species is a group of <u>closely-related</u> organisms that can breed to produce <u>fertile offspring</u> (see page 60).

4) The <u>binomial system</u> that's used to name organisms uses the Latin names of the genus and the species they belong to.

   For example, humans are <u>Homo sapiens</u> — 'Homo' is our <u>genus</u> name and 'sapiens' is our <u>species</u>.

Living things *can be* **plants**, **animals** *or* **something else**

1) To be a member of the plant kingdom, organisms must contain <u>chloroplasts</u> and therefore be able to <u>make their own food</u> using photosynthesis (see page 161).

2) Members of the <u>animal</u> kingdom move about from place to place and have <u>compact</u> bodies (unlike plants, which spread out to catch as much light and water as possible and can't move about freely).

   Animals <u>can't make their own food</u> so they have to find things to eat, such as plants or other animals.

3) Other organisms, like <u>fungi</u> and <u>bacteria</u>, don't have animal or plant features and are put in <u>other kingdoms</u>.

4) Some single-celled organisms have features of <u>both</u> plants and animals.

   <u>Euglena</u> can <u>move</u> from place to place by thrashing its <u>flagellum</u>, but also has <u>chloroplasts</u> which allow it to make its own food.

   It's put into a kingdom called <u>Protoctista</u>, along with some other single-celled organisms.

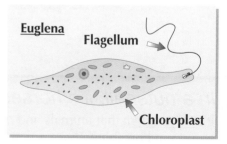

Classification

Vertebrates have backbones

The animal kingdom is divided into <u>vertebrates</u> and <u>invertebrates</u>.

Vertebrates are animals with a <u>backbone</u> and an <u>internal skeleton</u>. Invertebrates don't have these structures — some do have an <u>external skeleton</u> though.

<u>Vertebrates</u> are divided into five groups, called <u>classes</u> — fish, amphibians, reptiles, birds and mammals.

1) <u>FISH</u> live in water. They have <u>scales</u>, and <u>gills</u> for gas exchange.

2) <u>AMPHIBIANS</u> exchange gas partly through their skin, so gases must be able to move in and out — their skin's got to be <u>permeable</u> and <u>moist</u>.

3) <u>REPTILES</u> are more adapted to live on the land. They've got a <u>dry scaly skin</u> which stops them losing too much water.

4) Most <u>BIRDS</u> can fly and they've got <u>feathers</u> to help them do this. You'll also find a <u>beak</u> — useful for cracking seeds or catching prey.

5) <u>MAMMALS</u> have <u>fur</u> covering their bodies to keep them warm. They give birth to their young (rather than laying eggs like other vertebrates) and <u>produce milk</u> to feed them.

The rules of the classification system were made up using the animals and plants that were known about at the time.

Sometimes <u>newly discovered species</u> don't really fit into any of the categories. These can be <u>living species</u> or <u>fossil ones</u>, such as <u>archaeopteryx</u>, which had reptilian teeth, clawed hands and a long bony tail, like a dinosaur, but also had wings and flight feathers, like a bird.

Warm-Up and Exam Questions

Learning facts and practising exam questions is the only recipe for success.
That's what the questions on this page are all about. All you have to do — is do them.

Warm-Up Questions

1) Why is a small body surface area compared to its volume an advantage for an animal living in cold conditions?
2) Give two adaptations that a wasp has developed to help deter predators.
3) Explain the meaning of the term species.
4) Give two of the defining characteristics of a mammal.

Exam Questions

1   Arctic animals are adapted to their environment.
The table below is about the adaptations of a polar bear.
Match each adaptation, **A**, **B**, **C** and **D** in the list with its purpose (**1 - 4**).

    A   Large feet

    B   Thick layer of blubber

    C   White fur

    D   Greasy fur

	Purpose
1	Prevents cooling due to evaporation.
2	Stops them sinking into snow.
3	Helps them retain body heat.
4	Makes it hard for prey to spot them.

(4 marks)

2   Explain how the features of a cactus help it to survive in desert conditions.

(3 marks)

3   Match each of the classes of vertebrate on the left with one of their features on the right.

    A AMPHIBIANS   **1** Have dry scaly skin.

    B REPTILES   **2** Have a beak used for catching prey or cracking seeds.

    C BIRDS   **3** Can exchange gases over their skin surface.

(3 marks)

Ecosystems

An <u>ecosystem</u> is all the <u>different organisms</u> living together in a <u>particular environment</u>. Sounds cosy.

Artificial ecosystems can be carefully controlled

1) There are <u>two types of ecosystem</u> you need to know about:

> A <u>natural ecosystem</u> is one where humans <u>don't control the processes</u> going on within it.
>
> An <u>artificial ecosystem</u> is one where humans <u>deliberately</u> promote the growth of certain living organisms and get rid of others which threaten their well-being.

2) Humans <u>might</u> affect <u>natural ecosystems</u> in some way, but they <u>don't take deliberate steps</u> to decide what animals and plants should be there.

3) <u>Artificial ecosystems</u> are most common in money-making enterprises, e.g. <u>farms</u> and <u>market gardens</u>. Things like weedkillers, pesticides and fertilisers are used to control conditions. <u>Artificial ecosystems</u> normally have a <u>smaller number of species</u> (less <u>biodiversity</u>) than natural ones.

Estimate population sizes in an ecosystem using a quadrat

A <u>quadrat</u> is a square frame enclosing a known area.
You just place it on the ground, and look at what's inside it.

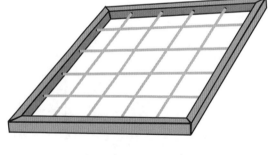

A quadrat

> To estimate <u>population size</u>:
>
> 1) Count all the organisms in a <u>1 m² quadrat</u>.
>
> 2) Multiply the number of organisms by the <u>total area</u> (in m²) of the habitat.
>
> 3) ...and there you go, easy as that.

Two important points about this kind of counting method...

1) The <u>sample size</u> affects the <u>accuracy</u> of the estimate — the bigger your sample, the more accurate your estimate of the total population is likely to be. (So it'd be better to use the quadrat more than once, get an <u>average</u> value for the number of organisms in a 1 m² quadrat, then multiply that by the total area.)

2) The sample may not be <u>representative</u> of the population, i.e. what you find in your sample might be different from what you'd have found if you'd looked somewhere else.

Species

Organisms are <u>classified</u> depending on how <u>closely related</u> they are to other groups of organisms. It's just sometimes quite <u>difficult</u> to work out how closely related two groups are...

Different **organisms** belong to different **species**

1) Organisms are of the <u>same species</u> if they can <u>breed</u> to produce <u>fertile offspring</u>.

2) If you interbreed a male from one species with a female from a <u>different</u> species you'll get a <u>hybrid</u> (that's if you get anything at all). For example, a <u>mule</u> is a cross between a donkey and a horse. But hybrids are <u>infertile</u> so they <u>aren't</u> new species.

Unrelated species may have **similar features**

1) Similar species often share a <u>recent common ancestor</u>, so they're <u>closely related</u> in evolutionary terms. They often look <u>alike</u> and tend to live in similar types of <u>habitat</u>, e.g. whales and dolphins.

2) This isn't always the case though — closely related species may look <u>very different</u> if they have evolved to live in <u>different habitats</u>, e.g. llamas and camels.

3) Species that are <u>very different genetically</u> may also end up looking alike. E.g. dolphins and sharks look pretty similar and swim in a similar way. But they're totally different species — dolphins are <u>mammals</u> and sharks are <u>fish</u>.

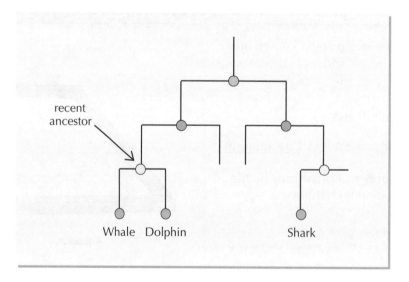

4) So to explain the similarities and differences between species, you have to consider how they're related in <u>evolutionary terms</u> AND the <u>type of environment</u> they've adapted to survive in.

Organisms of different species produce infertile offspring

It's possible to breed lions and tigers together... it's true — they produce <u>hybrids</u> called tigons and ligers. They look a bit like lions and a bit like tigers... as you'd expect. The offspring produced when lions and tigers breed are infertile though — this shows that they are from different species.

Populations and Competition

Organisms have to <u>compete for resources</u> in the environment where they live.

Population size is limited by available resources

<u>Population size</u> is limited by:

> 1) The <u>total amount of food</u> or nutrients available
> (plants don't eat, but they get <u>minerals</u> from the soil).

> 2) The amount of <u>water</u> available.

> 3) The <u>amount of light available</u> (this applies only to plants really).

> 4) The quality and amount of <u>shelter</u> available.

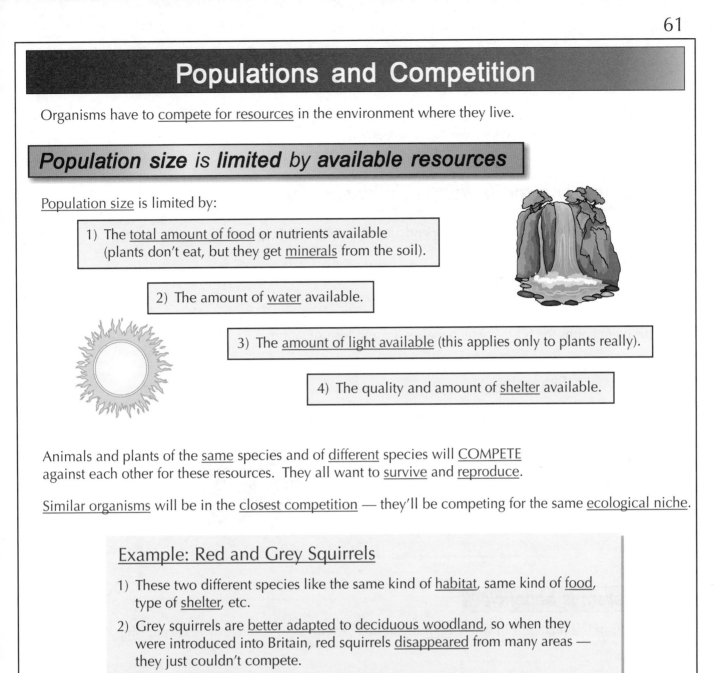

Animals and plants of the <u>same</u> species and of <u>different</u> species will <u>COMPETE</u> against each other for these resources. They all want to <u>survive</u> and <u>reproduce</u>.

<u>Similar organisms</u> will be in the <u>closest competition</u> — they'll be competing for the same <u>ecological niche</u>.

Example: Red and Grey Squirrels

1) These two different species like the same kind of <u>habitat</u>, same kind of <u>food</u>, type of <u>shelter</u>, etc.
2) Grey squirrels are <u>better adapted</u> to <u>deciduous woodland</u>, so when they were introduced into Britain, red squirrels <u>disappeared</u> from many areas — they just couldn't compete.

Populations of prey and predators go in cycles

In a community containing <u>prey</u> and <u>predators</u> (as most of them do of course):

1) The <u>population</u> of any species is usually <u>limited</u> by the amount of <u>food</u> available.

2) If the population of the <u>prey</u> increases, then so will the population of the <u>predators</u>.

3) However as the population of predators <u>increases</u>, the number of prey will <u>decrease</u>.

E.g. <u>More grass</u> means <u>more rabbits</u>. More rabbits means <u>more foxes</u>. But more foxes means <u>less rabbits</u>. Eventually less rabbits will mean <u>less foxes again</u>. This <u>up and down pattern</u> continues...

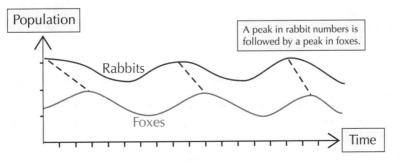

> A peak in rabbit numbers is followed by a peak in foxes.

Parasites and Mutualism

All organisms <u>depend</u>, at least to some extent, on other organisms in their <u>ecosystem</u>.
There are some species that take this to the <u>extreme</u>.

Parasites and mutualistic relationships

The <u>survival</u> of some organisms can <u>depend</u> almost entirely on the presence of <u>other species</u>.

Parasites live off a host

Parasites <u>take</u> what they need to survive, <u>without</u> giving anything <u>back</u>.
This often <u>harms</u> the host — which makes it a win-lose situation.

Examples:

- <u>Tapeworms</u> absorb lots of <u>nutrients</u> from the host, causing them to suffer from <u>malnutrition</u>.

- <u>Fleas</u> are parasites. Dogs gain nothing from having fleas (unless you count hundreds of bites).

Mutualism is beneficial

Mutualism is a relationship where <u>both</u> organisms benefit — so it's a win-win relationship.

Examples:

- Most plants have to rely on <u>nitrogen-fixing bacteria</u> in the soil to get the <u>nitrates</u> that they need. But <u>leguminous plants</u> carry the bacteria in <u>nodules</u> in their <u>roots</u>. The bacteria get a constant supply of <u>sugar</u> from the plant, and the plant gets essential <u>nitrates</u> from the bacteria.

- '<u>Cleaner species</u>' are fantastic. E.g. <u>oxpeckers</u> live on the backs of <u>buffalo</u>. Not only do they <u>eat pests</u> on the buffalo, like ticks, flies and maggots (providing the oxpeckers with a source of food), but they also <u>alert</u> the animal to any <u>predators</u> that are near, by hissing.

The organisms in an ecosystem depend upon each other

In the exam you might get asked about the distribution of <u>any</u> animals or plants. Just think about what they would need to survive. And remember, if things are in <u>limited supply</u> then there's going to be <u>competition</u>. And the more similar the needs of the organisms, the more they'll have to compete.

Warm-Up and Exam Questions

I know that you'll be champing at the bit to get into the exam questions, but these basic warm-up questions are invaluable to get the basic facts straight first.

Warm-Up Questions

1) What is a quadrat and what is it used for?
2) What is the difference between a natural ecosystem and an artificial ecosystem?
3) State three factors that limit the population size for any organism.
4) What is mutualism?

Exam Questions

1 Which of the following is an example of mutualism?

   A   Tapeworms absorbing nutrients from its host.

   B   A bee getting nectar from a plant which it pollinates with pollen from another plant.

   C   Fleas feeding on the blood of a vertebrate host.

   D   Foxes depending on rabbits for a source of nutrients.

(1 mark)

2 Which of the following statements is **never** true about organisms of the same species?

   A   They are able to breed to produce a sterile hybrid.

   B   They live in similar types of habitat.

   C   They are able to breed to produce fertile offspring.

   D   They look similar.

(1 mark)

3 The graph below shows the changes in a population of owls and in a population of mice over a number of years in an area.

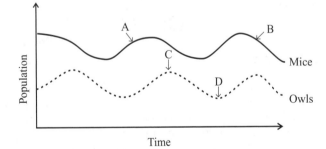

(a) At which point, A, B, C or D, are there fewest owls?

(1 mark)

(b) Suggest why the number of owls falls after point C.

(2 marks)

(c) Suggest what might happen to the owl population if another species was introduced that also eats mice as its main food source.

(1 mark)

Evolution

So far about <u>1.5 million different species</u> have been identified. There are probably many more still to find. But how life first got started on planet Earth is still a mystery.

No one knows how life began

We know that <u>living things</u> come from <u>other</u> living things — that's easy enough.
But where the <u>first</u> living thing came from... that's a much more difficult question.

1) There are various <u>theories</u> suggesting how life first came into being, but no one really <u>knows</u>.

2) Maybe the first life forms came into existence in a primordial <u>swamp</u> (or under the <u>sea</u>) here on <u>Earth</u>.

   Maybe simple organic molecules were brought to Earth on <u>comets</u> — these could have then become more <u>complex</u> organic molecules, and eventually very simple <u>life forms</u>.

3) These ideas, and others, have their supporters. But we just don't know — the evidence was lost long ago. All we know is that life started <u>somehow</u>. And after that, we're on slightly firmer ground.

The fossil record shows that organisms have evolved

1) A <u>fossil</u> is <u>any evidence</u> of an animal or plant that lived ages ago.

2) Fossils form in rocks as <u>minerals</u> replace <u>slowly decaying</u> tissue (or in places where no decay happens) and show features like <u>shells</u>, <u>skeletons</u>, <u>soft tissue</u> (occasionally), <u>footprints</u>, etc.

   They show what was on Earth millions of years ago. They can also give clues about an organism's <u>habitat</u> and <u>food</u>.

3) We also know that the <u>layers of rock</u> where fossils are found were made at <u>different times</u>. This means it's possible to tell how long ago a particular species <u>lived</u>.

4) From studying the <u>similarities</u> and <u>differences</u> between fossils in rocks of different ages, we can see how species have <u>evolved</u> (changed and developed) over <u>billions of years</u>.

> THEORY OF EVOLUTION: Life began as <u>simple organisms</u> from which <u>more complex organisms</u> <u>evolved</u> (rather than just popping into existence).

6) In theory, you could put all species on a 'family tree' — where each new branch shows the <u>evolution</u> of a new species. Then you could easily find the most recent <u>common ancestor</u> of any two species.

   The more <u>recent</u> the common ancestor, the more <u>closely related</u> the two species.

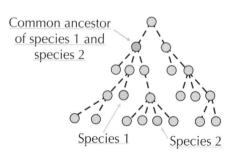

Common ancestor of species 1 and species 2

Species 1   Species 2

5) Unfortunately, very few organisms <u>turn into fossils</u> when they die — most decay away completely. This leaves <u>gaps</u> in the <u>fossil record</u>, which means there are many species that we'll never know about.

Evolution

The evidence in the <u>fossil record</u> supports the theory of <u>evolution</u>.
You can use the fossil record to trace the evolution of <u>individual species</u>.

The *evolution* of the *horse*

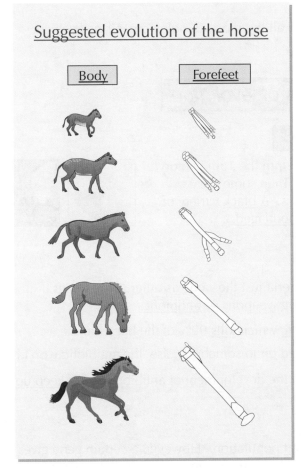

Suggested evolution of the horse

Body   Forefeet

1) The fossil record of the <u>horse</u> provides <u>strong evidence</u> for the <u>theory of evolution</u>.

   But things are a little more complicated than we first thought.

2) If you stick all the fossil bones in order of age, they seem to show the modern horse evolving gradually from a creature about the size of a <u>dog</u>, with the <u>middle toe</u> slowly getting bigger to form the familiar <u>hoof</u>.

3) At first some fossils didn't seem to fit.

   But now we know that <u>several now-extinct kinds</u> of horse evolved at the same time, and it all makes <u>sense</u>.

There are *other views* about the fossil record

Some people interpret the fossil evidence differently.

For example, <u>creationists</u> believe that <u>each species</u> was created separately by God and will <u>never evolve</u> into new species.

They don't think the fossil record is evidence for <u>gradual evolution</u>, but simply shows <u>a lot of different organisms</u>, some of which are now extinct.

Fossils give us information about the history of life on Earth
The fossil record provides <u>good evidence</u> for evolution, but it <u>can't prove it</u>. But proving a theory about something that happens over millions of years was never going to be straightforward.

Evolution

The <u>theory of evolution</u> states that one of your (probably very distant) ancestors was a <u>blob</u> in a swamp somewhere. Something like that, anyway.

Make sure you know the **Theory of Evolution**

1) Don't forget what you learnt over the last couple of pages — the theory of evolution states that all of the animals and plants on Earth gradually '<u>evolved</u>' over <u>millions</u> of years, rather than just suddenly appearing.

2) Life on Earth began as <u>simple organisms</u> from which all the more complex organisms evolved. And it only took about <u>3 000 000 000 years</u>.

There are lots of **modern examples** *of evolution*

1) **Peppered moths** *adapted their colour*

<u>Peppered moths</u> are often seen on the <u>bark</u> of trees. Until the 19th century, the only ones found in England were <u>light</u> in colour. Then some areas became <u>polluted</u> and the soot darkened the tree trunks. A <u>black</u> variety of moth was found. The moths had <u>adapted</u> to stay <u>camouflaged</u>.

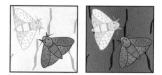

2) **Bacteria** *adapt to beat antibiotics*

The "<u>survival of the fittest</u>" (see next page) affects bacteria just the same as other living things. They adapt to become <u>resistant</u> to our bacteria-fighting weapons — <u>antibiotics</u>.

1) If someone gets ill they might be given an <u>antibiotic</u> which <u>kills</u> 99% of the bacteria.

2) The 1% that survive are <u>resistant</u> so if they're passed on to somebody else, the antibiotic won't help.

Nowadays bacteria are getting resistant at such a rate the development of antibiotics <u>can't keep up</u>.

3) **Rats** *adapt to beat poison*

The poison <u>warfarin</u> was widely used to control the <u>rat</u> population. However, a certain gene gives rats <u>resistance</u> to it, so rats which carry it are more likely to survive and breed. This gene has become more and more <u>frequent</u> in the rat population, so warfarin isn't as much use any more.

Environmental change can cause **extinction**

1) The <u>dinosaurs</u> and <u>woolly mammoths</u> became <u>extinct</u>, and it's only <u>fossils</u> that tell us they ever existed.

There are <u>three ways</u> a species can become <u>extinct</u>:

1. The <u>environment changes</u> more quickly than the species can adapt.

2. A new <u>predator</u> or <u>disease</u> kills them all.

3. They can't <u>compete</u> with another (new) species for <u>food</u>.

2) As the environment changes, it'll <u>gradually</u> favour certain characteristics (see p.68).

3) Over many generations those features will be present in <u>more</u> of the population. In this way, the species constantly <u>adapts</u> to its changing environment.

4) But if the environment changes too <u>fast</u> the whole species may become <u>extinct</u>.

Natural Selection

Charles Darwin developed a theory about how evolution actually happened.
He called it the theory of <u>natural selection</u>. This is how he came up with it...

Darwin made *four* important *observations*...

1) All organisms produce <u>more offspring</u> than could possibly survive
   (e.g. only a few frogspawn survive and become frogs).

2) But in fact, population numbers tend to remain
   <u>fairly constant</u> over long periods of time.

3) Also, organisms in a species show <u>wide variation</u> in <u>characteristics</u>.

4) <u>Some</u> of the variations are <u>inherited</u>, and so <u>passed on</u>
   to the next generation.

...and then made these *two deductions*:

1) Since most offspring don't survive, all organisms must have to <u>struggle for survival</u>.
   <u>Being eaten</u>, <u>disease</u> and <u>competition</u> cause large numbers of individuals to die.

2) The ones who have characteristics that allow them to <u>survive and reproduce</u> better
   (i.e. the most useful <u>adaptations</u> to the environment) will <u>pass on these</u>
   <u>characteristics</u>.

This is the famous "<u>survival of the fittest</u>" statement.
Organisms with slightly less survival value will
probably perish first, leaving the <u>fittest</u> to pass on
their <u>genes</u> to the next generation.

Natural selection — the fittest pass on their characteristics

This is a good example of how scientific theories come about — someone <u>observes</u> something and
tries to <u>explain</u> it. Their theory will then be <u>tested</u> by other scientists using <u>evidence</u> — if the theory
passes these tests, it gains in credibility. If not, it's <u>rejected</u>. Natural selection <u>hasn't</u> been rejected yet.

Natural Selection

Have a look at this example to see how a <u>whole population</u> can change its <u>characteristics</u> pretty easily.

Organisms with certain **characteristics** will **survive** better

Here's an example...

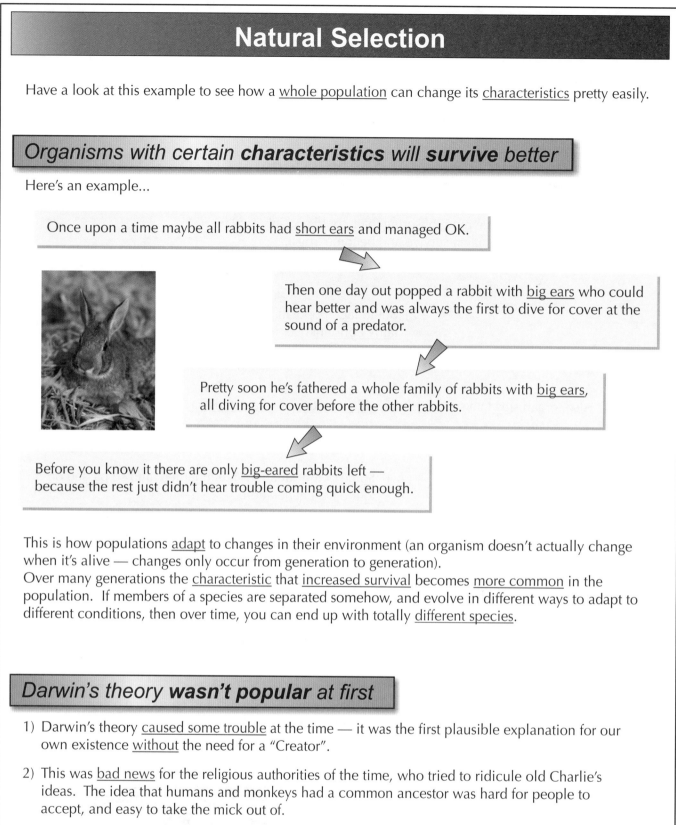

Once upon a time maybe all rabbits had <u>short ears</u> and managed OK.

Then one day out popped a rabbit with <u>big ears</u> who could hear better and was always the first to dive for cover at the sound of a predator.

Pretty soon he's fathered a whole family of rabbits with <u>big ears</u>, all diving for cover before the other rabbits.

Before you know it there are only <u>big-eared</u> rabbits left — because the rest just didn't hear trouble coming quick enough.

This is how populations <u>adapt</u> to changes in their environment (an organism doesn't actually change when it's alive — changes only occur from generation to generation).
Over many generations the <u>characteristic</u> that <u>increased survival</u> becomes <u>more common</u> in the population. If members of a species are separated somehow, and evolve in different ways to adapt to different conditions, then over time, you can end up with totally <u>different species</u>.

Darwin's theory **wasn't popular** at first

1) Darwin's theory <u>caused some trouble</u> at the time — it was the first plausible explanation for our own existence <u>without</u> the need for a "Creator".

2) This was <u>bad news</u> for the religious authorities of the time, who tried to ridicule old Charlie's ideas. The idea that humans and monkeys had a common ancestor was hard for people to accept, and easy to take the mick out of.

3) Some <u>scientists weren't keen</u> either, at first. Darwin didn't provide a proper explanation of exactly <u>how</u> individual organisms passed on their survival characteristics to their offspring.

4) Later, the idea of <u>genetics</u> was understood — which <u>did</u> explain how characteristics are inherited.

You'll increase your chances of survival by learning this stuff

Darwin was ridiculed by the Church about his theory, but it wasn't the first time a scientist or philosopher was picked on by the Church... Galileo was put under house arrest by the Church for nine years for supporting Copernicus' theory that the Earth was not the centre of the Universe.

Warm-Up and Exam Questions

The warm-up questions run quickly over the basic facts you'll need in the exam. The exam questions come later — but unless you've learnt the facts first you'll find the exams tougher than stale bread.

Warm-Up Questions

1) What can a fossil of an organism tell us?
2) Explain why there are gaps in the fossil record.
3) What is meant by the term 'survival of the fittest'?
4) Explain the difference between evolution and natural selection.

Exam Questions

1   Which of the following could **not** cause a species to become extinct?

   A   Competition from another species for food.

   B   The environment changing more quickly than the species can adapt.

   C   The species producing too many offspring.

   D   A new disease emerging.

(1 mark)

2   The picture on the right shows what scientists believe the dinosaur **Stegosaurus** looked like.

   (a)   What evidence is there that Stegosaurus existed?

(1 mark)

   (b)   It is estimated that Stegosaurus lived about 150 million years ago. How can scientists tell approximately how old a fossil is?

(1 mark)

   (c)   Fossils of Stegosaurus teeth have been discovered. What useful information about Stegosaurus might the fossils of its teeth provide?

(1 mark)

   (d)   Scientists believe that all dinosaurs have a common ancestor.
   Why might it be difficult to find evidence of this common ancestor?

(1 mark)

3   Charles Darwin developed the theory of evolution by natural selection.

   (a)   Give one observation he made that led him to this theory.

(1 mark)

   (b)   According to Darwin's theory, explain how natural selection occurs.

(4 marks)

   (c)   Why did Darwin have trouble getting his theory accepted?

(1 mark)

Revision Summary for Section Three

There's a lot to remember in this section and you need to know all the facts... so here are some questions to help you. If you get any wrong, there's no shame in it and nobody will shout at you — just go back and learn the stuff again AND DO IT PROPERLY THIS TIME.

1) Give four ways in which a desert animal may be adapted to its environment, and two ways that a desert plant might be adapted.

2) Explain how an animal that lives in the Arctic might be adapted to its environment.

3) State three ways that plants and animals might be adapted to deter predators.

4) Name two different kingdoms.

5) What do all vertebrates have in common?

6) Name the five different types of vertebrate.

7) Why are euglena and archaeopteryx difficult to classify?

8) What is the difference between a natural and an artificial ecosystem?

9) How could you estimate a population size in a habitat using a quadrat?
Give two reasons why your results might not be 100% accurate.

10) Explain two reasons why different species may look similar.

11) Name three things that:
a) plants compete for,
b) animals compete for.

12) Sketch a typical graph of prey and predator populations and explain the pattern shown.

13) What is the difference between a parasitic and a mutualistic relationship?
Give an example of each.

14) Briefly describe two theories that have been suggested as explanations of how life on Earth began.

15) Write down the theory of Evolution.

16) Why are there gaps in the fossil record.

17) Describe three modern examples of evolution.

18) Give three reasons why some species become extinct.

19) What were Darwin's four observations and two deductions that led to his theory of natural selection?

20) Why was Darwin's theory controversial?

Variation in Plants and Animals

The word 'variation' sounds far too fancy for its own good. All it means is how animals or plants of the same species look or behave slightly differently from each other. You know, a bit taller or a bit fatter or a bit more scary-to-look-at etc. There are two kinds of variation — genetic and environmental.

Genetic variation is caused by genes

1) All animals (including humans) are bound to be slightly different from each other because their genes are slightly different.

2) Genes are the code which determines how your body turns out — they control your inherited traits, e.g. eye colour. We all end up with a slightly different set of genes. The exceptions to this rule are identical twins, because their genes are exactly the same.

See page 73 for more about genes.

Most variation in animals is due to genes and environment

1) Most variation in animals is caused by a mixture of genetic and environmental factors.

2) Almost every single aspect of a human (or other animal) is affected by our environment in some way, however small. In fact it's a lot easier to list the factors which aren't affected in any way by environment:

If you're not sure what "environment" means, think of it as "upbringing" instead.

> 1) Eye colour,
> 2) Hair colour in most animals (in humans, vanity plays a big part),
> 3) Inherited disorders like haemophilia, cystic fibrosis, etc.,
> 4) Blood group.

3) Environment can have a large effect on human growth even before someone's born. For example, a baby's weight at birth can be affected by the mother's diet.

4) And having a poor diet whilst you're growing up can stunt your growth — another environmental variation.

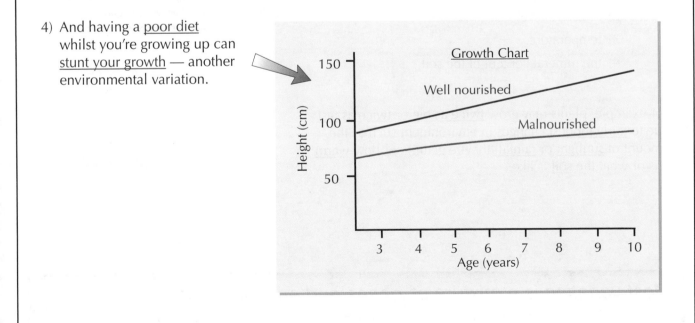

Growth Chart

Well nourished

Malnourished

Height (cm)

150

100

50

3 4 5 6 7 8 9 10
Age (years)

Variation in Plants and Animals

Sometimes it's **hard** to tell which **factor** is **more important**

For some characteristics, it's hard to say which factor is more important — genes or environment...

1) <u>Health</u> — Some people are more likely to get certain <u>diseases</u> (e.g. <u>cancer</u> and <u>heart disease</u>) because of their genes. But <u>lifestyle</u> also affects the risk, e.g. if you smoke or only eat junk food.

2) <u>Intelligence</u> — One theory is that although your <u>maximum possible IQ</u> might be determined by your <u>genes</u>, whether you get to it depends on your <u>environment</u>, e.g. your <u>upbringing</u> and <u>school</u> life.

3) <u>Sporting ability</u> — Again, genes probably determine your <u>potential</u>, but training is important too.

Environmental variation in **plants** is much **greater**

Plants are strongly affected by:

1) sunlight,
2) moisture level,
3) temperature,
4) the mineral content of the soil.

Think about it — if you give your pot plant some plant food (full of lovely minerals), then your plant grows loads faster. Farmers and gardeners use <u>mineral fertilisers</u> to improve crop yields.

For example, plants may grow <u>twice as big</u> or <u>twice as fast</u> due to <u>fairly modest</u> changes in environment such as the amount of <u>sunlight</u> or <u>rainfall</u> they're getting, or how <u>warm</u> it is or what the <u>soil</u> is like.

Most variation is a mixture of genes and environment

So there you go... the "<u>nature versus nurture</u>" debate (*Are you like you are because of the genes you're born with, or because of the way you're brought up?*) summarised in two pages. And the winner is... well, <u>both</u> of them. Your genes are pretty vital, but then so is your environment. What an anticlimax.

Genes and Chromosomes

This page is a bit tricky, but it's dead important you get to grips with all the stuff on it
— because you're going to hear a <u>lot more</u> about it over the next few pages...

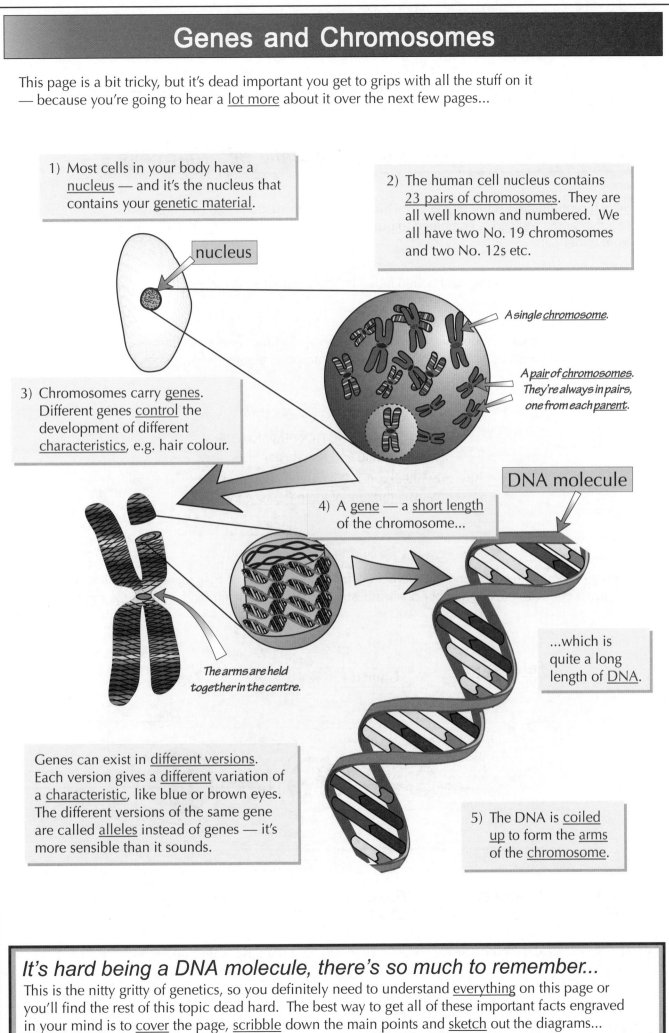

1) Most cells in your body have a
<u>nucleus</u> — and it's the nucleus that
contains your <u>genetic material</u>.

2) The human cell nucleus contains
<u>23 pairs of chromosomes</u>. They are
all well known and numbered. We
all have two No. 19 chromosomes
and two No. 12s etc.

nucleus

A single <u>chromosome</u>.

*A <u>pair</u> of <u>chromosomes</u>.
They're always in pairs,
one from each <u>parent</u>.*

3) Chromosomes carry <u>genes</u>.
Different genes <u>control</u> the
development of different
<u>characteristics</u>, e.g. hair colour.

4) A <u>gene</u> — a <u>short length</u>
of the chromosome...

DNA molecule

...which is
quite a long
length of <u>DNA</u>.

*The arms are held
together in the centre.*

Genes can exist in <u>different versions</u>.
Each version gives a <u>different</u> variation of
a <u>characteristic</u>, like blue or brown eyes.
The different versions of the same gene
are called <u>alleles</u> instead of genes — it's
more sensible than it sounds.

5) The DNA is <u>coiled
up</u> to form the <u>arms</u>
of the <u>chromosome</u>.

It's hard being a DNA molecule, there's so much to remember...

This is the nitty gritty of genetics, so you definitely need to understand <u>everything</u> on this page or
you'll find the rest of this topic dead hard. The best way to get all of these important facts engraved
in your mind is to <u>cover</u> the page, <u>scribble</u> down the main points and <u>sketch</u> out the diagrams...

Sexual Reproduction and Variation

Everyone is slightly different. This is partly due to differences in environment, but also partly because we all have different genes (except identical twins). And that's down to sexual reproduction.

Sexual reproduction produces genetically different cells

1) Sexual reproduction is the process in which genetic information from two organisms (a father and a mother) is combined to produce offspring which are genetically different from either parent.

2) In sexual reproduction the mother and father produce gametes — e.g. egg and sperm cells in animals.

3) In humans, each gamete contains 23 chromosomes — half the number of chromosomes in a normal cell. (Instead of having two of each chromosome, a gamete has just one of each.)

> SEXUAL REPRODUCTION involves the fusion of male and female gametes.
>
> Because there are TWO parents, the offspring contains a mixture of the parents' genes.

4) The egg (from the mother) and the sperm cell (from the father) then fuse together (fertilisation) to form a cell with the full number of chromosomes (half from the father, half from the mother).

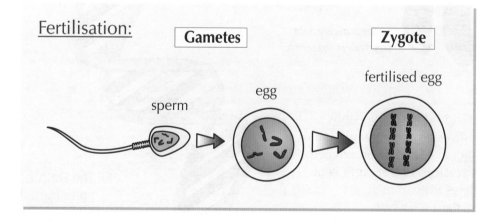

Fertilisation:　Gametes　Zygote

fertilised egg

sperm　egg

5) The offspring inherits features from both parents — it's received a mixture of chromosomes from its mum and its dad (and it's the chromosomes that decide how you turn out).

6) This is why sexual reproduction produces more variation than asexual reproduction (see page 84).

Mutations and Variation

Not all genetic differences are down to sexual reproduction.
Some are the result of <u>mutations</u> — changes in your DNA sequence.

Mutations are changes to the genetic code

1) Occasionally a gene may <u>mutate</u>. Mutations <u>change the sequence</u> of the <u>DNA bases</u> (see page 109). This could <u>stop the production</u> of a <u>protein</u>, or it might mean a <u>different</u> protein is produced instead. This can lead to <u>new characteristics</u>, <u>increasing variation</u>.

2) Mutations can happen <u>spontaneously</u> — when a chromosome doesn't quite copy itself properly. However, the chance of mutation is <u>increased</u> by exposing yourself to:

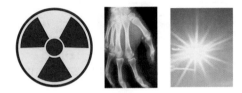

- <u>nuclear radiation</u>, <u>X-rays</u> or <u>ultraviolet light</u>.

- <u>chemicals</u> called <u>mutagens</u>. <u>Cigarette smoke</u> contains mutagens. If the mutations lead to cancer, the chemicals are called <u>carcinogens</u>.

3) Mutations are usually <u>harmful</u>.

> If a mutation occurs in <u>reproductive cells</u>, the offspring might develop <u>abnormally</u> or <u>die</u>.
>
> If a mutation occurs in body cells, the mutant cells may start to <u>multiply</u> in an <u>uncontrolled</u> way and <u>invade</u> other parts of the body (which is <u>cancer</u>).

Mutations can create new characteristics

<u>Very occasionally</u>, mutations are beneficial and give an organism a survival <u>advantage</u>, so it can live on in conditions where the others die. This is <u>natural selection</u> at work.

> For example, a mutation in a bacterium might make it <u>resistant</u> to <u>antibiotics</u>. If this mutant gene is passed on, you might get a <u>resistant</u> "<u>strain</u>" of bacteria, which antibiotics can't kill.

Sexual reproduction and mutations both create genetic variation

The main messages here are that: 1) <u>Sexual reproduction</u> needs <u>two</u> parents to form offspring that are <u>genetically different</u> to both, so it leads to <u>lots</u> of variation. 2) <u>Mutations</u> can also lead to an increase in variation and can occasionally be <u>beneficial</u> — although they're more likely to be <u>harmful</u>.

Warm-Up and Exam Questions

Take a deep breath and go through these warm-up questions one by one.
If you don't know these basic facts there's no way you'll cope with the exam questions.

Warm-Up Questions

1) State four environmental factors that can affect the growth of plants
2) Where is DNA found in an animal or plant cell?
3) What are genes?
4) Why does sexual reproduction lead to variation?
5) Give an example of a mutation that could prove beneficial to an organism.

Exam Questions

1   (a)   What are the male and female human gametes?

(2 marks)

(b)   How many chromosomes does a human gamete contain?

(1 mark)

Two human gametes fuse to form a zygote.

(c)   How many chromosomes does the zygote contain?

(1 mark)

(d)   What fraction of its chromosomes has the zygote inherited from its mother?

(1 mark)

2   This is Ruth, and her little brother Mark.

(a)   Ruth's eyes are blue.
Mark's eyes are brown.
Why do Ruth and Mark have different colour eyes?

(1 mark)

(b)   Explain why sexual reproduction produces variation.

(3 marks)

(c)   Ruth and Mark are going to have a new baby sister.

Which **one** of the following statements about the baby's eye colour is true?

A   The baby's eyes will be the same colour as Ruth's eyes.

B   The baby's eye colour will depend on the genes that it inherits from both parents.

C   The baby's eyes will be the same colour as its mother's eyes.

D   The baby's eyes will definitely be a different colour to both parents' eyes.

(1 mark)

Exam Questions

3   Which of the following statements about sperm cells and egg cells is correct?

     A   They contain twice as much genetic information as normal body cells.

     B   They contain the same amount of genetic information as normal body cells.

     C   They do not contain any genetic information.

     D   They contain half the genetic information of normal body cells.

          (1 mark)

4   How many chromosomes does a human liver cell contain?

     A   2

     B   23

     C   23 pairs

     D   46 pairs

          (1 mark)

5   The following piece of advice is taken from a cigarette packet: Smoking Causes Cancer.

    (a)   What is cancer?

          (1 mark)

    (b)   Cancers are the result of mutations. What is a mutation?

          (1 mark)

    (c)   Give two things (other than cigarette smoke) that can increase the risk of mutation.

          (2 marks)

    (d)   Explain why some mutations can be beneficial.

          (2 marks)

6   Andrew and Peter are identical twins. Peter is heavier than Andrew but Andrew is taller.

    (a)   Some people find it hard to tell Andrew and Peter from each other.
        Why do identical twins, such as Andrew and Peter, look very similar?

          (1 mark)

    (b)   Andrew and Peter are not completely identical.
        Explain why Andrew and Peter look slightly different from each other.

          (1 mark)

    (c)   (i)   Give one human characteristic that is determined only by genes.

          (1 mark)

        (ii)   Give one human characteristic that is not affected by genes.

          (1 mark)

Genetic Diagrams

When a <u>single gene</u> controls the inheritance of a characteristic, you can work out the odds of getting it...

Alleles are different versions of the same gene

1) Most of the time you have <u>two</u> of each gene (i.e. two alleles) — one from each parent.

2) If the alleles are different you have instructions for two different versions of a characteristic (e.g. blue eyes or brown eyes), but you only show one version of the two (e.g. brown eyes). The version of the characteristic that appears is caused by the <u>dominant allele</u>. The other allele is said to be <u>recessive</u>.

3) In genetic diagrams <u>letters</u> are used to represent <u>genes</u>. <u>Dominant</u> alleles are always shown with a <u>capital letter</u> (e.g. 'C') and <u>recessive</u> alleles with a <u>small letter</u> (e.g. 'c').

4) You'll need to know the definitions of homozygous and heterozygous:

Homozygous

If you're <u>homozygous</u> for a trait you have <u>two alleles the same</u> for that particular gene, e.g. CC or cc.

Heterozygous

If you're <u>heterozygous</u> for a trait you have <u>two different alleles</u> for that particular gene, e.g. Cc.

You need to be able to construct and explain genetic diagrams

Imagine you're cross-breeding <u>hamsters</u>, and that some have a normal, boring disposition while others have a leaning towards crazy acrobatics. And suppose you know the behaviour is due to one gene...

Let's say that the allele which causes the crazy nature is <u>recessive</u> — so use a '<u>b</u>'.
And normal (boring) behaviour is due to a <u>dominant allele</u> — call it '<u>B</u>'.

1) For an organism to display a <u>recessive</u> characteristic, <u>both</u> its alleles must be <u>recessive</u> — so a crazy hamster must have the alleles 'bb' (i.e. it must be homozygous for this trait).

2) However, a <u>normal hamster</u> could be BB (homozygous) or Bb (heterozygous), because the dominant allele (B) <u>overrules</u> the recessive one (b).

Genetic Diagrams

So if you cross a <u>thoroughbred crazy hamster</u>, genetic type bb,
with a <u>thoroughbred normal hamster</u>, BB, you get this:

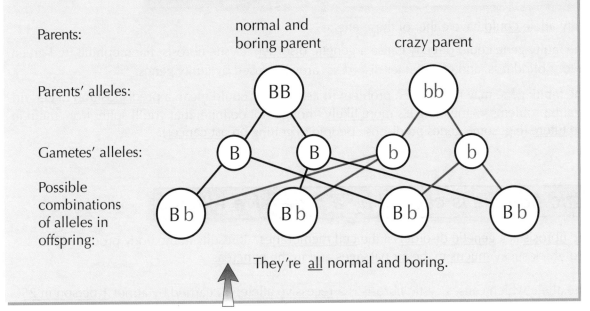

Parents: normal and boring parent   crazy parent

Parents' alleles: BB   bb

Gametes' alleles: B   B   b   b

Possible combinations of alleles in offspring: B b   B b   B b   B b

They're <u>all</u> normal and boring.

The lines show <u>all the possible</u> ways the parents' alleles <u>could</u> combine.

Remember, only <u>one</u> of these possibilities would <u>actually happen</u> for any one offspring.

When you breed two organisms together to look at one characteristic it's called a MONOHYBRID CROSS.

If two of the offspring from the cross above now breed,
they will produce a <u>new combination</u> of offspring:

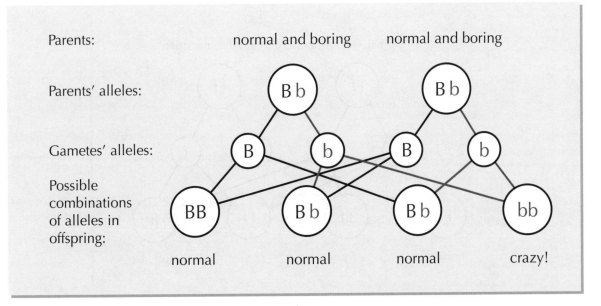

Parents: normal and boring   normal and boring

Parents' alleles: B b   B b

Gametes' alleles: B   b   B   b

Possible combinations of alleles in offspring: BB   B b   B b   bb

normal   normal   normal   crazy!

This time, there's a 75% chance of having a normal, boring hamster, and a 25% chance of a crazy
one. (To put that another way... you'd expect a 3:1 ratio of normal:crazy hamsters.)

Genetic diagrams can only give you a probability

Interestingly (maybe), you can draw a similar diagram to show the probability of having a <u>boy or a girl</u>.
(It's not a single gene that determines sex, but a <u>chromosome</u> — the diagram's exactly the same though.)
Women have 2 <u>X-chromosomes</u>, whereas men have <u>an X and a Y</u>, the Y-chromosome being <u>dominant</u>.
It turns out the odds are <u>50:50</u>. Have a go at drawing the genetic diagram to show this.

Genetic Disorders

Sometimes an allele might be faulty and not work properly. It can cause more than a few problems...

Genetic disorders are caused by faulty alleles

A faulty allele could have either of these effects...

1) The faulty gene could directly cause a genetic disorder. Cystic fibrosis, haemophilia, red-green colour blindness (and many other disorders) are all caused by faulty genes.

2) The faulty gene may not cause a problem in itself, but it could mean a predisposition to certain health problems — meaning it's more likely (though not definite) that you'll suffer from them in the future (e.g. some genes predispose people to getting breast cancer).

Cystic fibrosis is caused by a recessive allele

Cystic fibrosis is a genetic disorder of the cell membranes. It results in the body producing a lot of thick sticky mucus in the air passages and in the pancreas.

1) The allele which causes cystic fibrosis is a recessive allele, 'f', carried by about 1 person in 25.

2) Because it's recessive, people with only one copy of the allele won't have the disorder — they're known as carriers.

3) For a child to have a chance of inheriting the disorder, both parents must be either carriers or sufferers.

4) As the diagram shows, there's a 1 in 4 chance of a child having the disorder if both parents are carriers.

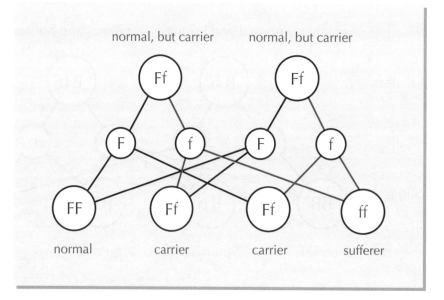

That's three genetic diagrams in two pages. Get scribbling

Cystic fibrosis is a terrible condition that affects a lot of people. Luckily for you, you just need to know the symptoms and draw a genetic diagram to show how it's inherited (just like the one above).

Genetic Disorders

There are all sorts of problems with preventing and treating genetic disorders.

Knowing about genetic disorders opens up a *whole can of worms*

Knowing there are inherited conditions in your family raises <u>difficult issues</u>:

- Should all family members be <u>tested</u> to see if they're carriers? Some people might prefer <u>not to know</u>, but is this <u>fair</u> on any partners or future children they might have?

- Is it <u>right</u> for someone who's at risk of passing on a genetic condition to have <u>children</u>? Is it <u>fair</u> to put them under pressure <u>not to</u>, if they decide they want children?

- It's possible to <u>test</u> a foetus for some genetic conditions while it's still in the <u>womb</u>. But if the test is positive, is it right to <u>terminate</u> the pregnancy? The family might not be able to <u>cope</u> with a sick or disabled child, but why should that child have a lesser <u>right to life</u> than a healthy child? Some people think abortion is <u>always wrong</u> under any circumstances.

Gene therapy is being developed to *treat genetic disorders*

Gene therapy means <u>correcting faulty genes</u> — usually a <u>healthy copy</u> of the gene is added.

Example — Treating cystic fibrosis

1) At the moment scientists are trying to cure cystic fibrosis (CF) with gene therapy. One method being trialled is the use of a virus to insert a <u>healthy copy</u> of the gene into cells in the airways.

2) There are still problems — for example, at the moment the effect wears off after a <u>few days</u>. But there are big hopes that gene therapy will one day mean CF can be treated effectively.

3) However, since this kind of gene therapy involves only body cells (and not reproductive cells), the faulty gene would still be passed on to children.

Learn the facts then see what you know

On a related note... the <u>Human Genome Project</u> aimed to map all the genes in a human. This has now been completed, and the results could help with future gene therapies. Exciting stuff.

Warm-Up and Exam Questions

There's no better preparation for exam questions than doing... err... practice exam questions. Hang on, what's this I see...

Warm-Up Questions

1) What are alleles?
2) What are genetic disorders caused by?
3) What are the symptoms of the genetic disorder cystic fibrosis?
4) Give the names of two genetic disorders (other than cystic fibrosis).
5) If someone has genes that predispose them to breast cancer, will they definitely develop breast cancer?

Exam Questions

1   Whether you are right-handed or left-handed is determined by the handedness genes that you inherit from your parents.
The allele for right-handedness, H, is dominant over the allele for left-handedness, h.

(a) Complete the genetic diagram below to show the possible combinations of alleles in the offspring of these two parents.

parent's alleles

	H	h
H		
h		

parent's alleles

(1 mark)

(b) What is the chance of a child of these two parents being left-handed?

A   25%

B   50%

C   75%

D   100%

(1 mark)

2   Jack found out that his father is a carrier of a genetic disorder. Which of the following is a reason why Jack may **not** want to be tested for the same disorder?

A   Not knowing might be unfair on any partners.

B   If he is a carrier, he might feel under pressure not to have children.

C   If he had the genetic disorder he could prepare for its onset.

D   He could pass on the disorder to his children.

(1 mark)

Exam Questions

3   Which of the following statements about the use of gene therapy to treat cystic fibrosis is **not** correct?

     A   At the moment, the effects are only temporary.

     B   It can involve the use of viruses.

     C   It involves inserting a working gene into cells in the airways.

     D   The healthy gene can be passed on to children of the sufferer.

(1 mark)

4   Cystic fibrosis is a disease caused by recessive alleles.

        F = the normal allele
        f = the faulty allele that leads to cystic fibrosis

    The genetic diagram below shows the possible inheritance of cystic fibrosis from one couple.

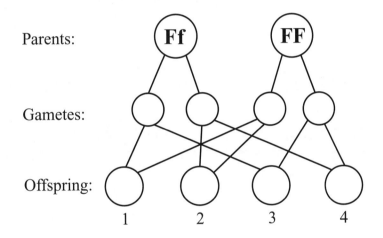

    (a)   Complete the genetic diagram.

(2 marks)

    (b)   Which of the possible offspring will be sufferers and which will be unaffected?

(1 mark)

    (c)   (i)   What proportion of the possible offspring are homozygous?

(1 mark)

          (ii)   Which of the possible offspring are carriers of the disease?

(1 mark)

    (d)   Explain why someone might want to be tested to see if they are a carrier for cystic fibrosis.

(1 mark)

Cloning

Sexual reproduction isn't the only way of producing offspring.

Asexual reproduction produces **genetically identical cells**

An ordinary cell can make a new cell by simply dividing in two. The new cell has exactly the same genetic information (i.e. genes) as the parent cell — this is known as asexual reproduction.

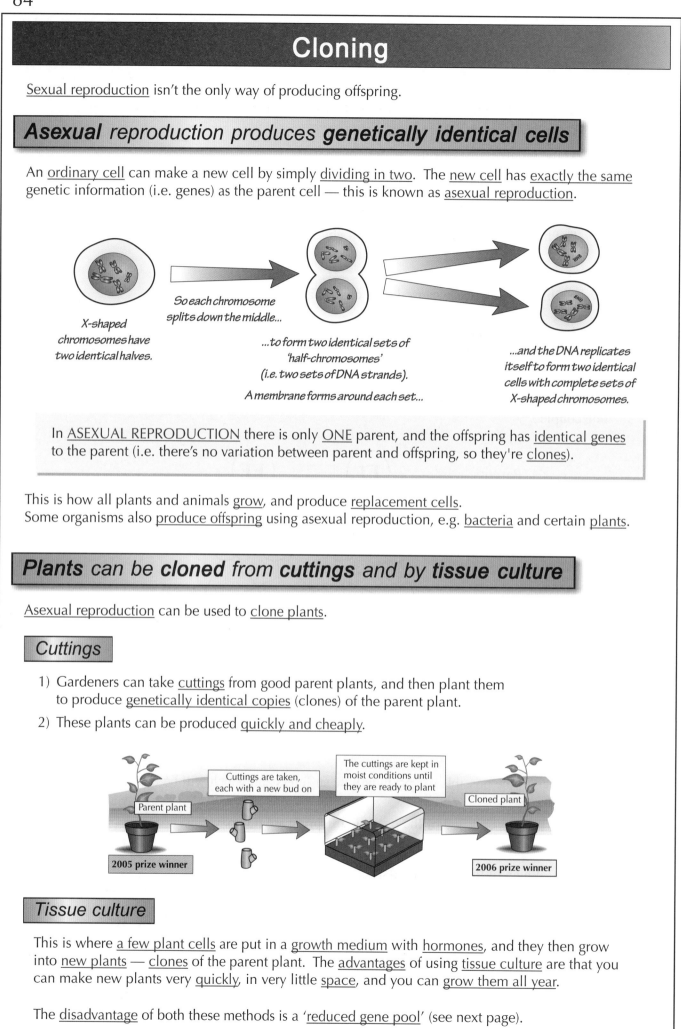

X-shaped
chromosomes have
two identical halves.

So each chromosome
splits down the middle...

...to form two identical sets of
'half-chromosomes'
(i.e. two sets of DNA strands).

A membrane forms around each set...

...and the DNA replicates
itself to form two identical
cells with complete sets of
X-shaped chromosomes.

> In ASEXUAL REPRODUCTION there is only ONE parent, and the offspring has identical genes to the parent (i.e. there's no variation between parent and offspring, so they're clones).

This is how all plants and animals grow, and produce replacement cells.
Some organisms also produce offspring using asexual reproduction, e.g. bacteria and certain plants.

Plants can be **cloned** from **cuttings** and by **tissue culture**

Asexual reproduction can be used to clone plants.

Cuttings

1) Gardeners can take cuttings from good parent plants, and then plant them to produce genetically identical copies (clones) of the parent plant.

2) These plants can be produced quickly and cheaply.

Parent plant

Cuttings are taken,
each with a new bud on

The cuttings are kept in
moist conditions until
they are ready to plant

Cloned plant

2005 prize winner

2006 prize winner

Tissue culture

This is where a few plant cells are put in a growth medium with hormones, and they then grow into new plants — clones of the parent plant. The advantages of using tissue culture are that you can make new plants very quickly, in very little space, and you can grow them all year.

The disadvantage of both these methods is a 'reduced gene pool' (see next page).

Cloning

It isn't only plants that can be cloned — you can <u>clone animals</u> too.
Which is ideal if you want an animal to produce lots of <u>identical offspring</u>.

You need to know about *embryo transplants* in *cows*

Normally, farmers only breed from their <u>best</u> cows and bulls. However, traditional methods would only allow the <u>prize cow</u> to produce <u>one new offspring each year</u>. These days the whole process has been transformed using <u>embryo transplants</u>:

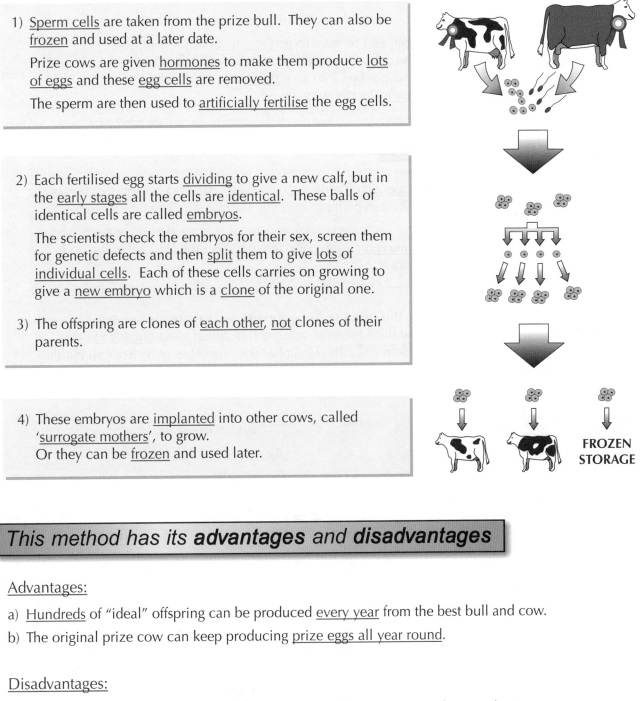

1) <u>Sperm cells</u> are taken from the prize bull. They can also be <u>frozen</u> and used at a later date.

   Prize cows are given <u>hormones</u> to make them produce <u>lots of eggs</u> and these <u>egg cells</u> are removed.

   The sperm are then used to <u>artificially fertilise</u> the egg cells.

2) Each fertilised egg starts <u>dividing</u> to give a new calf, but in the <u>early stages</u> all the cells are <u>identical</u>. These balls of identical cells are called <u>embryos</u>.

   The scientists check the embryos for their sex, screen them for genetic defects and then <u>split</u> them to give <u>lots</u> of <u>individual cells</u>. Each of these cells carries on growing to give a <u>new embryo</u> which is a <u>clone</u> of the original one.

3) The offspring are clones of <u>each other</u>, <u>not</u> clones of their parents.

4) These embryos are <u>implanted</u> into other cows, called '<u>surrogate mothers</u>', to grow.
   Or they can be <u>frozen</u> and used later.

FROZEN STORAGE

This method has its *advantages* and *disadvantages*

Advantages:

a) <u>Hundreds</u> of "ideal" offspring can be produced <u>every year</u> from the best bull and cow.

b) The original prize cow can keep producing <u>prize eggs all year round</u>.

Disadvantages:

The main problem is that the <u>same alleles</u> keep appearing (and many others are <u>lost</u>).
So there's a <u>greater risk</u> of <u>genetic disorders</u>, and a <u>disease</u> could wipe out an entire population if there are no <u>resistant alleles</u>.

Cloning

There's a second way to clone animals, and it's even more controversial than the first...

Adult cell cloning is another way to make a clone

Adult cell cloning can be <u>reproductive</u> or <u>therapeutic</u>.

Reproductive cloning

1) <u>Reproductive cloning</u> involves taking the genetic material from an adult cell to make a new organism that is a clone of that adult.

2) It's now been done in lots of mammals, including sheep, horses and cats.

3) Basically, you take an <u>egg cell</u> and remove its <u>genetic material</u>. A <u>complete set</u> of <u>chromosomes</u> from the cell of the <u>adult</u> you're cloning is then inserted into the 'empty' egg cell, which grows into an <u>embryo</u> and eventually into an animal that's <u>genetically identical</u> to the original adult.

Therapeutic cloning

1) The aim of <u>therapeutic cloning</u> is to produce 'spare' body parts for disease sufferers without them being rejected by the sufferer's immune system.

2) A cloned embryo is created that is genetically identical to the sufferer and special cells (<u>embryonic stem cells</u>) that can become any cell in the body are extracted from it.

Some people think it's <u>unethical</u> to do this because the <u>embryos</u> used to provide the stem cells are <u>destroyed</u>. <u>Fusion cloning</u> could avoid this. Here, an adult cell is joined to an <u>already existing</u> (but <u>genetically different</u>) embryonic stem cell. The result has the properties of a stem cell but the same genes as the adult.

Adult cell cloning

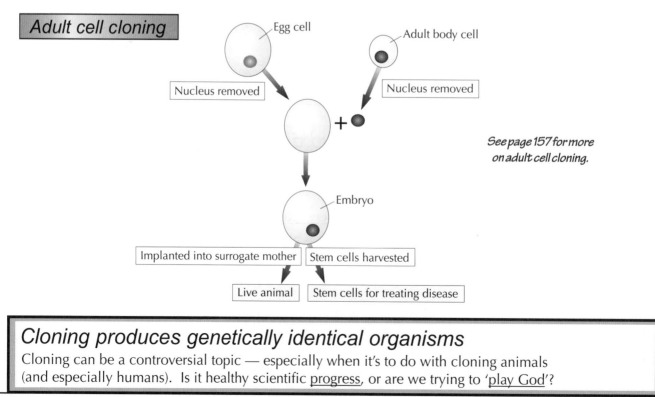

See page 157 for more on adult cell cloning.

Cloning produces genetically identical organisms

Cloning can be a controversial topic — especially when it's to do with cloning animals (and especially humans). Is it healthy scientific <u>progress</u>, or are we trying to '<u>play God</u>'?

Genetic Engineering

Scientists can now <u>add</u>, <u>remove</u> or <u>change</u> an organism's <u>genes</u> to alter its characteristics.

Genetic engineering uses enzymes to cut and paste genes

The basic idea is to move <u>useful genes</u> from one organism's chromosomes into the cells of another...

1) A useful gene is "<u>cut</u>" from one organism's chromosome using <u>enzymes</u>.

2) <u>Enzymes</u> are then used to <u>cut</u> another organism's chromosome and to <u>insert</u> the useful gene. This technique is called <u>gene splicing</u>.

3) Scientists use this method to do all sorts of things — for example, the human insulin gene can be inserted into <u>bacteria</u> to <u>produce human insulin</u>:

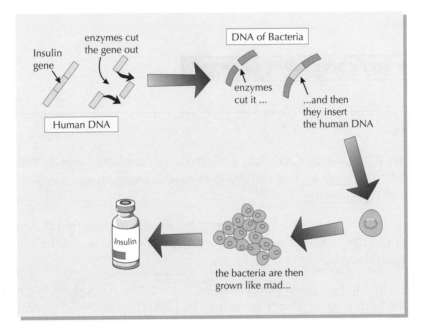

Genes can be transferred into animals and plants

The same method can be used to <u>transfer useful genes</u> into <u>animals</u> and <u>plants</u> at the <u>very early stages</u> of their development (i.e. shortly after <u>fertilisation</u>). This has (or could have) some really <u>useful applications</u>.

1) <u>Genetically modified (GM) plants</u> have been developed that are <u>resistant to viruses</u> and <u>herbicides</u> (chemicals used to kill weeds). And <u>long-life</u> tomatoes can be made by changing the gene that causes the fruit to ripen.

'Bt corn' contains a gene from a bacterium that protects against corn borer insects.

2) Genes can also be inserted into <u>animal embryos</u> so that the animal grows up to have more <u>useful characteristics</u>. For example, <u>sheep</u> have been genetically engineered to produce substances (e.g. drugs) in their <u>milk</u> that can be used to treat <u>human diseases</u>.

3) <u>Genetic disorders</u> like cystic fibrosis are caused by faulty genes. Scientists are trying to cure these disorders by <u>inserting working genes</u> into sufferers. This is called <u>gene therapy</u> — see page 81.

Genetic Engineering

On the face of it, genetic engineering is great. But like most other things, there are benefits and risks that you need to consider.

But genetic engineering is a **controversial** topic

So, genetic engineering is an exciting new area in science which has the potential for solving many of our problems (e.g. treating diseases, more efficient food production etc.) but not everyone likes it.

1) Some people strongly believe that we shouldn't go tinkering about with genes because it's not natural.

2) There are also worries that changing an organism's genes might accidentally create unforeseen problems — which could then get passed on to future generations.

There are **pros** and **cons** with GM crops

Disadvantages

1) Some people say that growing GM crops will affect the number of weeds and flowers (and therefore wildlife) that usually lives in and around the crops — reducing farmland biodiversity.

2) Not everyone is convinced that GM crops are safe. People are worried they may develop allergies to the food — although there's probably no more risk for this than for eating usual foods.

3) A big concern is that transplanted genes may get out into the natural environment. For example, the herbicide resistance gene may be picked up by weeds, creating a new 'superweed' variety.

Advantages

1) On the plus side, GM crops can increase the yield of a crop, making more food.

2) People living in developing nations often lack nutrients in their diets. GM crops could be engineered to contain nutrients that are missing. For example, they're testing 'golden rice' that contains beta-carotene — lack of this substance can cause blindness.

3) GM crops are already being used elsewhere in the world (not the UK), often without any problems.

Genetic engineering has exciting and frightening possibilities

It's up to the Government to weigh up all the evidence before making a decision on how this knowledge is used. All scientists can do is make sure the Government has all the information it needs.

Warm-Up and Exam Questions

By doing these warm-up questions, you'll soon find out if you've got the basic facts straight.
If not, you'll really struggle, so take the time to go back over the bits you don't know.

Warm-Up Questions

1) What is a clone?
2) Name two ways that plant clones can be produced.
3) Give one advantage of cloning using cow embryo transplantation.
4) What is gene splicing?
5) Give two applications of genetic engineering.

Exam Questions

1 A gardener has a prize-winning rose bush. He wants another plant that is the same, so he takes a cutting from it. The cutting grows into a new rose bush.

(a) What type of reproduction is this?

(1 mark)

(b) Describe the stages involved in this kind of reproduction at the cellular level.

(3 marks)

(c) Complete the following sentences using words from this list:

clone   gene   parent   bud   identical   leaf

The gardener takes a cutting from the .... plant. The cutting must have a
.... on it. He plants the cutting, and takes care of it. The cutting grows into
a new rose bush that is a .... of the original plant.

(3 marks)

2 The advantage of using tissue culture to produce new plants is that

A it is expensive

B useful genes can be added

C defective genes can be removed

D new plants can be produced very quickly

(1 mark)

3 Cloning organisms results in a reduced gene pool.

(a) What is meant by 'reduced gene pool'?

(1 mark)

(b) Describe the problems associated with a reduced gene pool.

(1 mark)

Exam Questions

4   Farmers can produce cloned offspring from their best bull and cow using embryo transplants.

   (a)   Why do farmers use this procedure?

   (1 mark)

   (b)   Describe the process of embryo transplantation.

   (4 marks)

5   Organisms can be genetically modified.

   (a)   Explain what is meant by 'genetically modified'.

   (2 marks)

   (b)   Give three functions of enzymes used in genetic engineering.

   (3 marks)

   (c)   Suggest one useful way that plants can be genetically modified.

   (1 mark)

   (d)   Suggest one useful way that animals can be genetically modified.

   (1 mark)

   (e)   Some people think that it is wrong to genetically modify plants.
         Give two different objections that people might have.

   (2 marks)

6   In 1997 scientists the Roslin Institute issued a press release to tell the world about the birth of Dolly, a sheep that had been cloned using adult cells.

   (a)   Explain how Dolly was made using adult cell cloning.

   (3 marks)

   (b)   Human adult cell cloning could be used to help treat various diseases.

      (i)   Suggest how this could be done.

   (2 marks)

      (ii)   Explain why some people are opposed to human adult cell cloning.

   (1 mark)

Revision Summary for Section Four

There's a lot to remember in this section and quite a few of the topics are controversial, e.g. cloning, genetic engineering, and so on. You need to know all sides of the story, as well as all the facts. So, here are some questions to help you. If you get any wrong, go back and learn that bit again.

1) What are the two types, or causes, of variation?

2) Describe the relative importance of each type for plants and for animals.

3) List four features of animals which aren't affected at all by their environment, and three which are.

4) Draw a set of diagrams showing the relationship between: cell, nucleus, chromosomes, DNA.

5) How many pairs of chromosomes does a normal human cell nucleus contain?

   Which cells, found in every adult human, have a different number of chromosomes in their nucleus?

6) Explain why sexual reproduction results in offspring that are genetically different from either parent.

7) Name three things that cause genetic mutations.

8) Give an example of how a genetic mutation could be:

   a) harmful,   b) beneficial.

9) What does it mean if you are homozygous for a particular trait?

10)*Draw a genetic diagram showing a cross between a woman who can roll her tongue (Tt) and a man who can't roll his tongue (tt). Having the dominant allele (T) means that you can roll your tongue.

11) Describe two ways in which a faulty gene could lead to health problems.

12) It is now possible to test whether or not you are a carrier for many genetic disorders.

   Outline some of the reasons in favour of this testing, and also suggest reasons why an individual might prefer not to be tested.

13) What's the basic idea behind gene therapy?

14) Give a definition of asexual reproduction.

15) Describe how to make plant clones from:

   a) cuttings,   b) tissue culture.

16) Give an advantage and a disadvantage of producing cloned plants.

17) Describe two different ways to clone an animal.

18) Give an account of the important stages of genetic engineering.

19) Give an example of an application of genetic engineering, and explain why it is useful.

20) Why are some people concerned about genetic engineering?

* Answers on page 287.

There's Too Many People

We have an <u>impact</u> on the world around us — and the more humans there are, the bigger the impact.

There are **six billion people** in the world...

1) The <u>population</u> of the world is currently <u>rising</u> very quickly, and it's not slowing down — look at the graph below...

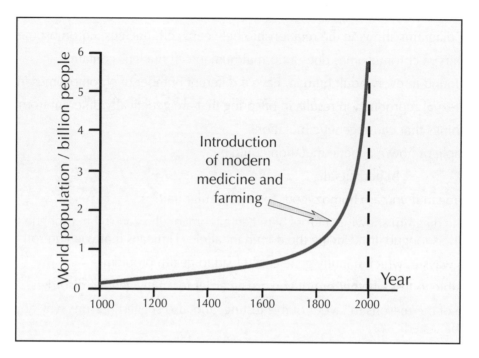

2) This rise is mostly due to modern <u>medicine</u> and <u>farming</u> methods, which have <u>reduced</u> the number of <u>people dying</u> from <u>disease</u> and <u>hunger</u>.

3) This is great for all of us <u>humans</u>, but it means we're having a <u>bigger effect</u> on the <u>environment</u> we live in.

...with **increasing demands** on the **environment**

When the <u>Earth's population</u> was much smaller, the effects of <u>human activity</u> were usually <u>small</u> and <u>local</u>. Nowadays though, our actions can have a far more <u>widespread</u> effect.

1) Our rapidly increasing <u>population</u> puts pressure on the <u>environment</u>, as we take the resources we need to <u>survive</u>.

2) People around the world are also demanding a higher <u>standard of living</u> (and so demand luxuries to make life more comfortable — cars, computers, etc.). So we use more <u>raw materials</u> (e.g. oil to make plastics), and we also use more <u>energy</u> for the manufacturing processes. This all means we're taking more and more <u>resources</u> from the environment more and more <u>quickly</u>.

3) Unfortunately, many raw materials are being used up more quickly than they're being replaced. So if we carry on like we are, one day we're going to <u>run out</u>.

There's Too Many People

It's not just that we're using more <u>resources</u>, more and more quickly — we're also making an awful lot of <u>rubbish</u> in the process.

We're producing **more waste**

As we manufacture more and more, we produce more and more <u>waste</u>. And unless this waste is properly handled, more <u>harmful pollution</u> will be caused. This affects water, land and air.

Water

<u>Sewage</u> and <u>toxic chemicals</u> from industry can pollute lakes, rivers and oceans, affecting the plants and animals that rely on them for survival (including humans). And chemicals used on farmland (e.g. fertilisers) can be washed into the water too.

Land

We use <u>toxic chemicals</u> for farming (e.g. pesticides and herbicides). We also bury <u>nuclear waste</u> underground, and we dump a lot of <u>household waste</u> in landfill sites.

Air

<u>Smoke</u> and <u>gases</u> released into the atmosphere can pollute the air (see page 100 for more info). For example, <u>sulfur dioxide</u> can cause <u>acid rain</u>.

More people means **less land** for plants and other animals

Humans also <u>reduce</u> the amount of <u>land and resources</u> available to other <u>animals</u> and <u>plants</u>. The <u>four</u> main human activities that do this are:

1) <u>Building</u>

2) <u>Farming</u>

3) <u>Dumping waste</u>

4) <u>Quarrying</u>

More people, more mess, less space, fewer resources

Well, I feel guilty, I don't know about you. Not only are we taking more and more <u>land</u> for building and farming and quarrying but we're also <u>polluting</u> what little there is left over. In the exam you might be given some data about environmental impact, so make sure you understand what's going on...

The Greenhouse Effect

The <u>greenhouse effect</u> is always in the news. We need it, since it makes Earth a suitable temperature for living on. But there's concern all us humans are causing it to trap more heat than is necessary.

Carbon dioxide and *methane trap heat* from the *Sun*

1) The <u>temperature</u> of the Earth is a <u>balance</u> between the heat it gets from the Sun and the heat it radiates back out into space.

2) Gases in the <u>atmosphere</u> naturally act like an <u>insulating layer</u>. They absorb most of the heat that would normally be radiated out into space, and re-radiate it in all directions (including back towards the Earth).

This is what happens in a greenhouse. The sun shines in, and the glass helps keep some of the heat in.

3) If this didn't happen, then at night there'd be nothing to keep any heat <u>in</u>, and we'd quickly get <u>very cold</u> indeed. But recently we've started to worry that this effect is getting a bit out of hand...

4) There are several different gases in the atmosphere which help keep the <u>heat in</u>. They're called '<u>greenhouse gases</u>' (oddly enough) and the <u>main ones</u> we worry about are <u>carbon dioxide</u> and <u>methane</u> — because the levels of these two gases are rising quite sharply.

5) There is good evidence that the Earth is gradually heating up, at least a little bit because of the increasing levels of greenhouse gases — this is <u>global warming</u>, and it may cause <u>climate change</u>.

We need greenhouse gases in the atmosphere, but not too much

Some people find the idea of the greenhouse effect quite confusing — it's more physics than biology really, with heat being <u>absorbed</u> and <u>radiated</u> all over the place. Don't waste time worrying about <u>why</u> the Earth radiates heat and <u>why</u> the gases absorb it — just remember the facts for your exam.

The Greenhouse Effect

On the last page you read that levels of <u>carbon dioxide</u> and <u>methane</u> are rising sharply —
now read on to find out why.

Human activity produces lots of carbon dioxide

1) <u>Humans</u> release <u>carbon dioxide</u> into the atmosphere all the time as
part of our <u>everyday lives</u> — in <u>car exhausts</u>, <u>industrial processes</u>,
as we <u>burn fossil fuels</u>, etc.

2) People around the world are also <u>cutting down</u> large areas of forest
(<u>deforestation</u>) for <u>timber</u> and to clear land for <u>farming</u> — and this
activity affects the <u>level of carbon dioxide</u> in the <u>atmosphere</u> in
various ways:

- Carbon dioxide is <u>released</u> when trees are <u>burnt</u> to clear land.
(Carbon in wood is 'locked up' and doesn't contribute to
atmospheric pollution — until it's released by burning.)

- <u>Microorganisms</u> feeding on bits of <u>dead wood</u>
release CO_2 as a waste product of <u>respiration</u>.

- Cutting down <u>loads of trees</u> means that the amount of carbon
dioxide <u>removed</u> from the atmosphere during <u>photosynthesis</u> is <u>reduced</u>.

So we're putting <u>more</u> CO_2 <u>into</u> the atmosphere and taking <u>less out</u>.

Methane is also a problem

1) <u>Methane gas</u> is also contributing to the <u>greenhouse effect</u>.

2) It's produced <u>naturally</u> from various sources, e.g. <u>rotting plants</u> in <u>marshland</u>.

3) However, two '<u>man-made</u>' sources of methane are <u>on the increase</u>:

   a)   <u>Rice growing</u>

   b)   <u>Cattle rearing</u> — it's the cows' "pumping" that's the problem,
believe it or not.

Levels of methane and carbon dioxide are both on the increase

Remember, climate change due to greenhouse gases is still just a <u>theory</u> — lots of scientists putting
together some pieces in a jigsaw. And whilst the theory is very popular in the scientific community,
it hasn't been accepted yet, so be careful when you're describing what we <u>know</u>...

Climate Change

Most climate scientists agree that the Earth is getting <u>warmer</u>. They're now trying to work out what the <u>effects</u> of global warming might be — sadly, it's not as simple as everyone having nicer summers.

*The **consequences** of **global warming** could be pretty **serious***

If climate scientists are right, there are several reasons to be <u>worried</u> about global warming. Here are a few:

1) As the sea gets warmer, it will <u>expand</u>, causing sea levels to <u>rise</u>. This would be bad news for people living in low-lying places, like the Netherlands, East Anglia and the Maldives — they'd be flooded.

2) <u>Hurricanes</u> form over water that's warmer than 26 °C — so if there's more warm water, you would expect <u>more hurricanes</u>.

3) Higher temperatures make <u>ice melt</u>. Water that's currently 'trapped' on land (as ice) will run into the sea, causing sea levels to rise even more.

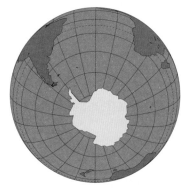

There's a lot of ice at the poles, but is it melting?

4) There's another problem too — lots of cold fresh water entering the sea from the melting ice caps could disrupt the <u>ocean currents</u>. This would be <u>very</u> bad news for us in Britain — we'd actually get a lot <u>colder</u> without the warm currents we have at the moment.

5) As weather patterns change, the <u>food</u> we grow will be affected, all over the world. <u>Droughts</u> in some places could force millions of people to move.

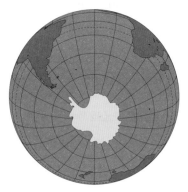

You'll notice that the word "could" pops up quite a bit on this page. That's because the climate is such a <u>complicated</u> system. For instance, if the ice melts, there's less white stuff around to reflect the sun's rays out to space, so maybe we'll absorb more heat and get <u>even warmer</u>.

But... when the sea's warmer, more water evaporates, making more <u>clouds</u> — and they reflect the Sun's rays, so maybe we'd <u>cool down</u> again. It's hard to predict exactly what will happen, but lots of people are currently working on it and so far it's not looking too good.

Climate Change

At GCSE level, it's not as simple as just learning all the facts any more (if that was ever simple). Sometimes you've got to be able to look at the <u>scientific evidence</u> and <u>judge</u> how useful it really is.

*Scientists collect various data as **evidence** of **climate change***

To find out if our climate is really changing, scientists are busy collecting <u>data</u> about the environment. For example:

1) <u>Satellites</u> are used to monitor <u>snow</u> and <u>ice cover</u>.

2) Satellites can also be used to measure the <u>temperature</u> of the <u>sea surface</u>.

3) The <u>temperature</u> and <u>speed</u> of <u>ocean currents</u> are monitored for any changes.

4) Automatic weather stations are constantly recording <u>atmospheric temperatures</u>.

*You need to **weigh** the **evidence** before **making judgements***

All this data is only useful if it covers a <u>wide enough area</u> and a <u>long enough time scale</u>.

AREA

Generally, observations of a very <u>small area</u> aren't much use. Noticing that your <u>local glacier</u> seems to be melting does <u>not</u> mean that ice everywhere is melting, and it's certainly <u>not</u> a valid way to show that <u>global temperature</u> is changing. (That would be like going to Wales, seeing a stripy cow and concluding that all the cows in Wales are turning into zebras.) Looking at the area of ice cover over a <u>whole continent</u>, like Antarctica, would be better.

<u>TIME</u>

The same thing goes for <u>time</u>. It's no good going to the Arctic, seeing four polar bears one week but only two the next week and concluding that polar bears are dying out because the ice is disappearing. You need to do your observations again and again, year after year.

Scientists can make mistakes — so don't take one person's word for something, even if they've got a PhD. But if <u>lots</u> of scientists get the <u>same result</u> using different methods, it's probably right. That's why most governments around the world are starting to take climate change seriously.

Not all scientific studies are equally useful

We humans have created some <u>big environmental problems</u> for ourselves. Many people, and some governments, think that we ought to start cleaning up the mess. Scientists can help, mainly in understanding the problems and suggesting solutions, but it's society as a whole that has to <u>act</u>.

Warm-Up and Exam Questions

Warm-Up Questions

1) Give two reasons why the human population of the world has increased so much over the last 200 years.

2) Why, apart from the increased population, is pollution by humans increasing?

3) Name one way in which humans pollute: (a) air   (b) land   (c) water

4) What is meant by the 'greenhouse effect'?

5) What are the two main gases that are causing an increase in the greenhouse effect?

6) List four possible harmful effects of global warming.

Exam Questions

1   The graph shows the carbon dioxide concentration in the Earth's atmosphere between AD 1000 and AD 2000.

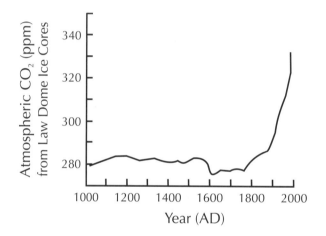

(a)   Use the graph to describe the trend in carbon dioxide concentration:

   (i)   between AD 1000 and AD 1500.

(1 mark)

   (ii)   between AD 1850 and AD 2000.

(1 mark)

(b)   Name two human activities that may have caused the changes in concentration between AD 1850 and AD 2000.

(2 marks)

2   (a)   Explain how global warming could lead to a rise in sea levels.

(1 mark)

(b)   Explain how global warming might cause:

   (i)   a decrease in average temperature in some parts of the world.

(1 mark)

   (ii)   more hurricanes.

(1 mark)

Exam Questions

3   The tropical island of Hannaria has an area of approximately 2000 km². Most of the island is covered with tropical rainforest. However, the inhabitants of Hannaria want to clear large areas of the rainforest to make room for more housing. Opponents say that this development will contribute to global warming.

(a) Explain how clearing the forest could contribute to global warming.

(2 marks)

(b) If the trees are cut down, they could be used as fuel or they could be used to make wooden buildings and furniture. Which of these uses is likely to contribute more to global warming? Explain your answer.

(2 marks)

4   John did an experiment to demonstrate the greenhouse effect. The diagram on the right shows the apparatus he used.

JAR 1 filled with air   JAR 2 filled with CO_2

John left both jars under a heat lamp for 15 minutes, and noted the temperature on the thermometers every minute.

(a) In which jar would you expect the temperature to increase faster, and why?

(2 marks)

(b) Explain why John included jar 1 in the experiment.

(1 mark)

(c) Give one condition that should be kept the same for both jars.

(1 mark)

5   A scientist was examining some data to see if there is a link between the global human population and the carbon dioxide concentration in the atmosphere.
Here are the two graphs that the scientist examined.

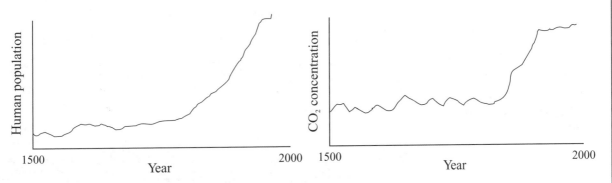

(a) The scientist said that there is a correlation between the two graphs. Explain what this means.

(1 mark)

(b) On their own, these graphs do not prove that the increased human population caused the increased carbon dioxide concentration. Explain why not.

(1 mark)

Air Pollution

As well as carbon dioxide and methane, there are <u>other gases</u> that can cause environmental problems.

CFCs *cause ozone* **depletion**

1) <u>CFCs</u> (chlorofluorocarbons) used to be used in <u>aerosols</u>, <u>fridges</u>, <u>air-conditioning units</u> and <u>polystyrene foam</u>.

2) They break down <u>ozone</u> in the upper atmosphere.

3) This allows more <u>harmful UV rays</u> to reach the Earth's surface.

4) Being exposed to more UV rays increases the risk of <u>skin cancer</u> (although this can be reduced with suncream). Australia has high levels of skin cancer because it is under an ozone hole.

5) The increase in UV rays might also <u>kill plankton</u> in the sea — this could have a massive effect on the <u>sea ecosystem</u> because plankton are at the bottom of the food chain. Scientists predict that <u>fish levels</u> will <u>drop</u> (meaning, amongst other things, <u>less food</u> for us to eat).

Carbon monoxide *is* **poisonous**

1) When <u>fossil fuels</u> are burnt <u>without enough air</u>, the gas <u>carbon monoxide</u> (CO) is produced.

2) It's a <u>poisonous</u> gas. If it <u>combines</u> with <u>red blood cells</u>, it stops them carrying oxygen.

3) Carbon monoxide is mostly released in <u>car emissions</u>. Most <u>modern cars</u> are fitted with <u>catalytic converters</u> that <u>oxidise</u> the <u>carbon monoxide</u> (to make carbon dioxide), decreasing the amount that's released into the atmosphere.

Acid rain *is caused by* **sulfur dioxide** *and* **oxides of nitrogen**

1) As well as releasing CO_2, burning fossil fuels releases other harmful gases. These include <u>sulfur dioxide</u> and various <u>nitrogen oxides</u>.

2) The <u>sulfur dioxide</u> (SO_2) comes from <u>sulfur impurities</u> in the <u>fossil fuels</u>. The <u>nitrogen oxides</u> are made in a <u>reaction</u> between nitrogen and oxygen <u>in the air</u>, caused by the <u>heat</u> of the burning.

3) When these gases <u>mix</u> with <u>rain clouds</u> they form dilute <u>sulfuric acid</u> and dilute <u>nitric acid</u>. This then falls as <u>acid rain</u>.

4) <u>Internal combustion engines</u> in cars and <u>power stations</u> are the <u>main causes</u> of acid rain.

Acid rain *kills* fish and trees and **damages** buildings

1) Acid rain can cause <u>lakes</u> to become more <u>acidic</u>. This has a <u>severe effect</u> on the <u>ecosystem</u>. Many organisms are <u>sensitive</u> to <u>changes in pH</u> and <u>can't survive</u> in more acidic conditions.

2) Acid rain can kill <u>plants</u>.

3) It also damages <u>limestone buildings</u> and statues.

Sustainable Development

There is a growing feeling among scientists and politicians that if we carry on behaving as we are, we may end up causing huge problems for <u>future generations</u>...

Sustainable development needs careful planning

1) Human activities can <u>damage</u> the environment (e.g. pollution). And some of the damage we do can't easily be <u>repaired</u> (e.g. the destruction of the rainforests).

2) We're also placing <u>greater pressure</u> on our planet's <u>limited resources</u> (e.g. oil is a non-renewable resource so it will eventually run out).

3) This means that we need to <u>plan carefully</u> to make sure that our activities today don't mess things up for <u>future generations</u> — this is the idea behind <u>sustainable development</u>...

> **SUSTAINABLE DEVELOPMENT** meets the needs of <u>today's</u> population <u>without</u> harming the ability of <u>future</u> generations to meet their own needs.

Learn this definition carefully so you can repeat it in the exam.

4) This isn't easy — it needs detailed thought at every level to make it happen. For example, <u>governments</u> around the world will need to make careful plans. But so will the people in charge at a <u>regional</u> level.

Reduction in biodiversity means fewer species

1) Biodiversity is the <u>variety of different species</u> in an area — the more species, the higher the biodiversity.

2) Ecosystems (especially ones like tropical <u>rainforests</u>) can contain a <u>huge number</u> of different species, so when a habitat like this is destroyed there is a danger of <u>many species becoming extinct</u>. If this happens, the biodiversity in the area is greatly <u>reduced</u>.

3) This causes a number of <u>lost opportunities</u> for humans and problems for those species that are left — some examples of this are described on the next page.

If we can't manage sustainable development, the future looks bleak

So we're <u>using up resources</u>, <u>destroying habitats</u>, <u>dumping waste</u>... all unavoidable as the human population grows, but also pretty harsh on future generations. They're going to be left with a great big mess and no resources if we're not careful. That's why we need to do <u>sustainable development</u> stuff like recycling, conserving energy, planting forests, protecting vulnerable habitats, etc.

Sustainable Development

For those of you who aren't bothered about your future grandchildren (yes, trouble really could be that close — or closer), there are other reasons not to let biodiversity disappear without a fight.

Learn these **examples** of why **biodiversity** is so important

Amazing new products

There are probably loads of useful products that we will never know about because the organisms that produced them have become extinct. Newly discovered plants and animals are a great source of new foods, new fibres for clothing and new medicines, e.g. the rosy periwinkle flower from Madagascar has helped treat Hodgkin's disease (a type of cancer), and a chemical in the saliva of a leech has been used to help prevent blood clots during surgery.

Organisms need each other to survive

Loss of one or more species from an ecosystem unbalances it, e.g. the extinct animal's predators may die out or be reduced. Loss of biodiversity can have a 'snowball effect' which prevents the ecosystem providing things we need, such as rich soil, clean water, and the oxygen we breathe.

Human impact can be **measured** using **indicator species**

Getting an accurate picture of the human impact on an environment is hard.
But one technique that's used involves indicator species.

1) Some organisms are very sensitive to changes in their environment and so can be studied to see the effect of human activities — these organisms are known as indicator species.

2) For example, air pollution can be monitored by looking at particular types of lichen, which are very sensitive to levels of sulfur dioxide in the atmosphere (and so can give a good idea about the level of pollution from car exhausts, power stations, etc.). The number and type of lichen at a particular location will indicate how clean the air is (e.g. the air is clean if there are lots of lichen).

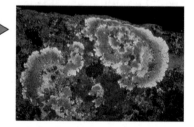

3) If raw sewage is released into a river, the bacterial population in the area increases and uses up a lot of the oxygen in the water. Animals like mayfly larvae are good indicators for water pollution, because they are very sensitive to the level of oxygen in the water. If you find mayfly larvae in a river, it indicates that the water is clean.

Conservation and Recycling

Conservation and recycling are two things that we can do to <u>reduce</u> our impact on the environment. They're an important part of sustainable development (see previous pages).

Conservation is important for protecting food, nature and culture

1) Conservation measures <u>protect species</u> by <u>maintaining</u> their <u>habitats</u> and <u>protecting</u> them from <u>poachers</u> and from <u>over-hunting</u> or <u>over-harvesting</u>.

2) There are several <u>reasons</u> why it's important to <u>conserve species and natural habitats</u>:

PROTECTING ENDANGERED SPECIES

Many species are now <u>endangered</u>, often due to hunting and the <u>destruction</u> of their <u>habitats</u>. They need to be protected to stop them becoming extinct.

PROTECTING THE HUMAN FOOD SUPPLY

Overfishing has greatly <u>reduced fish stocks</u> in the <u>sea</u>. Conservation measures (e.g. <u>quotas</u> on how many fish can be caught) encourage the survival and <u>growth</u> of fish stocks. This <u>protects the food supply</u> for future generations.

MAINTAINING BIODIVERSITY

Conserving the number of <u>species</u> in a particular area, and the total number on the Earth, is important for many reasons (see pages 101-102).

Learn these examples of woodland conservation measures

Conservation measures in a woodland habitat may include:

1) Coppicing

This is an ancient form of woodland management. It involves <u>cutting trees</u> down to just above ground level. The <u>stumps</u> sprout <u>straight, new stems</u> which can be regularly harvested.

2) Reforestation

Where forests have been cut down in the past, they can be <u>replanted</u> to <u>recreate</u> the <u>habitat</u> that has been lost.

2) Replacement planting

This is when <u>new trees</u> are <u>planted</u> at the <u>same rate</u> that others are <u>cut down</u>. So the total number of trees remains the same.

Conservation and Recycling

Recycling materials like aluminium and glass help to <u>conserve these resources</u> so that future generations will still be able to use them.

Recycling conserves our **natural resources**

If materials aren't recycled they get <u>thrown away as waste</u>. This means that:

1) There is <u>more waste</u>, so <u>more land</u> has to be used for <u>landfill sites</u> (waste dumps). Some waste is <u>toxic</u> (poisonous), so this also means more polluted land.

2) <u>More materials</u> have to be <u>manufactured</u> or <u>extracted</u> to make new products (rather than recycling existing ones) — using up more of the Earth's resources and more energy.

Recycling uses up less of the Earth's <u>natural resources</u>. <u>Recycling processes</u> usually use <u>less energy</u> and create <u>less pollution</u> than manufacturing or extracting materials from scratch. Recyclable materials include metals, paper, plastics and glass.

There are some **problems** with recycling

1) Recycling still <u>uses up energy</u>, e.g. for <u>collecting</u>, <u>sorting</u>, <u>cleaning</u> and <u>processing</u> the waste (though usually not as much as making a new product from scratch).

2) Some waste materials can be difficult and <u>time-consuming to sort</u> out, e.g. different types of <u>plastic</u> have to be separated from each other before they can be recycled.

3) The <u>equipment needed</u> for recycling can be <u>expensive</u>, e.g. equipment for automatically sorting plastics costs a lot.

4) In some cases, the <u>quality</u> of the recycled material <u>isn't as good</u> as that of the new material, e.g. recycled paper.

5) <u>Some materials</u> can only be <u>recycled</u> a <u>limited number of times</u> (e.g. plastics and paper). Others can be recycled indefinitely though (e.g. aluminium).

We need to conserve species, habitats, food stocks and resources.

The organisms in a habitat are <u>dependent</u> on each other, e.g. for food. You need to protect <u>all</u> species — animals, trees, fungi, bacteria... because if one of them dies out it affects the others (see page 102).

Warm-Up and Exam Questions

Now's your chance to practise some incredibly life-like exam questions — but do the warm-up first — you don't want to end up straining something.

Warm-Up Questions

1) What is meant by sustainable development?
2) What is conservation?
3) Give three reasons why conservation is important.
4) Give two advantages and two disadvantages of recycling.

Exam Questions

1   Copy and complete the table about air pollutants below.

Air Pollutant	Source of Pollution	Effect of Pollution
CFCs		
		prevents blood carrying oxygen
sulfur dioxide		

(6 marks)

2   (a)   Explain the meaning of the term biodiversity.

(1 mark)

(b)   Give two reasons why it is important to maintain biodiversity in ecosystems.

(2 marks)

(c)   (i)   Explain why sewage pollution can reduce biodiversity.

(1 mark)

(ii)   Explain how indicator species can be used to monitor sewage pollution in water.

(2 marks)

3   The graph shows how the pH of Lake Mudd changed between 1955 and 2005.

(a)   Describe how the pH of the lake changed between 1955 and 2005.

(2 marks)

(b)   Suggest a reason for the change after 1985.

(1 mark)

(c)   What effect would this pH change have on the fish in the lake?

(1 mark)

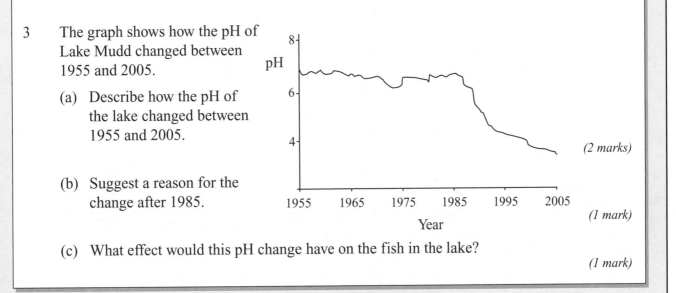

Revision Summary for Section Five

So, no cheerful stuff here. It's all doom and gloom. All these humans are hogging the land and filling the air with evil pollutants. In fact, planet Earth would be much better off if we all emigrated to Mars. Anyway, it's time for you to answer some questions on the woes of the world. You should know the drill by now. Try all the questions and if you get any wrong it's straight back to the page on that topic — do not pass go, do not collect £200. Before long, you'll be an environmental guru and won't be fazed by any question that turns up in the exam.

1) What is happening to the size of the world's population? What is largely responsible for this trend?
2) Suggest three ways in which an increasing population is affecting the environment.
3) What are the main four human activities that use up land?
4) Name two important greenhouse gases. Why are they called 'greenhouse' gases?
5) Draw and label a diagram to explain the greenhouse effect.
6) Give three ways that deforestation adds to the greenhouse effect.
7) Give two human activities (apart from deforestation) that release carbon dioxide.
8) Name two human activities that are increasing the release of methane.
9) What problems could global warming cause?
10) Give three different types of data that scientists are collecting to try and determine whether climate change as a result of global warming is really happening.
11)*Read the statement below and consider how valid it is.

> The Malaspina Glacier in Alaska is losing over 2.7 km³ of water each year. This proves global warming is happening.

12) Explain how CFCs could end up having a serious impact on the Earth's oceans.
13) Which gases cause acid rain?
14) Describe the damage that can be caused by acid rain.
15) Define sustainable development.
16)*The graph on the right shows human population growth and an estimate of the number of species that have become extinct between 1800 and 2000.
  a) How are the size of the human population and the number of extinct species related?
  b) Suggest a reason for this relationship.

17) Explain how lichen can be used as an indicator of air pollution.
18) What does it suggest about the cleanliness of the water if you find mayfly larvae in a river?
19) Give three reasons why it is important to conserve natural habitats and populations.
20)*Here is a graph of population and household waste (destined for landfill) produced by a small village.
  a) In 2002 how many people lived in the village?
  b) In what year did the village produce 12.5 tonnes of waste?
  c) Using your answer from part a), work out how many tonnes one person produced in 2002.
  d) What year did the village adopt a recycling scheme?
  e) Give two ways that a recycling scheme could benefit the environment.

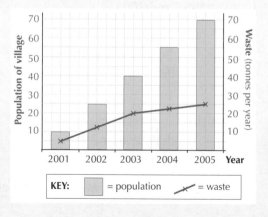

KEY: ▢ = population ✗ = waste

* Answers on page 288.

Cells

Ah, <u>cells</u>. After all that information on cloning and fretting over the state of the environment, it must come as quite a <u>relief</u> to get back to some good, old-fashioned science.

Most **animal** cells have certain **features** in common

Most <u>human cells</u>, like most <u>animal</u> cells, have the following parts — make sure you know them all:

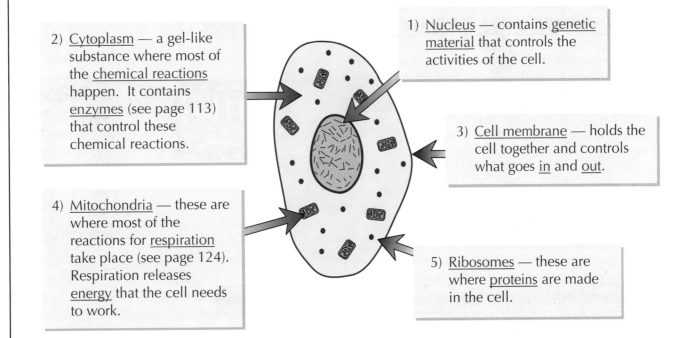

2) <u>Cytoplasm</u> — a gel-like substance where most of the <u>chemical reactions</u> happen. It contains <u>enzymes</u> (see page 113) that control these chemical reactions.

4) <u>Mitochondria</u> — these are where most of the reactions for <u>respiration</u> take place (see page 124). Respiration releases <u>energy</u> that the cell needs to work.

1) <u>Nucleus</u> — contains <u>genetic material</u> that controls the activities of the cell.

3) <u>Cell membrane</u> — holds the cell together and controls what goes <u>in</u> and <u>out</u>.

5) <u>Ribosomes</u> — these are where <u>proteins</u> are made in the cell.

Plant cells have some **extra features**

Plant cells usually have <u>all the bits</u> that <u>animal</u> cells have, plus a few <u>extra</u> things that animal cells <u>don't</u> have:

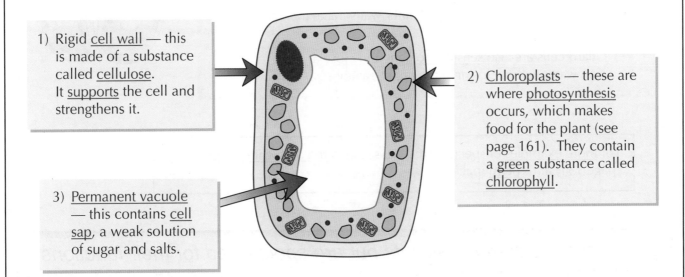

1) Rigid <u>cell wall</u> — this is made of a substance called <u>cellulose</u>. It <u>supports</u> the cell and strengthens it.

3) <u>Permanent vacuole</u> — this contains <u>cell sap</u>, a weak solution of sugar and salts.

2) <u>Chloroplasts</u> — these are where <u>photosynthesis</u> occurs, which makes food for the plant (see page 161). They contain a <u>green</u> substance called <u>chlorophyll</u>.

Cells

Most cells are specialised for their function

Similar cells are grouped together to make a <u>tissue</u>, and different tissues work together as an <u>organ</u>. Most cells are <u>specialised</u> for their function within a <u>tissue</u> or <u>organ</u>. In the exam you might have to explain <u>how</u> a particular cell is adapted for its function.

Here are a couple of plant examples:

1) *Palisade leaf cells* are adapted for *photosynthesis*

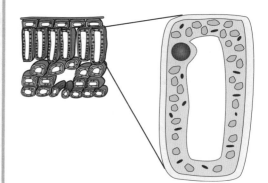

a) They're packed with <u>chloroplasts</u> for <u>photosynthesis</u>.

b) Their <u>tall</u> shape means a lot of <u>surface area</u> is exposed down the side for <u>absorbing CO_2</u> from the air in the leaf.

c) They're <u>thin</u>, so you can pack loads of them in at the top of a leaf (where most light falls).

Lots of palisade cells make up <u>palisade tissue</u> where most of the <u>photosynthesis</u> happens.

2) *Guard cells* are adapted to *open and close pores*

a) They have a special kidney shape which <u>opens</u> and <u>closes</u> pores (<u>stomata</u>) in a leaf.

b) When the plant has <u>plenty</u> of water the guard cells fill with it and go plump (<u>turgid</u>). This makes the stomata <u>open</u> so <u>gases</u> can be exchanged for <u>photosynthesis</u>.

c) When the plant is <u>short</u> of water, the guard cells lose water and go floppy (<u>flaccid</u>), making the stomata <u>close</u>. This helps to stop too much water vapour <u>escaping</u> through the pores.

d) <u>Thin</u> outer walls and <u>thickened</u> inner walls make the opening and closing work.

e) Guard cells are also <u>sensitive to light</u> and <u>close at night</u> to save water without losing out on photosynthesis.

For <u>more examples</u> of specialised cells, see also <u>red and white blood cells</u> (page 131) and <u>sperm</u> (page 146).

Cells have the same basic bits but are specialised for their functions

The cells on the opposite page are typical, with all the typical bits you need to know. But cells <u>aren't</u> all the same — they have different <u>structures</u> and make different <u>substances</u> depending on the <u>job</u> they do.

DNA

You probably first learnt about <u>DNA</u> long ago, when times were simple and all you had to know was that it lived in the nucleus and told cells what to do. Well, as I'm sure you're already aware, nowadays things are a whole lot more complicated...

Here are some **basic facts** about **DNA**

First, a quick recap:

1) <u>DNA</u> stands for <u>d</u>eoxyribose <u>n</u>ucleic <u>a</u>cid.

2) It contains all the <u>instructions</u> needed to put an organism together and <u>make it work</u>.

3) It's found in the <u>nucleus</u> of animal and plant cells in <u>long molecules</u> called <u>chromosomes</u> (see page 73).

DNA is a **double helix** of **paired bases**

1) A DNA molecule has <u>two strands</u> coiled together in the shape of a <u>double helix</u> (two spirals), as shown in the diagram below.

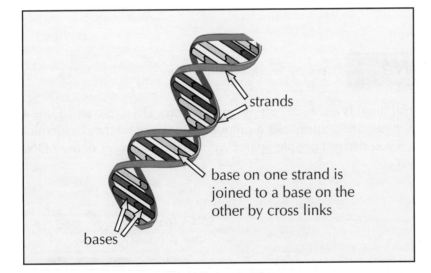

strands

base on one strand is joined to a base on the other by cross links

bases

2) Each strand is made up of lots of small groups called '<u>nucleotides</u>'.

3) Each <u>nucleotide</u> contains a small molecule called a '<u>base</u>'.

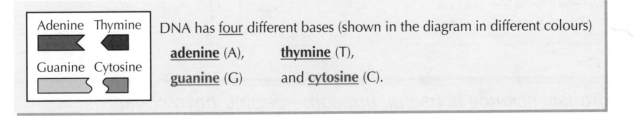

| Adenine | Thymine |
| Guanine | Cytosine |

DNA has <u>four</u> different bases (shown in the diagram in different colours)

<u>adenine</u> (A),   **<u>thymine</u>** (T),

<u>guanine</u> (G)   and **<u>cytosine</u>** (C).

4) The bases are <u>paired</u> in the DNA molecule, and they always pair up in the same way — it's always <u>**A**</u>–<u>**T**</u> and <u>**C**</u>–<u>**G**</u>. This is called <u>complementary base-pairing</u>.

DNA

Make sure you really understand the structure of DNA covered on the last page before you read on. You'll find this stuff about how the molecule replicates a lot easier if you do.

DNA can replicate itself

1) DNA copies itself every time a cell divides, so that each new cell still has the full amount of DNA.

2) In order to copy itself, the DNA double helix first 'unzips' to form two single strands.

3) As the DNA unwinds itself, new nucleotides (floating about freely in the nucleus) join on only where the bases fit (A with T and C with G), making an exact copy of the DNA on the other strand.

4) The result is two molecules of DNA identical to the original molecule of DNA.

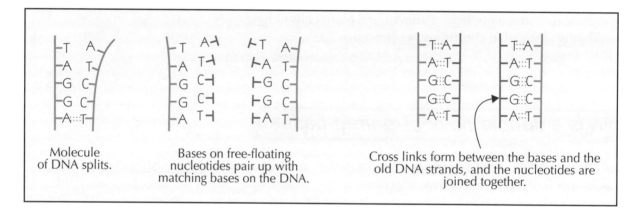

Molecule of DNA splits.

Bases on free-floating nucleotides pair up with matching bases on the DNA.

Cross links form between the bases and the old DNA strands, and the nucleotides are joined together.

Everyone has unique DNA...   ...except identical twins and clones.

DNA fingerprinting (or genetic fingerprinting) is a way of cutting up a person's DNA into small bits and then separating them. Every person's genetic fingerprint has a unique pattern (unless they're identical twins or clones of course). This means you can tell people apart by comparing samples of their DNA.

DNA fingerprinting is used in...

1) Forensic science

   DNA (from hair, skin flakes, blood, semen etc.) taken from a crime scene is compared with a DNA sample taken from a suspect. In the diagram, suspect 1's DNA has the same pattern as the DNA from the crime scene — so suspect 1 was probably at the crime scene.

2) Paternity testing

   To see if a man is the father of a particular child.

DNA from crime scene   suspect 1   suspect 2   suspect 3

Forensic science is useful, but some people have concerns

Some people want there to be a national genetic database of everyone in the country. Then any DNA from a crime scene could easily be identified. But others think this is a big invasion of privacy, and they worry about how safe the data would be and what else it might be used for. There are also scientific problems — false positives can occur if errors are made in the procedure or if the data is misinterpreted.

Making Proteins

Here is how life works — <u>DNA molecules</u> contain a <u>genetic code</u> which determines which <u>proteins</u> are built. These proteins include <u>enzymes</u> that control all the <u>reactions</u> going on in the body.

DNA controls the production of **proteins** in a cell

1) A <u>gene</u> is a <u>section of DNA</u> that 'codes' for a particular <u>protein</u>.

2) Proteins are made up of <u>chains</u> of molecules called <u>amino acids</u>.
   Each different type of protein has its own particular <u>number</u> and <u>order</u> of amino acids.

3) This gives each protein a different <u>shape</u>, which means each protein can have a different <u>function</u>.

4) It's the order of the <u>bases</u> in a strand of <u>DNA</u> that decides the order of <u>amino acids</u> in a <u>protein</u>.

5) Each amino acid is <u>coded for</u> by a sequence of <u>three bases</u> in the strand of DNA.

6) Proteins are made from <u>20</u> different amino acids, all found in the cytoplasm of cells.
   They're stuck together to make proteins, following the order of the <u>code</u> in the <u>DNA</u>.

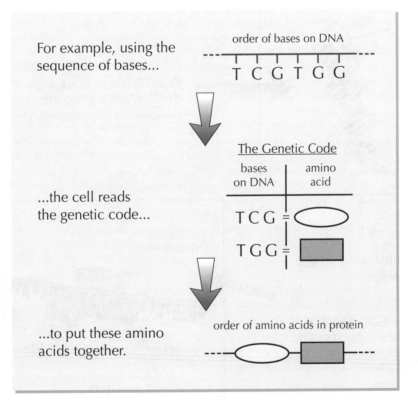

For example, using the sequence of bases...

order of bases on DNA

T C G T G G

...the cell reads the genetic code...

The Genetic Code

bases on DNA	amino acid
T C G =	⬭
T G G =	▬

...to put these amino acids together.

order of amino acids in protein

7) You get amino acids from your <u>diet</u>, but if you don't take in all the amino acids you need in the right amounts, your body can <u>change</u> some of them into others. This is called <u>transamination</u> and it happens in the <u>liver</u>.

8) DNA also determines which genes are <u>switched on or off</u> — and so which <u>proteins</u> the cell produces, e.g. haemoglobin or keratin. That in turn determines what <u>type of cell</u> it is, e.g. red blood cell or skin cell.

Making Proteins

So that's how DNA controls everything going on in the body — by controlling which proteins are made, and when and where. But it can't do it alone. Introducing <u>RNA</u> and the <u>ribosomes</u>...

Proteins are made by ribosomes

1) Proteins are made in the cell by <u>organelles</u> called <u>ribosomes</u> which are found in the cytoplasm.

2) DNA is found in the cell <u>nucleus</u> and can't move out of it because it's too big.

3) So the cell needs to get the information from the DNA to the ribosome in the cell cytoplasm, and it does this using a molecule called <u>RNA</u>. RNA is very similar to DNA, but it's much shorter and only a single strand.

4) RNA is like a <u>messenger</u> between the DNA in the nucleus and the ribosome.

Here's how it's done:

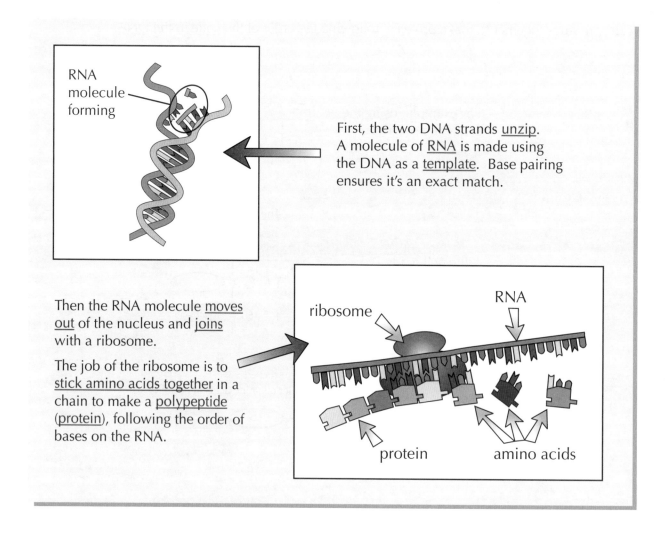

RNA molecule forming

First, the two DNA strands <u>unzip</u>. A molecule of <u>RNA</u> is made using the DNA as a <u>template</u>. Base pairing ensures it's an exact match.

Then the RNA molecule <u>moves out</u> of the nucleus and <u>joins</u> with a ribosome.

The job of the ribosome is to <u>stick amino acids together</u> in a chain to make a <u>polypeptide</u> (<u>protein</u>), following the order of bases on the RNA.

ribosome

RNA

protein

amino acids

RNA carries the genetic code, ribosomes build the proteins

So, the order of <u>bases</u> in your DNA decides what <u>amino acids</u> get joined together, and the order of the amino acids decides the type of <u>protein</u>. And proteins are pretty essential things — all your body's enzymes (see page 113) are proteins, and enzymes control the making of your other, non-protein bits.

Enzymes

There are more <u>reactions</u> going on in your body right now than you could possibly count, and they're all happening thanks to <u>enzymes</u>.

Enzymes are *catalysts* produced by *living things*

1) <u>Living things</u> have thousands of different <u>chemical reactions</u> going on inside them all the time.

2) These reactions need to be <u>carefully controlled</u> so that you get the <u>right</u> amounts of substances.

3) You can usually make a reaction happen more quickly by <u>raising the temperature</u>. This would speed up the useful reactions but also the unwanted ones too... not good. There's also a <u>limit</u> to how far you can raise the temperature inside a living creature before its <u>cells</u> start getting <u>damaged</u>.

4) So... living things produce <u>enzymes</u> which act as <u>biological catalysts</u>. Enzymes reduce the need for high temperatures and you <u>only</u> have enzymes to speed up the <u>useful chemical reactions</u> in the body.

> A <u>CATALYST</u> is a substance which <u>INCREASES</u> the speed of a reaction, without being <u>CHANGED</u> or <u>USED UP</u> in the reaction.

5) Enzymes are all <u>proteins</u>, which is one reason why proteins are so important to living things.

6) All proteins are made up of <u>chains</u> of <u>amino acids</u>. These chains are folded into <u>unique shapes</u>, which enzymes need to do their jobs (see below).

Enzymes have *special shapes* so they can *catalyse reactions*

1) <u>Chemical reactions</u> usually involve things either being <u>split apart</u> or <u>joined together</u>.

2) <u>Every</u> enzyme has a unique shape that <u>fits</u> onto the substance or substances involved in a reaction.

3) Enzymes are really <u>picky</u> — they usually only catalyse <u>one reaction</u>.

4) This is because, for the enzyme to work, each substance has to <u>fit</u> its special shape.

5) If a substance doesn't <u>match</u> the enzyme's shape, then the reaction <u>won't</u> be catalysed.

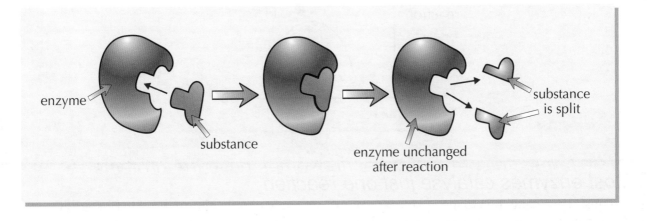

enzyme

substance

enzyme unchanged after reaction

substance is split

Enzymes

Enzymes are clearly very clever, but they're <u>not</u> very versatile. They need just the right <u>conditions</u> if they're going to work properly.

*Enzymes need the **right temperature** to work properly*

1) Changing the <u>temperature</u> changes the <u>rate</u> of an enzyme-catalysed reaction.

2) Like with any reaction, a higher temperature <u>increases</u> the rate at first.

3) But if it gets <u>too hot</u>, some of the <u>bonds</u> holding the enzyme together <u>break</u>. This destroys the enzyme's <u>special shape</u> and so it won't work any more. It's said to be <u>denatured</u>.

4) Enzymes in the <u>human body</u> normally work best at around <u>37 °C</u> — body temperature.

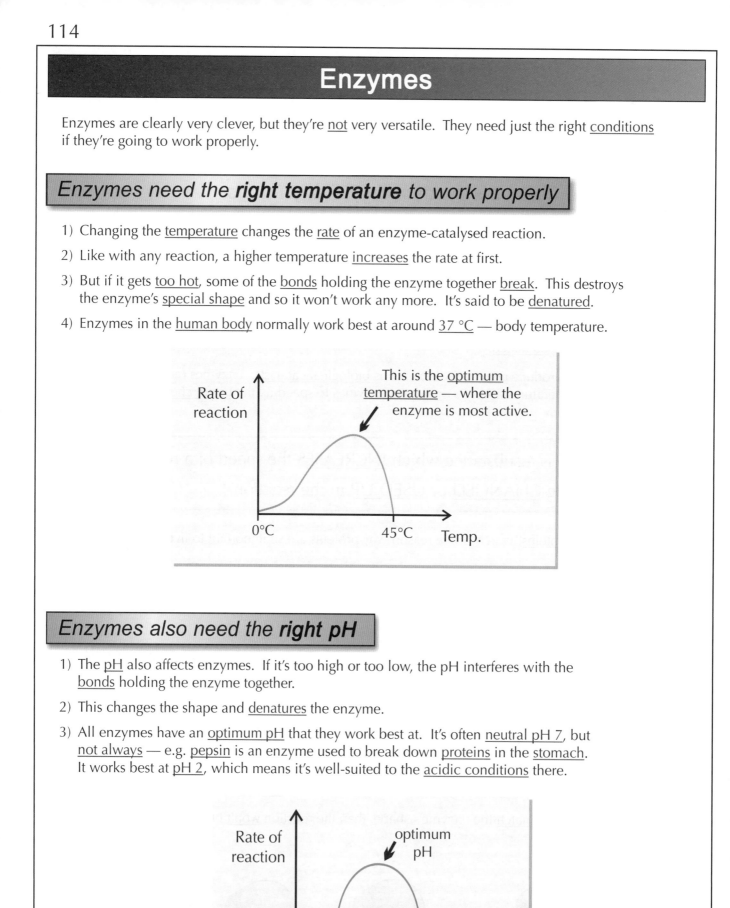

*Enzymes also need the **right pH***

1) The <u>pH</u> also affects enzymes. If it's too high or too low, the pH interferes with the <u>bonds</u> holding the enzyme together.

2) This changes the shape and <u>denatures</u> the enzyme.

3) All enzymes have an <u>optimum pH</u> that they work best at. It's often <u>neutral pH 7</u>, but <u>not always</u> — e.g. <u>pepsin</u> is an enzyme used to break down <u>proteins</u> in the <u>stomach</u>. It works best at <u>pH 2</u>, which means it's well-suited to the <u>acidic conditions</u> there.

Most enzymes catalyse just one reaction
Scientists have caught on to the idea that enzymes are <u>really useful</u>. They're used in biological <u>detergents</u> (to break down nasty stains) and in some <u>baby foods</u> (to predigest the food).

Warm-Up and Exam Questions

Warm-Up Questions

1) Give three ways in which plants cells are different from animal cells.
2) Name the four different bases in DNA and say how they pair up.
3) Which organelle is responsible for synthesising proteins?
4) Enzymes are sometimes referred to as 'biological catalysts'. What is a catalyst?
5) Sketch graphs to show how the rates of enzyme-controlled reactions are affected by temperature and pH.
6) What is meant by the optimum temperature or pH of an enzyme?

Exam Questions

1 The diagram shows a palisade cell from a leaf.

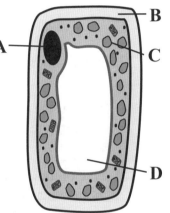

   (a) Which label points to a chloroplast?

(1 mark)

   (b) Name the green substance present in chloroplasts.

(1 mark)

   (c) Apart from having chloroplasts, state two other ways in which a palisade cell is adapted for photosynthesis.

(2 marks)

2 Part of one of the strands of a DNA molecule has this base sequence:

C — C — G — T — T — T — G — G — G

   (a) What is the base sequence of the equivalent part of the other DNA strand?

(1 mark)

   (b) How many amino acids does this piece of DNA code for?

(1 mark)

   (c) What kind of molecule is produced when amino acids are joined together?

(1 mark)

3 A leaf is a plant organ containing several tissues.

   (a) Explain what is meant by a tissue.

(1 mark)

   (b) Leaves contain guard cells. What is their function?

(1 mark)

   (c) Explain how the structure of guard cells' walls is important in their function.

(2 marks)

SECTION SIX — CELLS AND CELL FUNCTIONS

Exam Questions

4   Mr X and Mr Y are both suspects in a burglary. A blood stain has been found on a crowbar at the crime scene. The police carry out a DNA fingerprint on Mr X, Mr Y and the blood from the crime scene.

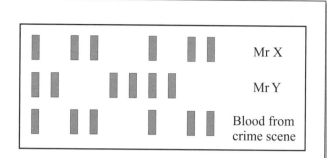

The diagram shows part of the test results.

(a) Do these results suggest that Mr X was at the crime scene? Explain your answer.

(2 marks)

(b) A police officer investigating the burglary says that no two people have exactly the same genetic fingerprint. Is he correct? Explain your answer.

(2 marks)

5   The graph shows the effect of temperature on the action of two different enzymes.

(a) What is the optimum temperature for enzyme A?

(1 mark)

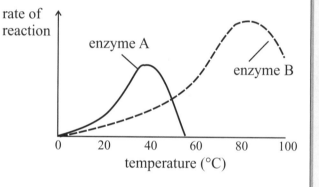

(b) One of these enzymes was extracted from human liver cells. The other was extracted from bacteria living in hot underwater vents.

Suggest which enzyme came from the bacteria, and explain your answer.

(2 marks)

(c) Enzyme B is a protein-digesting enzyme. Suggest why it might be useful in biological washing powders.

(2 marks)

6   The diagram represents the action of an enzyme in catalysing a biological reaction.

In terms of the enzyme's shape, explain the following:

(a) the enzyme's specificity.

(1 mark)

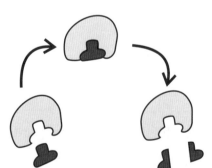

(b) what happens when the enzyme is denatured.

(1 mark)

Diffusion

Particles <u>move about randomly</u>, and after a bit they end up <u>evenly spaced</u>.

Don't be put off by the *fancy word*

<u>Diffusion</u> is just the <u>gradual movement</u> of particles from places where there are <u>lots</u> of them to places where there are <u>fewer</u> of them. Simple. Learn the fancy way of saying this, which is:

> <u>DIFFUSION</u> is the <u>passive movement</u> of <u>particles</u> from an area of <u>HIGHER CONCENTRATION</u> to an area of <u>LOWER CONCENTRATION</u>

Diffusion happens in both <u>liquids</u> and <u>gases</u> — that's because the particles are free to <u>move about</u> randomly. The <u>simplest type</u> is when different <u>gases</u> diffuse through each other, like when the smell of perfume diffuses through a room (see diagram).

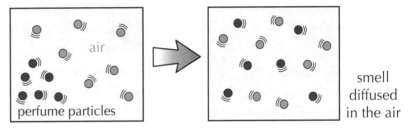

smell diffused in the air

The <u>bigger</u> the <u>difference</u> in concentration, the <u>faster</u> the diffusion rate.

Small molecules *diffuse* across *cell membranes*

Membranes are clever because they <u>hold</u> the cell together <u>but</u> they let stuff <u>in and out</u> as well. Substances can move in and out of cells by <u>diffusion</u> and <u>osmosis</u> (see page 120). Only very <u>small</u> molecules can <u>diffuse</u> through cell membranes though — things like <u>glucose</u>, <u>amino acids</u>, <u>water</u> and <u>oxygen</u>. <u>Big</u> molecules like <u>starch</u> and <u>proteins</u> can't fit through the membrane.

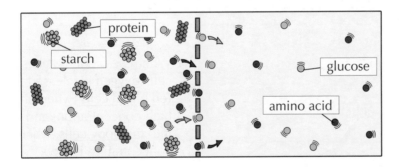

1) Just like with diffusion in air, particles flow through the cell membrane from where there's a <u>higher concentration</u> (more of them) to where there's a <u>lower concentration</u> (not such a lot of them).

2) They're only moving about <u>randomly</u> of course, so they go <u>both</u> ways — but if there are a lot <u>more</u> particles on one side of the membrane, there's a <u>net</u> (overall) movement <u>from</u> that side.

3) The <u>rate</u> of diffusion depends on three main things:

   a) <u>Distance</u> — substances diffuse <u>more quickly</u> when they haven't as <u>far</u> to move.

   b) <u>Concentration difference</u> (gradient) — substances diffuse faster if there's a <u>big difference</u> in concentration. If there are <u>lots more</u> particles on one side, there are more there to move across.

   c) <u>Surface area</u> — the <u>more surface</u> there is available for molecules to move across, the <u>faster</u> they can get from one side to the other.

Diffusion in Cells

You need to know some examples of where diffusion happens in our bodies.
First up, diffusion of carbon dioxide and oxygen in the lungs and in body cells.

Alveoli carry out gas exchange in the body

1) The lungs contain millions and millions of little air sacs called alveoli where gas exchange happens.

2) The blood passing next to the alveoli has just returned to the lungs from the rest of the body, so it contains lots of carbon dioxide and very little oxygen.

3) Oxygen diffuses out of the alveolus (where it's at high concentration) into the blood (low concentration).

4) Carbon dioxide diffuses out of the blood (where it's at high concentration) into the alveolus (low concentration) to be breathed out.

air in and out

alveolus

CO_2

O_2

blood capillary

The blood carries oxygen to the body cells

body cells

CO_2

O_2

blood capillary

1) When the blood reaches body cells oxygen is released from the red blood cells (where there's a high concentration) and diffuses into the body cells (where the concentration is low).

2) At the same time, carbon dioxide diffuses out of the body cells (where there's a high concentration) into the blood (where there's a low concentration). It's then carried back to the lungs.

Diffusion in Cells

Here are the other two examples you need of where diffusion happens in the body.
There's also a very nice <u>plant example</u> — diffusion in the leaf on page 165.

Small food molecules can *diffuse* into the *blood*

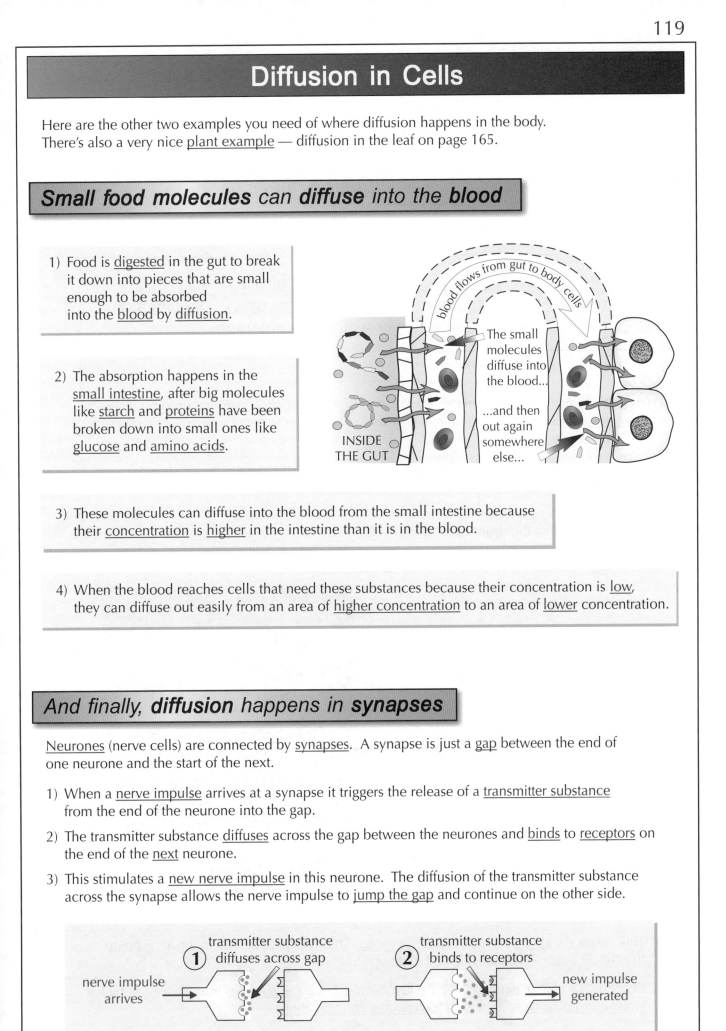

1) Food is <u>digested</u> in the gut to break it down into pieces that are small enough to be absorbed into the <u>blood</u> by <u>diffusion</u>.

2) The absorption happens in the <u>small intestine</u>, after big molecules like <u>starch</u> and <u>proteins</u> have been broken down into small ones like <u>glucose</u> and <u>amino acids</u>.

blood flows from gut to body cells

The small molecules diffuse into the blood...

...and then out again somewhere else...

INSIDE THE GUT

3) These molecules can diffuse into the blood from the small intestine because their <u>concentration</u> is <u>higher</u> in the intestine than it is in the blood.

4) When the blood reaches cells that need these substances because their concentration is <u>low</u>, they can diffuse out easily from an area of <u>higher concentration</u> to an area of <u>lower</u> concentration.

And finally, **diffusion** happens in **synapses**

<u>Neurones</u> (nerve cells) are connected by <u>synapses</u>. A synapse is just a <u>gap</u> between the end of one neurone and the start of the next.

1) When a <u>nerve impulse</u> arrives at a synapse it triggers the release of a <u>transmitter substance</u> from the end of the neurone into the gap.

2) The transmitter substance <u>diffuses</u> across the gap between the neurones and <u>binds</u> to <u>receptors</u> on the end of the <u>next</u> neurone.

3) This stimulates a <u>new nerve impulse</u> in this neurone. The diffusion of the transmitter substance across the synapse allows the nerve impulse to <u>jump the gap</u> and continue on the other side.

nerve impulse arrives

(1) transmitter substance diffuses across gap

(2) transmitter substance binds to receptors

new impulse generated

Osmosis

If you've got your head round diffusion, <u>osmosis</u> will be a breeze.
And if you haven't, what are you doing looking at this page? Go back and learn it.

*Osmosis is a **special case** of **diffusion**, that's all*

Learn this definition of <u>osmosis</u>:

> <u>OSMOSIS</u> is the <u>movement of water molecules</u> across a <u>partially permeable membrane</u> from a region of <u>higher water concentration</u> to a region of <u>lower water concentration</u>.

1) A <u>partially permeable</u> membrane is just a membrane that <u>only allows certain substances</u> to <u>diffuse</u> through it. For example, it may only allow <u>water</u> to pass through — not other molecules like <u>starch</u>.

2) The water molecules actually pass <u>both ways</u> through the membrane during osmosis. This happens because water molecules <u>move about randomly</u> all the time.

3) But because there are <u>more</u> water molecules on one side than on the other, there's a steady <u>net flow</u> of water into the region with <u>fewer</u> water molecules, e.g. into the <u>stronger</u> sugar solution.

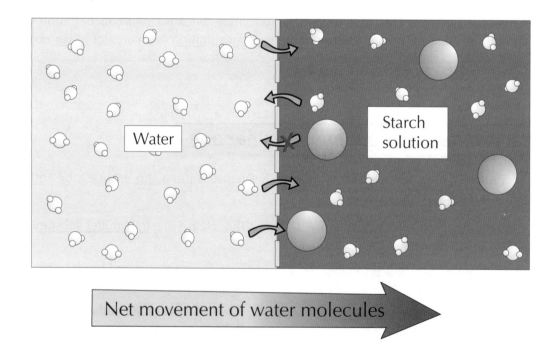

Water

Starch solution

Net movement of water molecules

4) This means the <u>strong</u> solution gets more <u>dilute</u>. The water acts like it's trying to '<u>even up</u>' the concentration on either side of the membrane.

5) Osmosis is a type of <u>diffusion</u> — passive movement of <u>water particles</u> from an area of <u>higher water concentration</u> to an area of <u>lower water concentration</u>.

Osmosis

You're not learning about osmosis just for fun — it's how water moves into and out of <u>cells</u>, so it's pretty important in biology.

Water moves into and out of **cells** by **osmosis**

1) <u>Tissue fluid</u> surrounds the cells in the body. It's basically just <u>water</u> with <u>oxygen</u> and <u>glucose</u> and stuff dissolved in it. It's squeezed out of the <u>blood capillaries</u> to supply the cells with everything they need.

2) The tissue fluid will usually have a <u>different concentration</u> to the fluid <u>inside</u> a cell. This means that water will either move <u>into the cell</u> from the tissue fluid, or <u>out of the cell</u> to the tissue fluid by <u>osmosis</u>.

3) If a cell is <u>short of water</u>, the solution inside it will become quite <u>concentrated</u>. This usually means the solution <u>outside</u> is more <u>dilute</u>, and so water will move <u>into</u> the cell by osmosis.

4) If a cell has <u>lots of water</u>, the solution inside it will be <u>more dilute</u>, and water will be <u>drawn out</u> of the cell and into the fluid outside by osmosis.

Osmosis Experiment

There's a fairly dull <u>experiment</u> you can do to show osmosis at work:

1) You cut up a <u>potato</u> into identical cylinders, and get some beakers with <u>different sugar solutions</u> in them.

2) One should be <u>pure water</u>, another should be a <u>very concentrated sugar solution</u>. Then you can have a few others with concentrations <u>in between</u>.

3) You measure the <u>length</u> of the cylinders, then leave a few in each beaker for half an hour or so. Then you take them out and measure their lengths <u>again</u>.

4) If the cylinders have drawn in water by osmosis, they'll be a bit <u>longer</u>. If water has been drawn out, they'll have <u>shrunk</u> a bit. Then you can plot a few <u>graphs</u> and things.

The <u>dependent variable</u> is the <u>cylinder length</u> and the <u>independent variable</u> is the <u>concentration</u> of the sugar solution. All <u>other</u> variables (volume of solution, temperature, time, type of sugar used, etc. etc.) must be kept the <u>same</u> in each case or the experiment won't be a <u>fair test</u>.

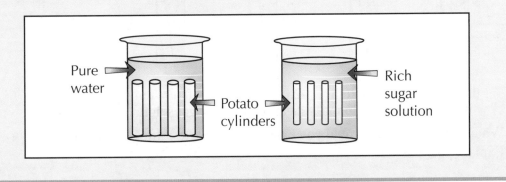

Pure water

Potato cylinders

Rich sugar solution

Water always moves into the more concentrated solution

That's why it's bad to drink sea water. The high <u>salt</u> content means you end up with a <u>lower water concentration</u> in your blood and tissue fluid than in your cells. Lots of water is sucked out of your cells by osmosis and they <u>shrivel and die</u>. So next time you're stranded at sea, remember this page...

Warm-Up and Exam Questions

So, hopefully you've read the last five pages. But could you cope if a question on diffusion or osmosis came up in the exam? Well, with amazing new technology we can simulate that very situation...

Warm-Up Questions

1) Define diffusion.
2) Name three places in the human body where diffusion is important.
3) In terms of osmosis, explain what will happen if an animal cell is placed in a concentrated sugar solution.
4) Explain what is meant by a partially permeable membrane.

Exam Questions

1   The lungs have a large surface area. This helps to make diffusion of gases (oxygen and carbon dioxide) more efficient.

   (a) Name two other factors, besides surface area, that influence the rate of diffusion.

   (2 marks)

   (b) Describe and explain the movement of carbon dioxide and oxygen as the blood moves past an alveolus in the lungs.

   (2 marks)

2   In an experiment, four 5 cm cylinders were cut from a fresh potato.
     The cylinders were then placed in different sugar solutions, as shown in the diagram.
     After four hours the potato cylinders were removed and measured.

 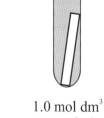

| Tube A | Tube B | Tube C | Tube D |

| distilled water | 1.0 mol dm³ sugar solution | 2.0 mol dm³ sugar solution | 3.0 mol dm³ sugar solution |

   (a) Which potato cylinder would you expect to be shortest after four hours?
        Explain your answer.

   (2 marks)

   (b) The potato cylinder in tube A increased in length during the four hours.
        Explain why this happened.

   (2 marks)

Revision Summary for Section Six

Well, look at this — it's another Revision Summary page. It's amazing the way they turn up at the end of each section, and they're always a right bundle of laughs, aren't they? I mean, just look at question one there — "Where in the cell does respiration happen?" HAAAH HAR HAR HAR. Good one.

1) Where in the cell does respiration happen?

2) Name five parts of a cell that both plants and animal cells have.
   What three things do plant cells have that animal cells don't?

3) Give three ways that a palisade leaf cell is adapted for photosynthesis.

4) Describe two ways that guard cells are adapted to open and close stomata.

5) What does DNA stand for?

6) What shape is DNA?

7) Name the four different bases found in DNA. How do they pair up?

8) Describe DNA replication.

9) How can DNA fingerprinting be used in forensic science?

10) What is a gene?

11) What does a triplet of three bases on a strand of DNA code for?

12) What is transamination?

13) Describe the stages of protein synthesis.

14) What name is given to biological catalysts?

15) What is a catalyst?

16) Give one reason why proteins are so important to living things.

17) What happens at the active site of an enzyme?

18) An enzyme with an optimum temperature of 37 °C is heated to 60 °C. Suggest what will happen to it.

19)*The graph on the right shows how the rate of an enzyme-catalysed reaction depends on pH:

   a) State the optimum pH of the enzyme.

   b) In which part of the human digestive system would you expect to find this enzyme?

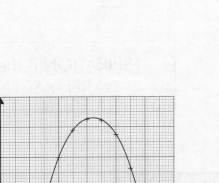

20) What is diffusion?

21) What three things does the rate of diffusion depend on?

22) Why does oxygen enter the blood in the alveoli and leave it when it reaches a respiring tissue?

23) Describe how a nerve impulse travels across a synapse.

24) What is osmosis?

25) A solution of pure water is separated from a concentrated sugar solution by a partially permeable membrane. What substance will move across the membrane and in which direction will it flow?

26) An osmosis experiment involves placing pieces of potato into sugar solutions of various concentrations and measuring their lengths before and after. What is:

   a) the independent variable,   b) the dependent variable?

* Answers on page 289.

Respiration and Exercise

Respiration happens in little tiny structures called <u>mitochondria</u> (see page 107).

Respiration *is NOT* 'breathing in and out'

<u>Respiration</u> is <u>really</u> important — it releases the <u>energy</u> that cells need to do <u>just about everything</u>.

1) Respiration is the process of <u>breaking down glucose to release energy</u>, and it goes on in <u>every cell</u> in your body. (Glucose contains energy in the form of chemical bonds.)

2) Respiration happens in <u>plants</u> too. <u>All</u> living things <u>respire</u>. It's how they get energy from their food.

3) This energy is used to do things like:

- build up <u>larger molecules</u> (like proteins)

- contract <u>muscles</u>

- maintain a steady <u>body temperature</u>

> <u>RESPIRATION</u> is the process of <u>BREAKING DOWN GLUCOSE TO RELEASE ENERGY</u>, which goes on <u>IN EVERY CELL</u>.

Respiration can be **aerobic** or **anaerobic**

<u>Aerobic respiration</u> is respiration using <u>oxygen</u> ('aerobic' just means '<u>with air</u>'). It's the most efficient way to release energy from glucose.

Learn the <u>word equation</u>:

> glucose + oxygen → carbon dioxide + water (+ ENERGY)

<u>Anaerobic respiration</u> happens when there's <u>not enough oxygen available</u> (e.g. when you're exercising hard). 'Anaerobic' means '<u>without air</u>' and it's <u>NOT the best way to release energy from glucose</u> — but it's useful in emergencies.

The overall word equation is:

> glucose → lactic acid (+ ENERGY)

Respiration and Exercise

The amount of respiration your body needs to do depends on how much <u>energy</u> you need.

*When you **exercise** you **respire more***

1) When you <u>exercise</u>, your muscles need <u>more energy</u> so you <u>respire more</u>.

2) You need to get <u>more oxygen</u> into the cells for respiration (see previous page). Your <u>breathing rate increases</u> to get more oxygen into the lungs, and your <u>heart rate increases</u> to get this oxygenated blood around the body faster.

3) During really <u>vigorous</u> exercise (like sprinting), your body can't supply enough <u>oxygen</u> to your muscles quickly enough, so they start respiring <u>anaerobically</u>.

4) Anaerobic respiration produces <u>lactic acid</u>, which builds up in your <u>muscles</u> and causes <u>pain</u>. When you stop exercising, you'll have an <u>oxygen debt</u>. You have to keep <u>breathing hard</u> to repay the oxygen that you didn't manage to get to your muscles. The oxygen <u>breaks down</u> the lactic acid.

5) Athletes monitor their <u>heart rate</u> and <u>breathing rate</u> to help with their training.

6) The current UK government recommendation is to exercise for at least <u>30</u> minutes, <u>five times</u> a week in order to stay fit and healthy. But the official advice changes all the time — not so long ago the recommendation was <u>20</u> minutes, <u>three times</u> a week.

Alveoli** are specialised for **gas exchange

1) The huge number of microscopic alveoli gives the lungs an <u>enormous surface area</u>.

2) There's a <u>moist lining</u> for gases to <u>dissolve</u> in.

3) The alveoli have very <u>thin walls</u> — only one cell thick, so the gas doesn't have far to diffuse.

4) They have a <u>great blood supply</u> to maintain a high concentration gradient.

5) The walls are <u>permeable</u> — so gases can diffuse across easily.

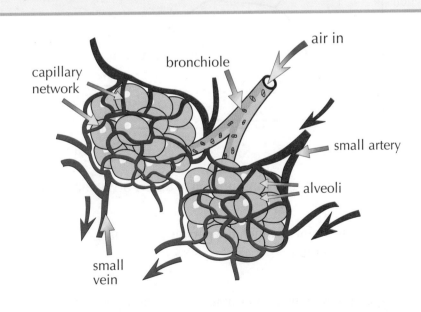

After respiring anaerobically you'll have an oxygen debt
Advice about exercise (and diet) is based on scientific evidence from <u>many</u> different surveys and studies.

Warm-Up and Exam Questions

Doing well in exams isn't just about remembering all the facts, although that's important. You have to get used to the way the exams are phrased and make sure you always read the question carefully.

Warm-Up Questions

1) Define respiration.
2) Write down the word equation for aerobic respiration.
3) Give the word equation for anaerobic respiration.
4) State three changes that take place in the body during vigorous exercise.
5) How are alveoli specialised for gas exchange?

Exam Questions

1   In the human body, respiration may be aerobic or anaerobic at different times.

   (a) Give two **differences** between anaerobic and aerobic respiration in humans.

   (2 marks)

   (b) Give two **similarities** between anaerobic and aerobic respiration in humans.

   (2 marks)

   (c) Give one advantage of each of these types of respiration.

   (2 marks)

2   The graph below shows the rate of oxygen use by a person before, during and after a period of exercise.

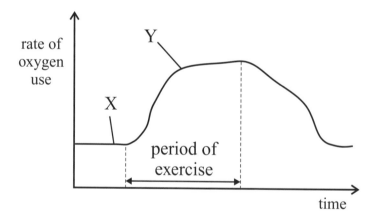

   (a) Explain why the rate of oxygen consumption is higher at Y than at X.

   (1 mark)

   (b) Mark on the graph the point at which the person's blood lactic acid concentration will be highest.

   (1 mark)

   (c) Why does oxygen use remain high even after the exercise ends?

   (1 mark)

Enzymes and Digestion

The enzymes used in <u>respiration</u> work <u>inside cells</u>. Various different enzymes are used in <u>digestion</u> too, but these enzymes are produced by specialised cells and then <u>released</u> into the gut to mix with the food.

Digestive enzymes break down *big molecules* into *smaller ones*

1) <u>Starch</u>, <u>proteins</u> and <u>fats</u> are BIG molecules. They're too big to pass through the walls of the digestive system.

2) <u>Sugars</u>, <u>amino acids</u>, <u>glycerol</u> and <u>fatty acids</u> are much smaller molecules. They can pass easily through the walls of the digestive system.

3) The <u>digestive enzymes</u> break down the BIG molecules into smaller ones.

Amylase converts *starch* into *simple sugars*

starch → amylase enzyme → maltose
and other simple sugars, e.g. dextrins

Amylase is made in <u>three</u> places:
1)   The <u>salivary glands</u>
2)   The <u>pancreas</u>
3)   The <u>small intestine</u>

Protease converts *proteins* into *amino acids*

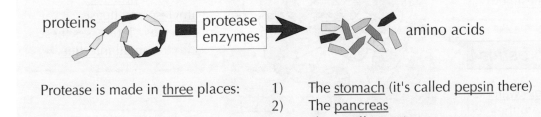

proteins → protease enzymes → amino acids

Protease is made in <u>three</u> places:
1)   The <u>stomach</u> (it's called <u>pepsin</u> there)
2)   The <u>pancreas</u>
3)   The <u>small intestine</u>

Lipase converts *fats* into *glycerol* and *fatty acids*

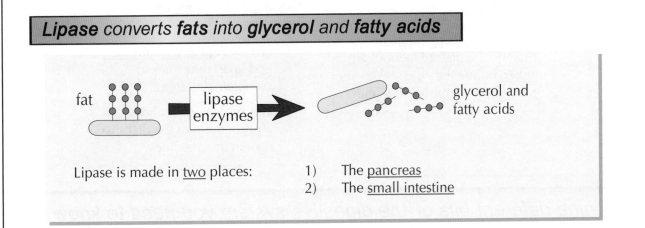

fat → lipase enzymes → glycerol and fatty acids

Lipase is made in <u>two</u> places:
1)   The <u>pancreas</u>
2)   The <u>small intestine</u>

The Digestive System

So now you know what the enzymes do, here's a nice big picture of the whole of the digestive system.

The breakdown of food is catalysed by enzymes

Enzymes used in the digestive system are produced by specialised cells in glands and in the gut lining.

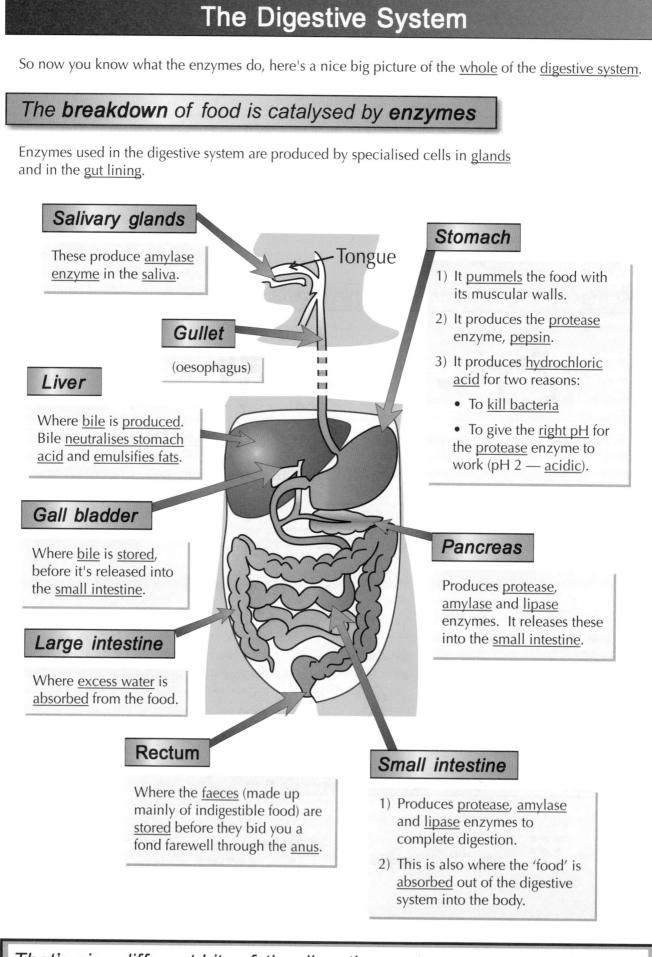

Salivary glands

These produce amylase enzyme in the saliva.

Tongue

Gullet

(oesophagus)

Liver

Where bile is produced. Bile neutralises stomach acid and emulsifies fats.

Gall bladder

Where bile is stored, before it's released into the small intestine.

Large intestine

Where excess water is absorbed from the food.

Stomach

1) It pummels the food with its muscular walls.

2) It produces the protease enzyme, pepsin.

3) It produces hydrochloric acid for two reasons:

- To kill bacteria

- To give the right pH for the protease enzyme to work (pH 2 — acidic).

Pancreas

Produces protease, amylase and lipase enzymes. It releases these into the small intestine.

Rectum

Where the faeces (made up mainly of indigestible food) are stored before they bid you a fond farewell through the anus.

Small intestine

1) Produces protease, amylase and lipase enzymes to complete digestion.

2) This is also where the 'food' is absorbed out of the digestive system into the body.

That's nine different bits of the digestive system you need to know

Did you know that pretty much the whole of your digestive system is actually a hole that goes right through your body? Think about it. It just gets loads of food, digestive juices and enzymes piled into it.

The Digestive System

The digested food is then <u>absorbed</u> into the body in the <u>small intestine</u>.

Villi in the **small intestine** help with **diffusion**

1) The <u>small intestine</u> is <u>adapted</u> for absorption of food.

2) It's very <u>long</u>, so there's time to break down and absorb <u>all</u> the food before it reaches the end.

3) There's a really <u>big surface area</u> for absorption, because the walls of the small intestine are covered in <u>millions and millions</u> of tiny little projections called <u>villi</u>.

4) Each <u>cell</u> on the surface of a villus also has its own <u>microvilli</u> — little projections that increase the surface area even more.

5) Villi have a <u>single permeable</u> layer of surface cells and a very <u>good blood supply</u> to assist <u>quick absorption</u>.

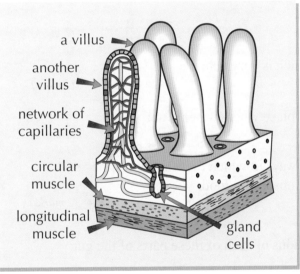

Bile neutralises the stomach acid and **emulsifies** fats

The digestive <u>enzymes</u> you need to know about are all on page 127, but there's <u>another</u> substance that helps to break down food — it's called <u>bile</u>.

1) Bile is <u>produced</u> in the <u>liver</u>. It's <u>stored</u> in the <u>gall bladder</u> until it's needed, and then it's released into the <u>small intestine</u>.

2) The <u>hydrochloric acid</u> in the stomach makes the pH <u>too acidic</u> for enzymes in the small intestine to work properly. Bile is <u>alkaline</u> — it <u>neutralises</u> the acid and makes conditions <u>alkaline</u>. The enzymes in the small intestine <u>work best</u> in these alkaline conditions.

3) It <u>emulsifies</u> fats. In other words it breaks the fat into <u>tiny droplets</u>. This gives a much <u>bigger surface area</u> of fat for the enzyme lipase to work on — which makes its digestion <u>faster</u>.

Bile is an important digesting agent but it's not an enzyme

This all happens inside your body, but there are some microorganisms which secrete their digestive enzymes <u>outside</u> their body onto their food. The food's digested, then the microorganism absorbs the nutrients. Nice. I wouldn't like to empty the contents of my stomach onto my food before eating it.

Warm-Up and Exam Questions

Warm-Up Questions

1) What is digestion?
2) Which enzymes digest: (a) starch (b) protein (c) fat?
3) What are the products of the digestion of: (a) starch (b) protein (c) fat?
4) What does bile do?

Exam Questions

1 The diagram shows the human digestive system.

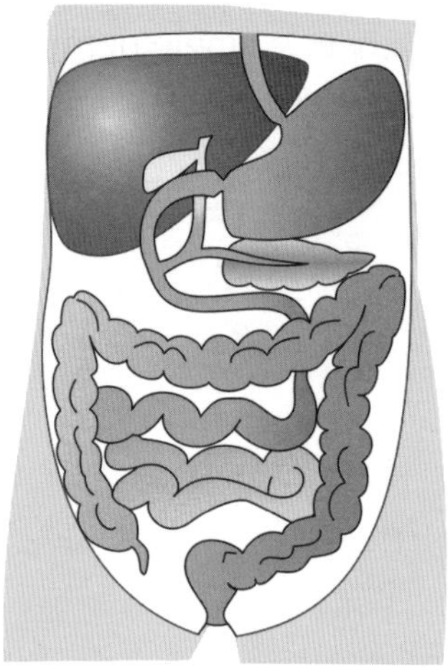

(a) Label the following parts on the diagram:

(i) the liver

(1 mark)

(ii) a part which is very acidic

(1 mark)

(iii) the main place where water is absorbed

(1 mark)

(b) Describe two ways in which the small intestine is adapted for absorbing food.

(2 marks)

2 Describe the functions of each of these parts of the gut:

(a) gall bladder

(1 mark)

(b) pancreas

(1 mark)

(c) liver

(1 mark)

3 Naz did an experiment to investigate the effect of pH on enzyme action. She took four test tubes and placed some starch solution in each one. Each solution was given a different pH value as shown below. Then a digestive enzyme was added to each tube.

Test tube	A	B	C	D
pH	2	5	8	11

(a) What type of digestive enzyme do you think should be added to the tubes?

(1 mark)

(b) Name three factors that should be kept constant during this experiment.

(3 marks)

(c) At which pH do you think the enzyme will work best? Explain your answer.

(2 marks)

Functions of the Blood

Blood is very useful stuff. It's a big <u>transport system</u> for moving things around the body.

Plasma is the liquid bit of blood

It's basically blood minus the blood cells (see below). Plasma is a pale yellow liquid which <u>carries just about everything</u> that needs transporting around your body:

1) <u>Red</u> and <u>white blood cells</u> (see below) and <u>platelets (used in clotting)</u>.

2) <u>Water</u>.

3) Digested food products like <u>glucose</u> and <u>amino acids</u> from the gut to all the body cells.

4) <u>Carbon dioxide</u> from the body cells to the lungs.

5) <u>Urea</u> from the liver to the kidneys (where it's removed in the urine).

6) <u>Hormones</u> — these act like chemical messengers.

7) <u>Antibodies</u> and <u>antitoxins</u> produced by the white blood cells (see below).

Red blood cells have the job of carrying oxygen

They transport <u>oxygen</u> from the <u>lungs</u> to <u>all</u> the cells in the body.
The <u>structure</u> of a red blood cell is adapted to its <u>function</u>:

1) Red blood cells are <u>small</u> and have a <u>biconcave shape</u> (which is a posh way of saying they look a bit like doughnuts, see diagram below) to give a <u>large surface area</u> for <u>absorbing</u> and <u>releasing oxygen</u>.

2) They contain <u>haemoglobin</u>, which is what gives blood its <u>colour</u> — it contains lots of <u>iron</u>. In the lungs, haemoglobin <u>reacts with oxygen</u> to become <u>oxyhaemoglobin</u>. In tissues the reverse reaction happens to <u>release oxygen to the cells</u>.

3) Red blood cells don't have a <u>nucleus</u> — this frees up <u>space</u> for more haemoglobin, so they can carry more oxygen.

4) Red blood cells are very <u>flexible</u>. This means they can easily pass through the <u>tiny capillaries</u> (see page 133).

White blood cells are used to fight disease

1) Their main role is <u>defence against disease</u>.

2) They produce <u>antibodies</u> to fight microbes.

3) They produce <u>antitoxins</u> to neutralise the toxins produced by microbes.

4) They have a <u>flexible shape</u>, which helps them to <u>engulf</u> any microorganisms they come across inside the body. Basically the white blood cell wraps around the microorganism until it's <u>totally surrounded</u>, and then <u>digests it</u> using enzymes.

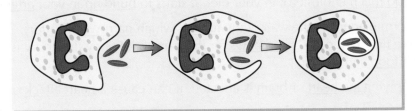

Blood Vessels

Blood needs a good system to move it around the body — it's called the <u>circulatory system</u>.

Blood vessels are *designed* for their *function*

There are <u>three</u> different types of <u>blood vessel</u>:

> 1) **<u>ARTERIES</u>** — these carry the blood <u>away</u> from the heart.

> 2) **<u>CAPILLARIES</u>** — these are involved in the <u>exchange of materials</u> at the tissues.

> 3) **<u>VEINS</u>** — these carry the blood <u>to</u> the heart.

Arteries carry blood under *pressure*

1) The heart pumps the blood out at <u>high pressure</u> so the artery walls are <u>strong</u> and <u>elastic</u>.

2) The walls are <u>thick</u> compared to the size of the hole down the middle (the '<u>lumen</u>').
   They contain thick layers of <u>muscle</u> to make them <u>strong</u>.

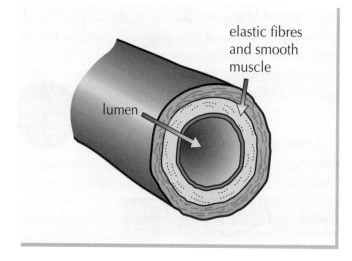

elastic fibres
and smooth
muscle

lumen

Cholesterol can build up in *arteries*

1) <u>Cholesterol</u> is a <u>fatty</u> substance. Eating a diet high in <u>saturated fat</u> has been linked to high levels of cholesterol in the blood.

2) You need some cholesterol for things like <u>making cell membranes</u>.
   But if you get <u>too much</u> cholesterol in your diet, it starts to <u>build up</u> in your <u>arteries</u>.

3) It can start to form <u>plaques</u> in the wall of the <u>lumen</u>, which <u>narrows</u> the artery.
   This <u>restricts</u> the flow of blood — <u>bad news</u> for the part of the body the artery is supplying with <u>food</u> and <u>oxygen</u>.

4) If an artery supplying the <u>heart</u> or <u>brain</u> is affected, it can cause a <u>heart attack</u> or <u>stroke</u>.

Blood Vessels

This page is about the other two types of blood vessel — <u>capillaries</u> and <u>veins</u>.

Capillaries are really small

1) Arteries branch into <u>capillaries</u>. Capillaries are really <u>tiny</u> — too small to see with the naked eye.

2) They carry the blood <u>really close</u> to <u>every cell</u> in the body to <u>exchange substances</u> with them.

3) They have <u>permeable</u> walls, so substances can <u>diffuse</u> in and out.

4) They supply <u>food</u> and <u>oxygen</u>, and take away <u>wastes</u> like <u>carbon dioxide</u>.

5) Their walls are usually <u>only one cell thick</u>. This <u>increases</u> the rate of diffusion by <u>decreasing</u> the <u>distance</u> over which it happens.

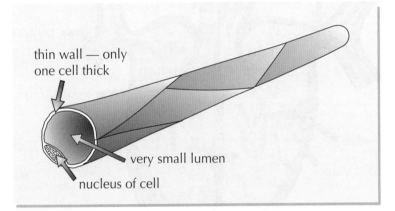

thin wall — only one cell thick

very small lumen

nucleus of cell

Veins take blood back to the heart

1) Capillaries eventually <u>join up</u> to form <u>veins</u>.

2) The blood is at <u>lower pressure</u> in the veins so the walls don't need to be as <u>thick</u> as artery walls.

3) They have a <u>bigger lumen</u> than arteries to help the blood <u>flow</u> despite the lower pressure.

4) They also have <u>valves</u> to help keep the blood flowing in the <u>right direction</u>.

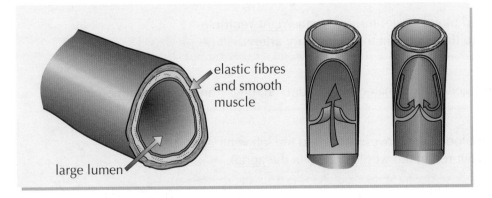

elastic fibres and smooth muscle

large lumen

Make sure you know the features of arteries, capillaries and veins

Here's an interesting(ish) fact for you — your body contains about <u>60 000 miles</u> of blood vessels. That's about <u>six times</u> the distance from <u>London</u> to <u>Sydney</u> in Australia. Of course, capillaries are really tiny, which is how there can be such a big length — they can only be seen with a <u>microscope</u>.

The Heart

Blood doesn't just move around the body <u>on its own</u>, of course. It needs a <u>pump</u>.

Learn *this* **diagram** *of the* **heart** *with all its* **labels**

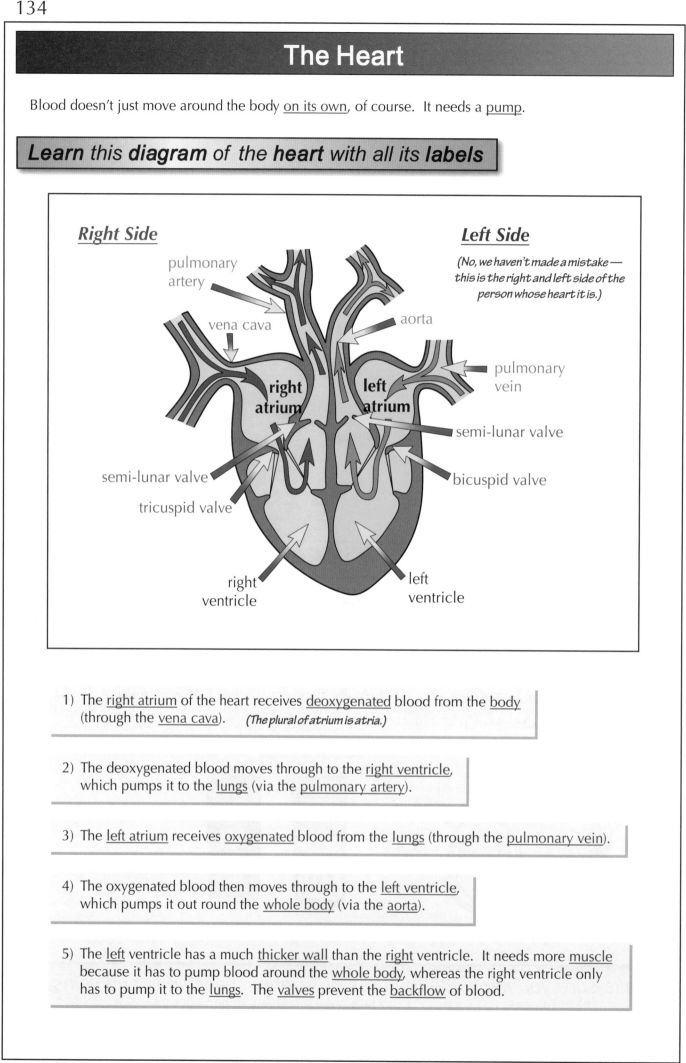

Right Side

pulmonary artery

vena cava

right atrium

semi-lunar valve

tricuspid valve

right ventricle

Left Side

(No, we haven't made a mistake — this is the right and left side of the person whose heart it is.)

aorta

pulmonary vein

left atrium

semi-lunar valve

bicuspid valve

left ventricle

1) The <u>right atrium</u> of the heart receives <u>deoxygenated</u> blood from the <u>body</u> (through the <u>vena cava</u>).   *(The plural of atrium is atria.)*

2) The deoxygenated blood moves through to the <u>right ventricle</u>, which pumps it to the <u>lungs</u> (via the <u>pulmonary artery</u>).

3) The <u>left atrium</u> receives <u>oxygenated</u> blood from the <u>lungs</u> (through the <u>pulmonary vein</u>).

4) The oxygenated blood then moves through to the <u>left ventricle</u>, which pumps it out round the <u>whole body</u> (via the <u>aorta</u>).

5) The <u>left</u> ventricle has a much <u>thicker wall</u> than the <u>right</u> ventricle. It needs more <u>muscle</u> because it has to pump blood around the <u>whole body</u>, whereas the right ventricle only has to pump it to the <u>lungs</u>. The <u>valves</u> prevent the <u>backflow</u> of blood.

The Heart

If you've learned the diagram on the previous page thoroughly enough, you've probably already noticed that the heart seems to be split into <u>two separate halves</u> — right and left. That's because mammals like us have a <u>double</u> circulatory system.

Mammals have a double circulatory system

1) The first one connects the <u>heart</u> to the <u>lungs</u>. <u>Deoxygenated</u> blood is pumped to the <u>lungs</u> to take in <u>oxygen</u>. The blood then <u>returns</u> to the heart.

2) The second one connects the <u>heart</u> to the <u>rest of the body</u>. The <u>oxygenated</u> blood in the heart is pumped out to the <u>body</u>. It <u>gives up</u> its oxygen, and then the <u>deoxygenated</u> blood <u>returns</u> to the heart to be pumped out to the <u>lungs</u> again.

3) Returning the blood to the <u>heart</u> after it's picked up oxygen at the <u>lungs</u> means it can be pumped out around the body with <u>much greater force</u>. This is needed so the blood can get to <u>every last tissue</u> in the body and <u>still</u> have enough push left to flow <u>back to the heart</u> through the veins.

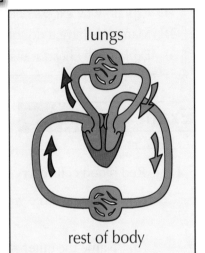

lungs

rest of body

If the heart stops working properly, bits can be replaced

1) The heart has a <u>pacemaker</u> — a group of cells which determine <u>how fast</u> it beats. If this stops working the heartbeat becomes <u>irregular</u>, which can be dangerous. The pacemaker can be <u>replaced</u> with an <u>artificial</u> one.

2) Defective <u>heart valves</u> can also be replaced — either with <u>animal</u> or with <u>mechanical</u> valves.

3) In extreme cases, the <u>whole heart</u> can be <u>removed</u> and <u>replaced</u> with another one from a <u>human donor</u> — this is called a <u>transplant</u>. It involves <u>major surgery</u> and a lifetime of <u>drugs</u> and <u>medical care</u>. They're only done on patients whose hearts are so damaged that the problems <u>can't</u> be solved in any other way. The new heart must be the <u>right size</u>, <u>relatively young</u> and a <u>close tissue match</u> to prevent <u>rejection</u> (see below).

Transplants can be rejected

One of the main problems with heart transplants is that the patient's <u>immune system</u> often recognises the new heart as '<u>foreign</u>' and <u>attacks</u> it — this is called <u>rejection</u>. Doctors use <u>drugs</u> that <u>suppress</u> the patient's immune system to help <u>stop</u> the donor heart being rejected, but that leaves the patient more <u>vulnerable</u> to <u>infections</u>.

Heart transplants can be risky so are usually a last resort
The human heart beats <u>100 000 times a day</u> on average. You can measure it by taking your <u>pulse</u>.

Warm-Up and Exam Questions

Hopefully I've persuaded you by now that it's a good idea to try these questions. So off you go...

Warm-Up Questions

1) List four things that are carried around the body in the blood plasma.
2) Give three ways in which the structure of an artery and a vein are different.
3) Explain why excess cholesterol in your blood is bad for you.
4) Mammals have a double circulatory system. Explain what this means.
5) Explain why heart transplants are only carried out in very serious cases of heart disease.

Exam Questions

1   Red blood cells carry oxygen around the body.

   (a) Describe three ways in which red blood cells are adapted for carrying out their function.

(3 marks)

   (b) Name the other main type of blood cell and state its function.

(2 marks)

2   (a) Karen was given a sheep's heart to look at. She made a drawing of the outside
          of the heart, and wrote some observations.

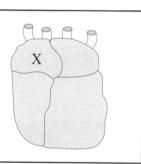

On the outside the heart is mainly red in colour,
with four big tubes coming out of the top.
The top part of the heart feels quite soft,
but at the bottom it feels much firmer.

   (i)   List the names of the four big tubes.

(4 marks)

   (ii) Name the part of the heart labelled X.

(1 mark)

   (b) Karen then dissected the heart. Inside she found the heart chambers,
        and some flaps between the chambers.

   (i)   How many heart chambers would you expect her to find?

(1 mark)

   (ii) What were the flaps she found between the chambers?

(1 mark)

   (iii) What is their function?

(1 mark)

The Kidneys and Homeostasis

The <u>kidneys</u> are really important in <u>homeostasis</u> (see p.20 – 21) — they control the content of the <u>blood</u>.

Kidneys basically act as filters to 'clean the blood'

The <u>kidneys</u> perform <u>three main roles</u>:

- <u>Removal of urea</u> from the blood.

- <u>Adjustment of ions</u> in the blood.

- <u>Adjustment of water content</u> of the blood.

Removal of urea

1) Proteins can't be <u>stored</u> by the body — so any excess amino acids are converted into <u>fats</u> and <u>carbohydrates</u>, which can be stored.

2) This process happens in the <u>liver</u>. <u>Urea</u> is produced as a <u>waste product</u> from the reactions.

3) Urea is <u>poisonous</u>. It's released into the <u>bloodstream</u> by the liver. The <u>kidneys</u> then filter it out of the blood and it's excreted from the body in <u>urine</u>.

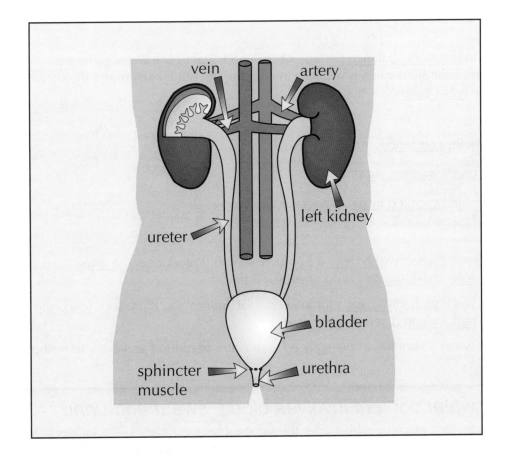

The Kidneys and Homeostasis

Urine contains some <u>water</u> and <u>ions</u> as well as urea, to help keep the balance right in the body.

Adjustment of **ion content**

1) <u>Ions</u> such as <u>sodium</u> are taken into the body in <u>food</u>, and then absorbed into the blood.

2) If the ion content of the body is <u>wrong</u>, this could mean too much or too little <u>water</u> is drawn into cells by <u>osmosis</u> (see page 120). Having the wrong amount of water can <u>damage</u> cells.

3) Excess ions are <u>removed</u> by the kidneys. For example, a salty meal will contain far too much sodium and so the kidneys will remove the <u>excess</u> sodium ions from the blood.

4) Some ions are also lost in <u>sweat</u> (which tastes salty, you may have noticed).

5) But the important thing to remember is that the <u>balance</u> is always maintained by the <u>kidneys</u>.

Adjustment of **water content**

Water is taken into the body in <u>food and drink</u> and is <u>lost</u> from the body in <u>three main ways</u>:

1) In <u>urine</u>

2) In <u>sweat</u>

3) In the air we <u>breathe out</u>

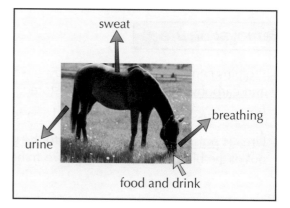

The body has to <u>constantly balance</u> the water coming in against the water going out.
Your body can't control how much you lose in your breath, but it can control the other factors.
This means the <u>water balance</u> is between:

1) Liquids <u>consumed</u>

2) Amount <u>sweated out</u>

3) Amount <u>excreted by the kidneys</u> in the <u>urine</u>

On a <u>cold</u> day you probably <u>won't sweat</u> as much, so you'll produce <u>more urine</u> which will be <u>pale</u> and <u>dilute</u> (to get rid of excess water).

On a <u>hot</u> day, you'll probably <u>sweat a lot</u> to keep cool, and so you'll produce <u>less urine</u> which will be <u>dark-coloured</u> and <u>concentrated</u>.

The water lost when it's hot has to be <u>replaced</u> with water from food and drink to restore the <u>balance</u>.

Adjusting water content involves blood, sweat and urine

Scientists have made a machine which does the same job as the kidneys — a <u>kidney dialysis machine</u>. People with <u>kidney failure</u> have to use it for 3–4 hours, three times a week. Unfortunately it's <u>not</u> something you can carry around with you, which makes life difficult for people with kidney failure.

The Pancreas and Diabetes

Scientific discoveries often take a <u>long time</u>, and a lot of <u>trial and error</u> — here's a rather famous example that led to a big advance in the control of <u>diabetes</u>.

*Insulin was discovered by **Banting and Best***

It has been known for sometime that people who suffer from diabetes have a lot of <u>sugar</u> in their <u>urine</u>.

In the 19th century, scientists <u>removed pancreases</u> from dogs, and the same sugary urine was observed — the dogs became <u>diabetic</u>. That suggested that the pancreas had to have something to do with the illness.

In the 1920s Frederick <u>Banting</u> and his assistant Charles <u>Best</u> managed to successfully <u>isolate insulin</u> — the hormone that controls blood sugar levels.

This is how they did it:

1) Banting and Best <u>tied string</u> around a dog's pancreas so that a lot of the organ <u>wasted</u> away — but the bits which made the <u>hormones</u> were left <u>intact</u>.

2) They <u>removed</u> the pancreas from the dog, and obtained an <u>extract</u> from it.

3) They then injected this extract into <u>diabetic dogs</u> and observed the effects on their <u>blood sugar levels</u>.

4) After the pancreatic extract was <u>injected</u>, the dogs' blood sugar levels <u>fell dramatically</u>. This showed that the <u>pancreatic extract</u> caused a <u>temporary decrease</u> in <u>blood sugar level</u>.

5) They went on to <u>isolate</u> the substance in the pancreatic extract — <u>insulin</u>.

After a <u>lot</u> more experiments, Banting and Best tried <u>injecting insulin</u> into a <u>human</u> with <u>diabetes</u>. And it <u>worked</u> — the patient's blood sugar level dropped.

This is still the basis of treatment today, although there have been certain advances (see next page).

Banting won a Nobel prize for this work in 1923
And, rather sweetly, he insisted on sharing the prize money with his young assistant and made sure his contribution was recognised. They also chose to make the <u>patent</u> for the treatment available <u>without charge</u>, rather than trying to make any money out of their discovery. How refreshing.

The Pancreas and Diabetes

Diabetes can be **controlled** by **regular injections** of **insulin**

Since Banting and Best's discovery of insulin, it has been <u>mass produced</u> to meet the <u>needs</u> of diabetics.

Diabetics have to inject themselves with insulin <u>often</u> — usually between two and four times a day. They also need to carefully control their <u>diet</u> and the amount of <u>exercise</u> they do (see page 23).

1) At first, the insulin was extracted from the pancreases of <u>pigs</u> or <u>cows</u>. Diabetics used <u>glass syringes</u> that had to be boiled before use.

2) In the 1980s <u>human</u> insulin made by <u>genetically engineered bacteria</u> became available. This didn't cause any <u>adverse reactions</u> in patients, which <u>animal</u> insulin sometimes did.

3) <u>Slow</u>, <u>intermediate</u> and <u>fast</u> acting insulins have been developed to make it easier for diabetics to <u>control</u> their blood sugar levels.

4) Ready sterilised, <u>disposable syringes</u> are now available, as well as <u>needle-free devices</u>.

These improved treatment methods allow diabetics to <u>control</u> their blood sugar <u>more easily</u>. This helps them avoid some of the damaging side effects of poor control, such as an increased risk of <u>heart disease</u>, <u>blindness</u> and <u>gangrene</u>.

Diabetics may have a **pancreas transplant**

Injecting yourself with insulin every day <u>controls</u> the effects of diabetes, but it doesn't help to <u>cure</u> it.

1) Diabetics can have a <u>pancreas transplant</u>. A successful operation means they won't have to inject themselves with insulin again.
   But as with any organ transplant, your body can <u>reject</u> the tissue. If this happens you have to take <u>costly immunosuppressive drugs</u>, which often have <u>serious side-effects</u>.

2) Another method, still in its <u>experimental stage</u>, is to transplant just the <u>cells</u> which produce insulin. There's been <u>varying success</u> with this technique, and there are still some problems with <u>rejection</u>.

3) Modern research into <u>artificial pancreases</u> and <u>stem cell research</u> may mean the elimination of organ rejection, but there's a way to go yet (see page 86).

Controlling diabetes is not the same as curing it

Insulin can't be taken in a pill or tablet — the <u>enzymes</u> in the stomach completely <u>destroy it</u> before it reaches the bloodstream. That's why diabetics usually have to <u>inject</u> it. Diabetes is growing more and more <u>common</u>, partly due to our society becoming increasingly overweight. It's very serious.

141

Warm-Up and Exam Questions

Warm-Up Questions

1) State the three main functions of the kidneys.
2) Where is urea produced and where is it removed from the body?
3) Give three ways in which water can be lost from the body.
4) Where in the body is insulin produced?
5) What is the effect of insulin on blood glucose levels?

Exam Questions

1   The diagram shows the human urinary system.

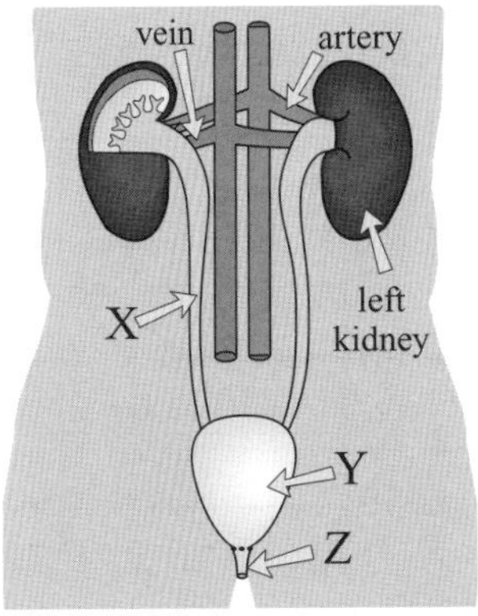

(a) Name the structures labelled X, Y and Z.

(3 marks)

(b) State three ways in which the composition
of the blood in the renal vein will be
different from the blood in the renal artery.

(3 marks)

2   The table shows the concentrations of some different
substances in samples of urine from three different people.

Substance	Conc. in sample A (%)	Conc. in sample B (%)	Conc. in sample C (%)
glucose	0.0	0.0	0.2
salt	0.8	0.2	0.1
urea	4.2	0.5	0.2

(a) One of the three people suffers from diabetes.
Suggest which person this is and explain your answer.

(2 marks)

(b) Suggest two possible reasons why sample A had a higher concentration
of urea than sample B.

(2 marks)

3   Diabetes can be treated using insulin injections or by a pancreas transplant.

(a) Insulin used to be extracted from the pancreases of animals, but today
most insulin is produced by genetically engineered bacteria.
Suggest two advantages of using the bacterial insulin.

(2 marks)

(b) Suggest one advantage and one disadvantage of treating diabetes
with a pancreas transplant rather than insulin injections.

(2 marks)

Footer*SECTION SEVEN — ORGANS AND SYSTEMS 1*

Revision Summary for Section Seven

And where do you think you're going? It's no use just reading through and thinking you've got it all — this stuff will only stick in your head if you've learnt it properly. And that's what these questions are for. I won't pretend they'll be easy — they're not meant to be, but all the information's in the section somewhere. Have a go at all the questions, then if there are any you can't answer, go back, look it up and try again. Enjoy...

1) Write down the word equations for aerobic respiration and anaerobic respiration.

2) Give one advantage and one disadvantage of anaerobic respiration.

3) Give three ways that alveoli are adapted for gaseous exchange.

4)* Danny measured his heart rate before, during and after exercise.
He plotted a graph of the results. Look at the graph and then answer the three questions below.

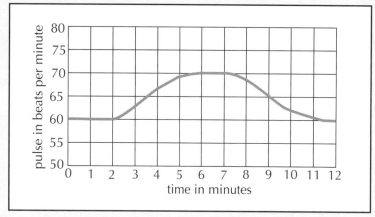

a) What was Danny's heart rate (in beats per minute) when he was at rest?

b) After how many minutes did Danny start exercising?

c) What was Danny's highest heart rate?

5) How much exercise does the UK government recommend you do per week?

6) In which three places in the body is amylase produced?

7) Explain why the stomach produces hydrochloric acid.

8) What is the main function of the small intestine?

9) Give three ways that the small intestine is adapted for absorption.

10) Where in the body is bile: a) produced?   b) stored?   c) used?

11) Name six things that blood plasma transports around the body.

12) Name the substance formed in red blood cells when haemoglobin reacts with oxygen.

13) Why do arteries need very muscular, elastic walls?

14) Explain how capillaries are adapted to carry out their function.

15) Name the blood vessel that joins to the right ventricle of the heart. Where does it take the blood?

16) Why does the left ventricle have a thicker wall than the right ventricle?

17) What three main jobs do the kidneys do in the body?

18) Where in the body is urea produced?

19) What damage could be done in the body if the ion content is wrong?

20) Explain why your urine is likely to be more concentrated on a hot day.

21) Describe the experiments by Banting and Best that led to the isolation of insulin.

22) What are the advantages and disadvantages of a pancreas transplant for someone who's diabetic?

* Answers on page 290.

Growth

This topic's about growth and development in plants and animals. Organisms grow using a combination of <u>cell division</u>, <u>cell elongation</u> and <u>cell differentiation</u> — which you'll learn all about in exquisite detail as you go through the topic. But first, here's a bit of general stuff about growth...

Growth *is an* increase *in* size *or* weight

You can <u>measure</u> the <u>growth</u> of an organism in these three ways:

1) Size

You can measure its:

- <u>height</u>   • <u>length</u>   • <u>width</u>   • <u>circumference</u>

2) Wet weight

Organisms <u>contain</u> a lot of <u>water</u>. The weight of the organism depends on how much water it has gained or lost (e.g. through drinking or sweating). The <u>wet weight</u> of the organism is its weight <u>including all the water</u> in its body — it can vary a lot from <u>one day to the next</u>.

3) Dry weight

The <u>dry weight</u> is the weight of an organism with <u>no water in its body</u>. This doesn't vary in the same way as wet weight, but you can only measure it once the organism's dead. The dead organism is <u>dried out</u> by leaving it in a hot oven overnight — then what's left is weighed.

Animals stop *growing, plants can grow* continuously

Plants and animals <u>grow differently</u>:

1) Animals tend to grow while they're <u>young</u>, and then they reach <u>full growth</u> and <u>stop</u> growing. Plants often grow <u>continuously</u> — even really old trees will keep putting out <u>new branches</u>.

2) In animals, growth happens by <u>cell division</u>, but in plants, growth in <u>height</u> is mainly due to <u>cell enlargement</u> (elongation) — cell <u>division</u> usually just happens in the <u>tips</u> of the <u>roots</u> and <u>shoots</u>.

Growth

Some animals are able to regenerate

1) A few animals have the ability to regrow (regenerate) part of their body if it is damaged:

- If some types of worm are cut in two, the front part can grow a new 'tail'.

- If a young spider loses a leg, it can grow a new one (adult spiders can't, though).

- Some reptiles, like lizards, can regrow a lost leg or tail.

2) The ability to regenerate parts of the body is pretty rare though. It tends to happen in fairly simple (or very young) animals which still contain lots of stem cells (see page 150).

Human growth can be monitored and manipulated

1) Humans, like other mammals, give birth to live young. The baby grows inside the uterus (womb) until it reaches a stage where it can survive outside — this period is called gestation and it lasts for 38 weeks in humans.

2) We don't grow evenly in the womb or in early life — certain organs grow faster than others, and the fastest-growing of all is the brain. This is because a large and well-developed brain gives humans a big survival advantage — it's our best tool for finding food, avoiding predators, etc.

3) A baby's growth rate can be monitored by measuring its head circumference. The actual values are not as important as the rate of growth. If the baby is growing too slowly, or if the head is relatively too large or small, it can alert the doctor to possible development problems.

4) Growth factors are chemicals that stimulate the body to grow. Some athletes have used growth factor drugs to improve their performance at sport. This is illegal because it gives them an unfair advantage over other competitors. It also has health risks:

- Growth factor drugs can have bad side effects for health: they can reduce fertility, can increase the risk of heart disease and can sometimes trigger mental illnesses like depression.

- Some growth factors cause women to develop male characteristics, e.g. a deeper voice.

The gestation period of an elephant is nearly two years...

... but of course, a baby elephant takes a lot of growing. Regeneration is an odd idea — I wonder what it'd be like to grow an extra leg. Could help in P.E., but finding clothes to fit might be tricky.

Cell Division — Mitosis

In order to survive and grow, our cells have got to be able to <u>divide</u>. And that means our <u>DNA</u> as well...

Mitosis makes new cells for **growth** and **repair**

1) <u>Body cells</u> are <u>diploid</u> — they normally have <u>two copies</u> of each chromosome, one from the organism's 'mother', and one from its 'father'. So, humans have two copies of chromosome 1, two copies of chromosome 2, etc.

2) The diagram shows the <u>23 pairs of chromosomes</u> from a human cell. The 23rd pair is a bit different (they control the baby's sex).

3) When a body cell <u>divides</u> it needs to make new cells <u>identical</u> to the <u>original</u> cell — with the <u>same number</u> of chromosomes.

4) This type of cell division is called <u>mitosis</u>. It's used when plants and animals <u>grow</u> or <u>replace</u> cells that have been <u>damaged</u>.

> "<u>MITOSIS</u> is when a cell reproduces itself <u>by splitting</u> to form <u>two identical offspring</u>."

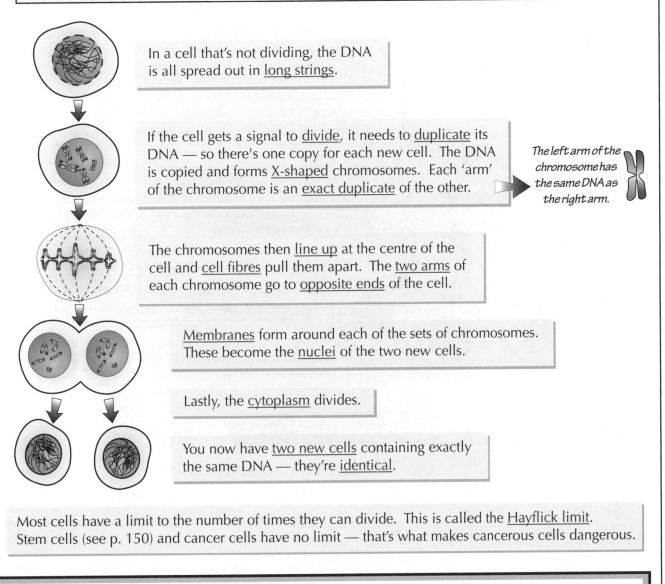

In a cell that's not dividing, the DNA is all spread out in <u>long strings</u>.

If the cell gets a signal to <u>divide</u>, it needs to <u>duplicate</u> its DNA — so there's one copy for each new cell. The DNA is copied and forms <u>X-shaped</u> chromosomes. Each 'arm' of the chromosome is an <u>exact duplicate</u> of the other.

The left arm of the chromosome has the same DNA as the right arm.

The chromosomes then <u>line up</u> at the centre of the cell and <u>cell fibres</u> pull them apart. The <u>two arms</u> of each chromosome go to <u>opposite ends</u> of the cell.

<u>Membranes</u> form around each of the sets of chromosomes. These become the <u>nuclei</u> of the two new cells.

Lastly, the <u>cytoplasm</u> divides.

You now have <u>two new cells</u> containing exactly the same DNA — they're <u>identical</u>.

Most cells have a limit to the number of times they can divide. This is called the <u>Hayflick limit</u>. Stem cells (see p. 150) and cancer cells have no limit — that's what makes cancerous cells dangerous.

Mitosis happens in most organisms for growth and repair

<u>Asexual reproduction</u> in some organisms uses mitosis — there's more on that back on page 84.

Cell Division — Meiosis

You thought mitosis was exciting. Hah. You ain't seen nothing yet.

Meiosis involves two divisions

Gametes (sperm and egg cells) only have half the number of chromosomes as a normal body cell. They are produced by meiosis. In humans it only happens in the reproductive organs (i.e. ovaries and testes).

> "MEIOSIS produces four haploid cells whose chromosomes are NOT identical."

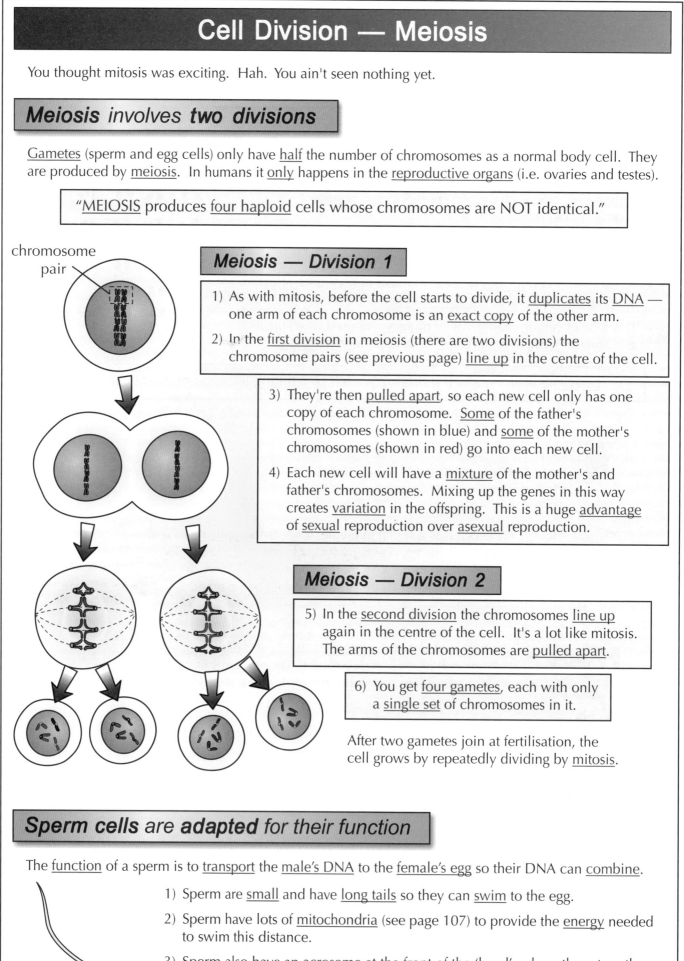

chromosome pair

Meiosis — Division 1

1) As with mitosis, before the cell starts to divide, it duplicates its DNA — one arm of each chromosome is an exact copy of the other arm.

2) In the first division in meiosis (there are two divisions) the chromosome pairs (see previous page) line up in the centre of the cell.

3) They're then pulled apart, so each new cell only has one copy of each chromosome. Some of the father's chromosomes (shown in blue) and some of the mother's chromosomes (shown in red) go into each new cell.

4) Each new cell will have a mixture of the mother's and father's chromosomes. Mixing up the genes in this way creates variation in the offspring. This is a huge advantage of sexual reproduction over asexual reproduction.

Meiosis — Division 2

5) In the second division the chromosomes line up again in the centre of the cell. It's a lot like mitosis. The arms of the chromosomes are pulled apart.

6) You get four gametes, each with only a single set of chromosomes in it.

After two gametes join at fertilisation, the cell grows by repeatedly dividing by mitosis.

Sperm cells are adapted for their function

The function of a sperm is to transport the male's DNA to the female's egg so their DNA can combine.

1) Sperm are small and have long tails so they can swim to the egg.

2) Sperm have lots of mitochondria (see page 107) to provide the energy needed to swim this distance.

3) Sperm also have an acrosome at the front of the 'head', where they store the enzymes they need to digest their way through the membrane of the egg cell.

4) They're produced in large numbers to increase the chance of fertilisation.

Warm-Up and Exam Questions

Warm-Up Questions

1) Give two measurements that could be taken to determine an organism's size.
2) What type of cell division is involved in the regeneration of body parts?
3) Give two reasons why the use of artificial growth factors to improve sporting performance is banned.
4) How many chromosomes are there in a human liver cell?
5) If a human cell divides by meiosis, how many chromosomes do the new cells each have?

Exam Questions

1   (a)   What type of cell division produces sperm cells in the testes?

(1 mark)

(b)   Explain the functions of each of these parts of a sperm cell:

(i) acrosome   (ii) mitochondria   (iii) tail

(3 marks)

2   Ed did an experiment to measure the growth of pea seeds. He took 200 seeds and soaked them in water, then allowed them to germinate. Every day he removed 20 seeds and measured their dry weight.

(a)   Explain what is meant by dry weight and suggest a reason why Ed measured the dry weight instead of the wet weight.

(2 marks)

(b)   Why did Ed measure the dry mass of 20 seeds instead of just one?

(1 mark)

(c)   Explain why Ed needed to use 200 seeds, instead of measuring the dry mass of the same 20 seeds throughout the experiment.

(1 mark)

3   (a)   The diagram below shows the chromosomes of a cell that is about to divide by meiosis.

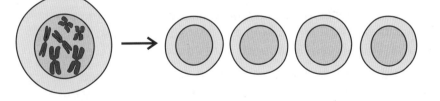

(i)   Complete the diagram to show the chromosomes at the end.

(2 marks)

(ii)   How is the genetic content of the new cells different from the original cell?

(1 mark)

(b)   State three ways in which meiosis is different from mitosis.

(3 marks)

Sexual Reproduction — Ethics

During sexual reproduction a sperm cell and an egg cell combine to produce an embryo.
It is possible to terminate a pregnancy — but this possibility raises some difficult ethical issues.

A pregnancy can legally be terminated up to 24 weeks

1) After the 8th week of pregnancy, the embryo starts to look a bit more human and is called a foetus.

2) In Britain, a termination (induced abortion) is legal until a foetus is 24 weeks old if two doctors agree that termination is necessary.

3) An abortion can be carried out later than this if the pregnancy is putting the mother's health at serious risk or if there is a major foetal abnormality.

4) The 24-week limit came into effect in 1991, but it remains the subject of some fairly heated debate:

Some people argue that abortion at any stage of pregnancy is unethical. They believe that a human life begins at fertilisation — and so ending a pregnancy is the same as killing a human being.

Other people think that the foetus doesn't become human until it's a conscious being — for example, when it starts being able to feel pain. They argue that abortion should be allowed up until this point.

But it's difficult to pinpoint exactly when the foetus becomes conscious and can feel pain — different people have different opinions.

For example, some people maintain that it's the point when pain receptors first develop at about 7 weeks. Others argue that the foetus can't feel pain until the pain receptors are connected up in the brain — which doesn't happen until about 26 weeks.

The legal limit in Britain is actually based on the 'viability' of the foetus — that is, whether or not the foetus can survive outside the womb (with medical help).

With advances in medicine, foetuses are becoming viable earlier in the pregnancy — babies have survived from as early as 21 weeks, so some people argue the limit should be dropped from 24 weeks to 20 weeks.

But babies born so prematurely can have serious problems. Only about a quarter of babies born at 24 weeks or under survive and, of those, over a third suffer severe disabilities.

Termination is an emotional topic...

...and a lot of people have very strong views about it. In the exam you've got to be able to back up your view with a valid argument and show that you have considered other points of view.

Sexual Reproduction — Ethics

In vitro fertilisation (IVF) is quite widely used now by people who have problems conceiving naturally. Part of the process involves screening for genetic disorders, but some people are unhappy about this.

Embryos can be screened for genetic disorders

For parents who are undergoing IVF, embryos can be tested for genetic disorders before they are implanted into the mother. But, like terminating a pregnancy, this is quite a controversial area.

1) During IVF, embryos are fertilised in a laboratory and then implanted into the mother's uterus. More than one egg is fertilised so that there's a better chance of the IVF being successful.

2) Before being implanted, it is possible to remove a cell from each of the embryos and analyse its genes.

3) Many genetic disorders can be detected in this way, such as cystic fibrosis and Huntington's disease.

4) Embryos with 'good' genes can then be implanted into the mother — the ones with genes that would cause a genetic disease in the baby are destroyed.

There is a huge debate raging about embryonic screening.
Below are some of the arguments for and against it.

Against Embryonic Screening

1) There may come a point when everyone wants to screen their embryos so they can pick the most 'desirable' one — e.g. a couple might decide they only want a blue-eyed, blonde-haired, intelligent boy.

2) The rejected embryos are destroyed — they could have developed into humans, so some people think that this is as bad as murder (it's the same issue as with termination).

3) Embryonic screening implies that people with genetic problems are 'undesirable' — which could increase prejudice.

For Embryonic Screening

1) It helps to stop people suffering.

2) There are laws to stop it going too far. At the moment parents cannot even select the sex of their baby (unless it's for health reasons).

3) During IVF, most of the embryos are destroyed anyway — screening just allows the selected one to be healthy.

4) Treating genetic disorders costs the Government (and the taxpayers) a lot of money.

Stem Cells and Differentiation

Stem cell research has exciting possibilities, but it's yet another controversial subject.

Embryonic stem cells can turn into **ANY** type of cell

1) Most cells in your body are <u>specialised</u> for a particular job. For example, white blood cells are brilliant at fighting invaders but they <u>can't</u> carry oxygen like red blood cells can.

2) <u>Differentiation</u> is the process by which a cell <u>changes</u> to become <u>specialised</u> for its job. In most <u>animal</u> cells, the ability to differentiate is <u>lost</u> at an early stage, but lots of <u>plant</u> cells <u>don't ever</u> lose this ability.

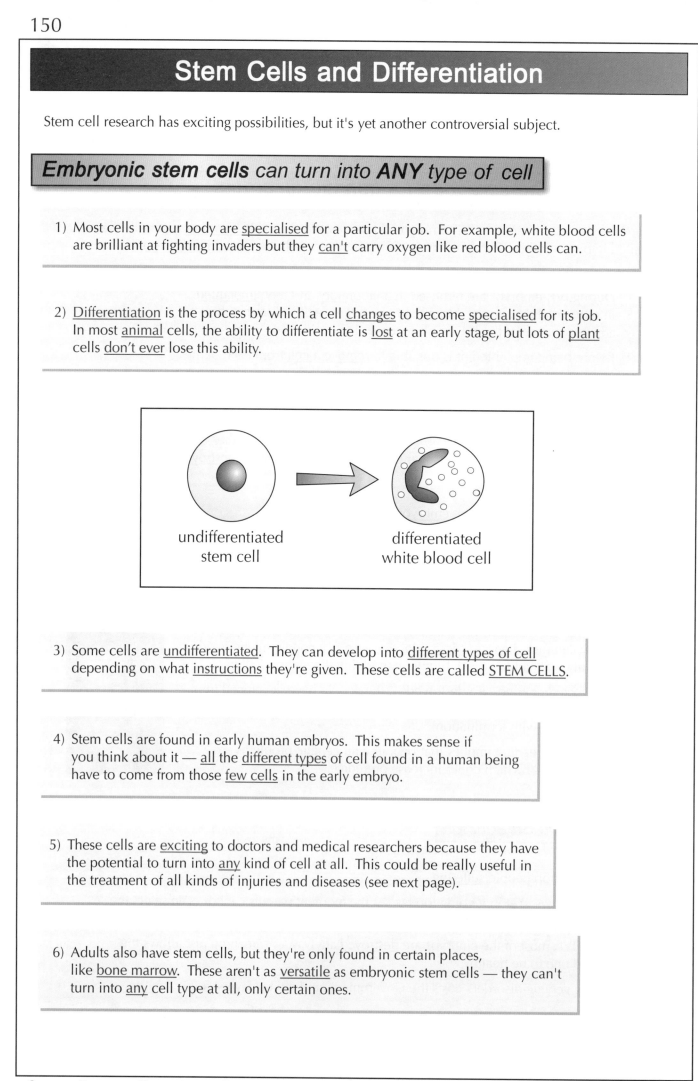

undifferentiated
stem cell

differentiated
white blood cell

3) Some cells are <u>undifferentiated</u>. They can develop into <u>different types of cell</u> depending on what <u>instructions</u> they're given. These cells are called <u>STEM CELLS</u>.

4) Stem cells are found in early human embryos. This makes sense if you think about it — <u>all</u> the <u>different types</u> of cell found in a human being have to come from those <u>few cells</u> in the early embryo.

5) These cells are <u>exciting</u> to doctors and medical researchers because they have the potential to turn into <u>any</u> kind of cell at all. This could be really useful in the treatment of all kinds of injuries and diseases (see next page).

6) Adults also have stem cells, but they're only found in certain places, like <u>bone marrow</u>. These aren't as <u>versatile</u> as embryonic stem cells — they can't turn into <u>any</u> cell type at all, only certain ones.

Stem Cells and Differentiation

Stem cells may be able to cure many diseases

1) Medicine <u>already</u> uses adult stem cells to cure <u>disease</u>. For example, people with some <u>blood diseases</u> (e.g. <u>sickle cell anaemia</u>) can be treated using <u>bone marrow transplants</u>. Bone marrow contains <u>stem cells</u> that can turn into <u>new blood cells</u> to replace the faulty old ones.

2) Scientists can also <u>extract</u> stem cells from very early human embryos and <u>grow</u> them.

3) These embryonic stem cells could be used to <u>replace faulty cells</u> in sick people — you could make <u>beating heart muscle cells</u> for people with <u>heart disease</u>, <u>insulin-producing cells</u> for people with <u>diabetes</u>, <u>nerve cells</u> for people <u>paralysed by spinal injuries</u>, and so on.

4) To get cultures of <u>one specific type</u> of cell, researchers try to <u>control</u> the differentiation of the stem cells by changing the environment they're growing in. So far, it's still a bit hit-and-miss — lots more <u>research</u> is needed.

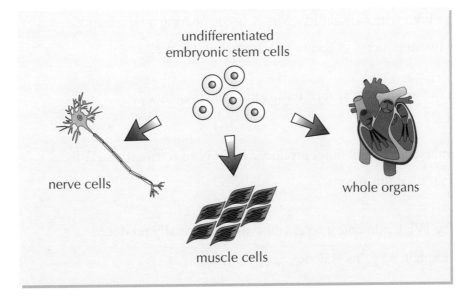

Some people are against stem cell research

1) Some people are <u>against</u> stem cell research because they feel that human embryos <u>shouldn't</u> be used for experiments since each one is a <u>potential human life</u>.

2) Others think that curing patients who <u>already exist</u> and who are <u>suffering</u> is more important than the rights of <u>embryos</u>.

3) One fairly convincing argument in favour of this point of view is that the embryos used in the research are usually <u>unwanted ones</u> from <u>fertility clinics</u> which would probably just be <u>destroyed</u> anyway. But of course, campaigners for the rights of embryos usually want this banned too.

4) These campaigners feel that scientists should concentrate more on finding and developing <u>other sources</u> of stem cells, so people could be helped <u>without</u> having to use embryos.

5) In some countries stem cell research is <u>banned</u> completely. It's allowed in the UK but must follow <u>strict guidelines</u>.

Alternative sources of stem cells would avoid the controversy

The <u>potential</u> of stem cells is huge — but it's early days yet. Research has recently been done into getting stem cells from alternative sources. For example, <u>umbilical cords</u> may be one possible source.

Warm-Up and Exam Questions

However strong your own opinions are, make sure you know both sides of the argument for the exam.

Warm-Up Questions

1) In Britain, what is the normal legal age limit (of the foetus) for abortion?
2) Why is this the limit?
3) What is meant by the **screening** of embryos produced by IVF?
4) What are stem cells?

Exam Questions

1   Mrs X is pregnant. The foetus is 20 weeks old. Doctors have found that the baby is likely to be born with a disability. Mrs X is considering a termination.

   (a) Give two arguments in favour of terminating the pregnancy.

   (2 marks)

   (b) Give two arguments against terminating the pregnancy.

   (2 marks)

2   Human embryos are sometimes produced by in vitro fertilisation (IVF).

   (a) Explain what this means.

   (1 mark)

   (b) During IVF treatment, several embryos are normally produced.

      (i)   Explain why this is done.

   (1 mark)

      (ii) Suggest one argument against producing several embryos.

   (1 mark)

   (c) Sometimes, unwanted embryos are used for medical research.
        Why are their cells particularly valuable for research purposes?

   (2 marks)

3   (a) Name one place in an adult human body that contains stem cells.

   (1 mark)

   (b) Explain how adult stem cells and embryonic stem cells are:

      (i)   similar.

   (1 mark)

      (ii) different.

   (1 mark)

   (c) Some people think that embryonic stem cells might one day be used to help treat people with spinal injuries. Briefly describe how this might work.

   (1 mark)

Growth in Plants

Plants don't grow randomly. Plant <u>hormones</u> make sure the plant grows in a useful direction —
for example, towards light.

*Auxins are plant **growth hormones***

1) <u>Auxins</u> are <u>plant hormones</u> which control <u>growth</u> near the <u>tips</u> of <u>shoots</u> and <u>roots</u>.

2) Auxin is produced in the <u>tips</u> and <u>diffuses backwards</u> to stimulate the <u>cell elongation</u>
   <u>(enlargement) process</u> which occurs in the cells <u>just behind</u> the tips.

3) If the tip of a shoot is <u>removed</u>, no auxin is available and the shoot may <u>stop growing</u>.

4) Auxins are involved in the responses of plants to <u>light</u>, <u>gravity</u> and <u>water</u>.

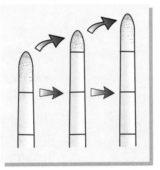

*Auxins change the **direction** of root and shoot growth*

Extra auxin <u>promotes</u> growth in the <u>shoot</u> but actually <u>inhibits</u> growth in the <u>root</u> —
this still produces the <u>desired result</u> in <u>both cases</u> though.

Shoots grow towards light

1) When a <u>shoot tip</u> is exposed to <u>light</u>, <u>more auxin</u>
   accumulates on the side that's in the <u>shade</u> than the
   side that's in the light.

2) This makes the cells grow (elongate) <u>faster</u> on the
   <u>shaded side</u>, so the shoot bends <u>towards</u> the light.

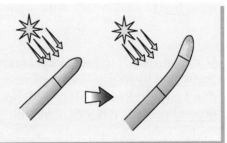

Shoots grow away from gravity

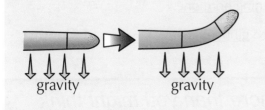

gravity   gravity

1) When a <u>shoot</u> is growing sideways, <u>gravity</u>
   produces an unequal distribution of auxin in the
   tip, with <u>more auxin</u> on the <u>lower side</u>.

2) This causes the lower side to grow <u>faster</u>, bending
   the shoot <u>upwards</u>.

Growth in Plants

And don't forget the <u>roots</u>, which are similar to the shoots but kind of opposite...

Roots grow towards gravity

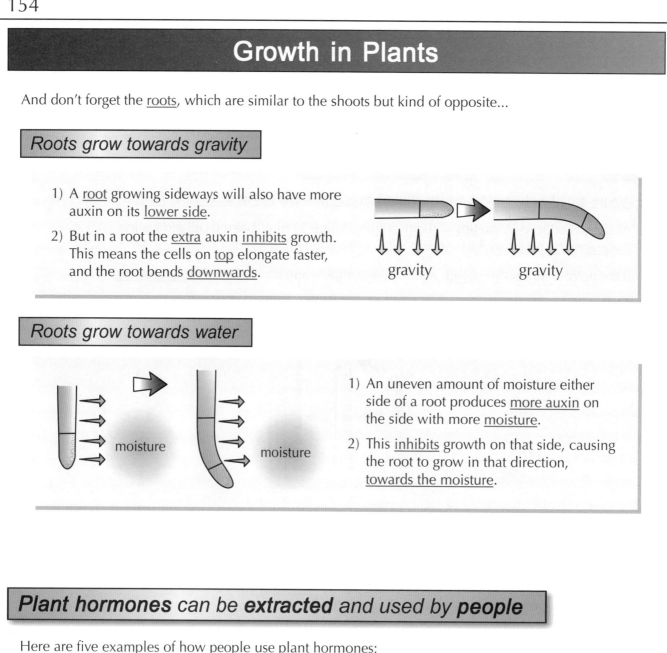

1) A <u>root</u> growing sideways will also have more auxin on its <u>lower side</u>.

2) But in a root the <u>extra</u> auxin <u>inhibits</u> growth. This means the cells on <u>top</u> elongate faster, and the root bends <u>downwards</u>.

gravity   gravity

Roots grow towards water

moisture   moisture

1) An uneven amount of moisture either side of a root produces <u>more auxin</u> on the side with more <u>moisture</u>.

2) This <u>inhibits</u> growth on that side, causing the root to grow in that direction, <u>towards the moisture</u>.

*Plant hormones can be **extracted** and used by **people***

Here are five <u>examples</u> of how people use plant hormones:

1) <u>Seedless fruits</u> can be made with <u>artificial hormones</u>. You need to learn the details of this one:

> Fruit (with seeds in the middle) normally only grows on plants which have been <u>pollinated by insects</u>. If the plant <u>doesn't</u> get pollinated, the fruit and seeds <u>don't grow</u>. However, if <u>growth hormones</u> are applied to the <u>unpollinated</u> <u>flowers</u> of some types of plant, the <u>fruit will grow</u> but the <u>seeds won't</u>.

2) <u>Selective weedkillers</u> have been developed from <u>plant growth hormones</u>.

3) <u>Cuttings</u> (see page 84) can be grown using <u>rooting powder</u> (containing a <u>plant growth hormone</u>).

4) <u>Fruit</u> can be <u>ripened</u> on its way to the shops using a <u>ripening hormone</u>.

5) <u>Seeds</u> can be forced to <u>germinate</u> using a hormone called <u>gibberellin</u>.

Plants respond to their environments more than you might think

Plants need plenty of water and light to grow well. But they don't just sit around passively and hope for the best. No, thanks to auxins they can grow in the <u>right directions</u> to <u>find</u> what they need.

Selective Breeding

Selective breeding is a way for humans to develop crops or herds with more <u>useful characteristics</u>.

Selective breeding the 'best' organisms gives the 'best' offspring

<u>Selective breeding</u> is when humans select the plants or animals that are going to breed and flourish, according to what <u>we</u> want from them. It's also called <u>artificial selection</u>.

This is the basic process involved in selective breeding:

1) From the existing stock, the organisms which have the <u>best characteristics</u> are selected.

2) They're <u>bred</u> with each other.

3) The <u>best</u> of the <u>offspring</u> are selected and <u>bred</u>.

4) This process is repeated over several generations to develop the <u>desired traits</u>.

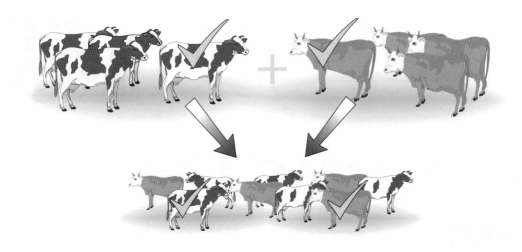

*There are **disadvantages** to selective breeding*

1) Only some of the original population is bred from — so there's <u>less variety</u> in the <u>gene pool</u> of the organisms. All the organisms in a crop or herd will be <u>closely related</u> and have <u>similar characteristics</u> — including their <u>level of disease-resistance</u>. Some diseases might be able to <u>wipe out</u> the whole lot.

2) Some of the characteristics encouraged by selective breeding are <u>beneficial for humans</u>, but <u>not</u> for the <u>organisms</u> themselves. E.g. selective breeding to <u>increase milk yields</u> means cows produce more milk than they would need to feed a calf. They often suffer from <u>mastitis</u> (inflammation of the udders).

Think about all the many breeds of dog — all from selective breeding

Selective breeding's <u>not</u> a new thing. People have been doing it for yonks. That's how we ended up with something like a poodle from a wolf. Somebody thought 'I really like this small, woolly, yappy wolf — I'll breed it with this other one'. And after thousands of generations, we got poodles. Hurrah.

Selective Breeding

Humans use other organisms for lots of things — we've selectively bred animals like the yappy poodle mentioned on the last page for <u>companionship</u>, we've selectively bred horses to make them sleek and fast so we can race them for <u>sport</u>, we've selectively bred flowers so that they <u>look pretty</u> in our gardens and houses. But selective breeding has been more important in <u>one</u> industry than in any other...

Selective breeding is very useful in farming

Here are three <u>examples</u> of how selective breeding can be used in <u>farming</u>:

Farmers can improve the yield and quality of milk from cattle

1) Cows can be selectively bred to produce offspring with particular characteristics, for example a <u>high milk yield</u> or <u>milk high in nutrients</u> (such as calcium or protein).

2) Cows are usually impregnated using <u>artificial insemination</u>. Semen from a <u>bull</u> which has <u>good characteristics</u> (or whose mother had good characteristics — bulls obviously don't produce milk) is used to artificially inseminate a <u>large number of cows</u>.

3) A typical dairy cow now produces between <u>5000 and 6000 litres</u> of milk a year. This is much more than dairy cows produced a hundred years ago. This is partly because of selective breeding and partly due to <u>intensive farming methods</u> (for example, giving the cows a special diet).

Farmers can increase the number of offspring in sheep

1) Farmers can selectively breed <u>sheep</u> to <u>increase</u> the number of <u>lambs born</u>.

2) Female sheep (ewes) that produce large numbers of offspring are bred with rams whose mothers had large numbers of offspring, or that have already fathered large numbers themselves in the past.

3) The <u>characteristic</u> of having large numbers of offspring is therefore likely to be <u>passed on</u> to appear in the next generation.

Farmers can increase the yields from dwarf wheat

1) Selective breeding can be used to combine <u>two different desirable characteristics</u>.

2) <u>Tall wheat plants</u> have a good grain yield but are easily damaged by wind and rain. <u>Dwarf wheat plants</u> can resist wind and rain but have a lower grain yield.

3) These two types of wheat plant were <u>cross-bred</u>, and the best resulting wheat plants were cross-bred again. This resulted in a <u>new variety</u> of wheat <u>combining</u> the <u>good characteristics</u> — dwarf wheat plants which could <u>resist bad weather</u> and had a <u>high grain yield</u>.

Adult Cloning

Ah, Dolly the sheep. It seems a long time ago now, but she was the <u>first mammal</u> to be cloned from an adult cell. She was born in 1996, the only success of 277 attempts by the team who created her.

Cloning an adult is done by transplanting a cell nucleus

The <u>first mammal</u> to be successfully cloned from an <u>adult cell</u> was a sheep called 'Dolly'.

This is the <u>method</u> that was used to produce Dolly:

1) The <u>nucleus</u> of a sheep's <u>egg cell</u> was removed —
   this left the egg cell without any <u>genetic information</u>.

2) Another nucleus was <u>inserted</u> in its place. This was a <u>diploid</u> nucleus from an udder
   cell of a <u>different sheep</u> (the one being cloned) and had all its <u>genetic information</u>.

3) The cell was <u>stimulated</u> so that it started <u>dividing by
   mitosis</u>, as if it was a normal <u>fertilised egg</u>.

4) The dividing cell was <u>implanted</u> into the <u>uterus</u> of
   another sheep to develop until it was ready to be born.

5) The result was <u>Dolly</u>, a clone of the sheep from which the <u>udder cell</u> came.

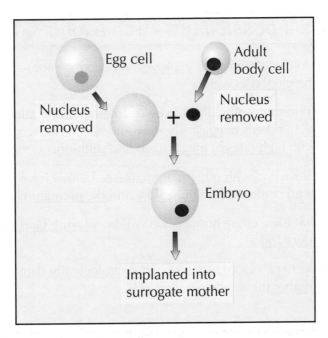

There are <u>risks</u> with cloning (see also next page), which the success with Dolly also highlighted. Embryos formed by cloning from adult cells often <u>don't develop normally</u>. There had been many <u>failed attempts</u> at producing a clone from an <u>adult</u> before Dolly was born.

Adult Cloning

There are both **benefits** and **risks** involved in **cloning**

There are many possible <u>benefits</u> of cloning:

1) Animals that can produce <u>medicines</u> in their <u>milk</u> could be cloned. Researchers have managed to transfer <u>human genes</u> that produce <u>useful proteins</u> into <u>sheep</u> and <u>cows</u>, so that they can produce, for example, the blood clotting agent <u>factor VIII</u> used for treating <u>haemophilia</u>. With cloning, you only need to transfer the genes <u>once</u>, and then you could <u>clone</u> the animal as many times as you liked.

2) Animals (probably pigs) that have organs suitable for <u>organ transplantation</u> into humans (<u>xenotransplantation</u>) could be developed by <u>genetic engineering</u> and then <u>cloned</u> in the same way.

3) The <u>study</u> of animal clones and cloned cells could lead to <u>greater understanding</u> of the <u>development</u> of the <u>embryo</u> and of <u>ageing</u> and <u>age-related disorders</u>.

4) Cloning could be used to help preserve <u>endangered species</u>.

But there are <u>risks</u> too:

1) There is some evidence that cloned animals might <u>not</u> be as <u>healthy</u> as normal ones.

2) Cloning is a <u>new</u> science and it might have consequences that we're <u>not yet aware of</u>.

3) People are worried that <u>humans</u> might be produced by cloning if research continues.

Cloning **humans** is a **possibility** — with a lot of ethical issues

1) As the technology used to clone mammals <u>improves</u>, it becomes more and more likely that <u>humans</u> could one day be <u>cloned</u> as well.

2) However, there are still enormous <u>difficulties</u> to be overcome, and it might well have to involve women willing to <u>donate</u> hundreds of <u>eggs</u>. There would have to be lots of <u>surrogate pregnancies</u>, probably with <u>high rates</u> of <u>miscarriage</u> and <u>stillbirth</u>.

3) The problems scientists have had with other mammals (see below) have shown that any human clones eventually produced could well be <u>unhealthy</u> and <u>die prematurely</u>.

4) There are also worries that if we clone humans we will be '<u>playing God</u>', and meddling with things we <u>don't fully understand</u>.

5) Even if a healthy clone were produced, it might be <u>psychologically damaged</u> by the knowledge that it's just a clone of <u>another</u> human being.

Human cloning is probably already possible — but would it be right?

Since Dolly, scientists have successfully cloned <u>all kinds</u> of mammals including goats, cows, mice, pigs, cats, rabbits, horses and dogs. Many of these clones suffered <u>health problems</u> and <u>died young</u> — Dolly seemed normal, but died aged just six (when the breed has a life expectancy of 11-12).

Warm-Up and Exam Questions

Warm-Up Questions

1) What are auxins?
2) Explain how auxins might be used for the production of seedless satsumas.
3) How is selective breeding done?
4) What is a clone?
5) Give two reasons why most people do not approve of the cloning of human beings.

Exam Questions

1   In 1918, a Hungarian scientist called Arpad Paal did experiments to investigate how plants grow. The diagram shows one experiment that he did.

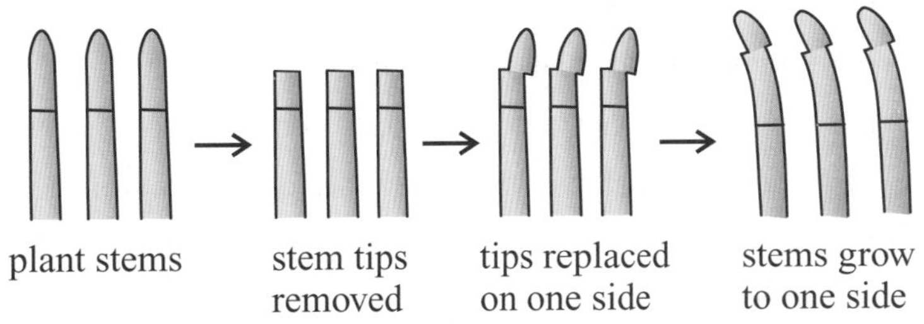

plant stems → stem tips removed → tips replaced on one side → stems grow to one side

(a) When a stem grows to the left as shown above, which side is growing faster?

(1 mark)

(b) Explain what makes the stems at the final stage grow to the left.

(3 marks)

(c) The stems were kept in the dark after the tips were replaced. Explain why.

(1 mark)

2   The Chestnut Stud Farm breeds racehorses. Over the years, each generation of horses was faster than their parents.

(a) Explain how this could be achieved as a result of a breeding programme.

(3 marks)

(b) Suggest one disadvantage of such a breeding programme.

(1 mark)

3   The diagram shows a method that scientists used for cloning mice. They used three adult mice for this — Beatrix, Brenda and Belinda.

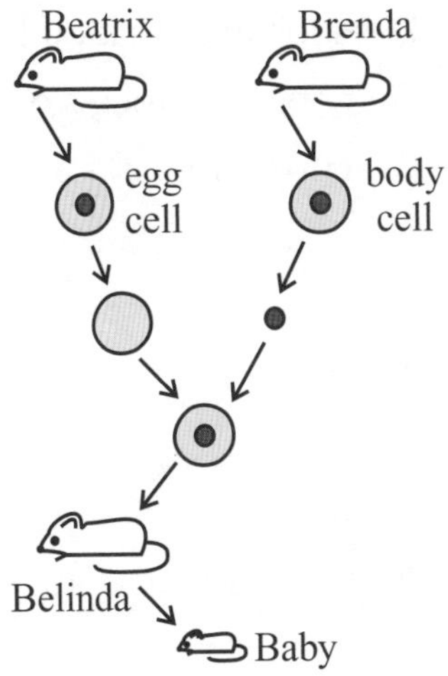

Beatrix   Brenda

egg cell   body cell

Belinda   Baby

(a) Explain why the egg cell from Beatrix had its nucleus removed.

(1 mark)

(b) One of the three adult mice had a useful property which the scientists wanted to clone. Which of them do you think this was, and why?

(2 marks)

SECTION EIGHT — GROWTH AND DEVELOPMENT

Revision Summary for Section Eight

And that's another section finished. Award yourself a gold star, relax, get a cup of tea, and take a leisurely glance through these beautiful revision summary questions. Once you've glanced through them, you'll have to answer them. And then you'll have to check your answers and go back and revise any bits you got wrong. And then do the questions again. In fact, it's not really a matter of relaxing at all. More a matter of knuckling down to lots of hard work. Oops. Sorry.

1) Give three ways that the growth of an organism can be measured.

2) Describe two differences in the way plant cells and animal cells grow and develop.

3) Name an animal that can regenerate parts of its body.

4) What is mitosis used for in the human body? Describe the four steps in mitosis.

5) What is the Hayflick limit? What two types of cell don't have a Hayflick limit?

6) Where does meiosis take place in the human body?

7) What type of cell division does a fertilised egg use to grow into a new organism?

8) Give three ways that sperm cells are adapted to their function.

9) Summarise the main arguments for and against the current 24 week time limit for aborting a foetus in the UK.

10) During in vitro fertilisation, it is possible to screen embryos for various genetic disorders before they're implanted into the mother. Only the 'good' embryos would be chosen for implantation. Summarise the main arguments for and against embryonic screening.

11) What is meant by the 'differentiation' of cells?

12) Describe one way that adult stem cells are currently used to cure diseases.

13) Give three examples of how embryonic stem cells could be used to cure diseases.

14) There are concerns about the ethics of stem cell research.
Give one argument in favour of stem cell research and one argument against stem cell research.

15) Explain how auxins cause plant shoots to grow towards light.

16) Explain how auxins cause plant roots to grow towards water.

17) Describe three ways that plant hormones are used commercially.

18) What is selective breeding?

19) Suggest three features that you might selectively breed for in a dairy cow.

20) Give three examples of the use of selective breeding in farming.

21) Describe two disadvantages of selective breeding.

22) Describe the process of cloning an animal from an adult cell (e.g. cloning a sheep).

23) Describe three risks associated with cloning animals.

Photosynthesis

Plants can make their own <u>food</u> — it's a very useful trick. Here's how they do it...

Photosynthesis produces glucose using sunlight

1) <u>Photosynthesis</u> is the process that produces 'food' in plants. The 'food' it produces is <u>glucose</u>.

2) Photosynthesis happens in the <u>leaves</u> of all <u>green plants</u> — this is largely what the leaves are for.

3) Photosynthesis happens inside the <u>chloroplasts</u>, which are found in leaf cells and in other <u>green</u> parts of a plant.

4) Chloroplasts contain a substance called <u>chlorophyll</u>, which absorbs <u>sunlight</u> and uses its energy to convert <u>carbon dioxide</u> and <u>water</u> into <u>glucose</u>. <u>Oxygen</u> is also produced.

$$\text{carbon dioxide} + \text{water} \xrightarrow[\text{chlorophyll}]{\text{SUNLIGHT}} \text{glucose} + \text{oxygen}$$

Four things are needed for photosynthesis to happen

If a plant <u>can't</u> get enough of any of these <u>four</u> things, it won't be able to make enough food. Its growth might be <u>stunted</u> as a result, and eventually it could <u>die</u>.

1) Light

Sunlight beating down on the leaf provides the <u>energy</u> for the reaction.

2) Chlorophyll

This is the <u>green substance</u> found in <u>chloroplasts</u> that makes leaves look <u>green</u>.

Chlorophyll absorbs the <u>energy</u> in sunlight and uses it to combine CO_2 and <u>water</u> to make <u>glucose</u>. Oxygen is just a <u>by-product</u> of this reaction.

3) Carbon dioxide

CO_2 diffuses into the leaf from the <u>air</u> around.

4) Water

<u>Water</u> is drawn up into the plant from the <u>soil</u>, up the roots and stem, and into the leaf via the <u>veins</u>.

Photosynthesis

So photosynthesis needs water, carbon dioxide, sunlight and chlorophyll and it produces glucose (plus oxygen as a by-product). Now you need to know what the plant <u>uses</u> the <u>glucose</u> for.

Plants use the glucose for six different things

1) For **respiration**

Respiration <u>releases the energy</u> that enables plants to <u>convert</u> the rest of the glucose into various other useful substances which they use to <u>build new cells</u> and <u>grow</u>.

2) For **making fruits**

<u>Glucose</u>, along with another sugar called <u>fructose</u>, is turned into <u>sucrose</u> for storing in <u>fruits</u>. Fruits <u>taste nice</u> so that animals will eat them and <u>spread the seeds</u> all over the place in their poo.

3) For **making cell walls**

<u>Glucose</u> in converted into <u>cellulose</u> for making <u>cell walls</u> (to support and strengthen the cells).

4) For **making proteins**

<u>Glucose</u> is combined with <u>nitrates</u> to make <u>amino acids</u> which are then made into <u>proteins</u>.

5) Stored in **seeds**

<u>Glucose</u> is turned into <u>lipids</u> (fats and oils) for storing in <u>seeds</u>.

6) Stored as **starch**

<u>Glucose</u> is turned into <u>starch</u> and <u>stored</u> in roots, stems and leaves, ready for use when photosynthesis isn't happening, like in <u>winter</u>. <u>Starch</u> is <u>insoluble</u>, which makes it much <u>better</u> for <u>storing</u> because it doesn't bloat the storage cells by causing <u>osmosis</u> like glucose would.

All life depends on photosynthesis

Plants are pretty crucial in ensuring the <u>flow of energy</u> through nature. They are able to use the Sun's energy to <u>make glucose</u>, the <u>energy source</u> which humans and animals need for <u>respiration</u> (see p.124). Make sure you know the photosynthesis equation inside out — it's important later in the section too.

Rate of Photosynthesis

A plant's rate of photosynthesis is affected by the amount of light, the amount of CO_2, and the temperature of its surroundings. Photosynthesis slows down or stops if the conditions aren't right.

*The **limiting factor** depends on the **conditions***

1) A limiting factor is something which stops photosynthesis from happening any faster. The amount of light, the amount of carbon dioxide and the temperature can all be the limiting factor.

2) The limiting factor depends on the environmental conditions. For example, in winter cold temperatures might be the limiting factor and at night light is likely to be the limiting factor.

3) It might seem strange that we haven't included water as a possible limiting factor. But the fact is that water is so important for all kinds of different reactions in a plant that by the time it starts to limit photosynthesis the plant will already be in a pretty bad state.

*Not enough **LIGHT** slows down the rate of **photosynthesis***

Chlorophyll uses light energy to carry out photosynthesis. It can only do it as quickly as the light energy is arriving.

1) If the light level is raised, the rate of photosynthesis will increase steadily, but only up to a certain point.

2) Beyond that, it won't make any difference because then it'll be either the temperature or the underline{CO_2} level which is now the limiting factor.

Rainforests have dense canopies which can cause low light intensity on the forest floor.

Rate of photosynthesis

CO_2 or temp needs to be increased

Plenty of CO_2 and warmth

light intensity

Rate of Photosynthesis

Too little CARBON DIOXIDE also slows it down

CO_2 is one of the raw materials needed for photosynthesis — only 0.04% of the air is CO_2, so it's pretty scarce as far as plants are concerned.

1) As with light intensity, increasing the amount of CO_2 will only increase the rate of photosynthesis up to a point. After this point the graph flattens out, showing that CO_2 is no longer the limiting factor.

2) As long as light and CO_2 are in plentiful supply then the factor limiting photosynthesis must be temperature.

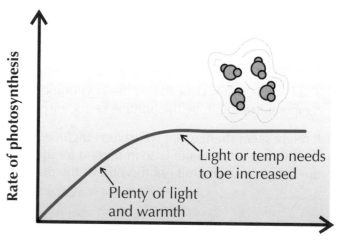

Rate of photosynthesis

Light or temp needs to be increased

Plenty of light and warmth

% level of CO_2

The TEMPERATURE has to be just right

Temperature affects the rate of photosynthesis because it affects the enzymes involved.

1) As the temperature increases, so does the rate of photosynthesis — up to a point.

2) If the temperature is too high (over about 45 °C), the plant's enzymes will be denatured (they stop working), so the rate of photosynthesis rapidly decreases.

3) Usually though, if the temperature is the limiting factor, it's because it's too low and things need warming up a bit.

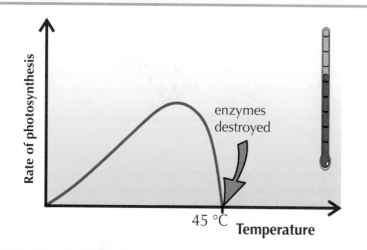

Rate of photosynthesis

enzymes destroyed

45 °C Temperature

Aren't plants fussy things, everything has to be just right...

First request is plenty of light, then is plenty of carbon dioxide, then the temperature has to be high, but not too high or enzymes denature and everything goes wrong. Add to all that their need for water and nitrates from the soil and it's a wonder that plants actually survive at all!

Leaf Structure

Now's a good time to flick back to page 119 and make sure that you thoroughly understand <u>diffusion</u>.

Leaves are designed for *making food* by *photosynthesis*

The whole structure of leaves is geared towards that.
You need to know all the different parts of a <u>typical leaf</u> shown on the diagram:

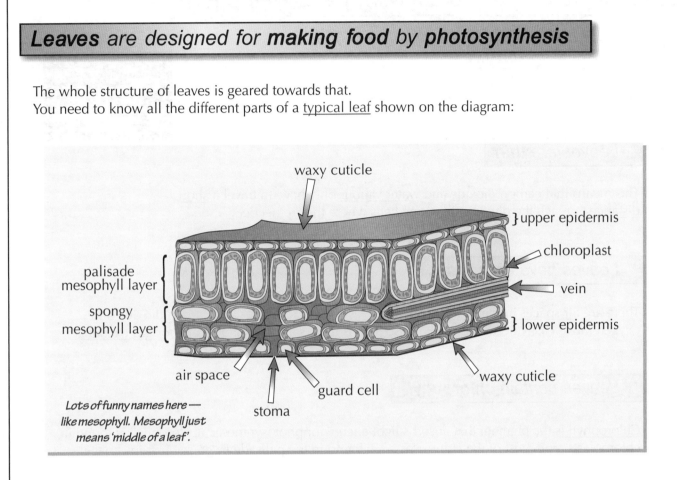

Lots of funny names here — like mesophyll. Mesophyll just means 'middle of a leaf'.

Plants exchange **gases** *by* **diffusion**

When plants photosynthesise they <u>use up carbon dioxide</u> from the atmosphere and <u>produce oxygen</u> as a by-product. Plants also <u>respire</u>, where they <u>use up oxygen</u> and <u>produce carbon dioxide</u> as a by-product. So there are lots of gases moving about in plants, and this happens by <u>diffusion</u>.

1) When the plant is photosynthesising it uses up lots of <u>carbon dioxide</u>, so there's hardly any inside the leaf. Luckily this makes <u>more carbon dioxide</u> move into the leaf by <u>diffusion</u> (from an area of <u>higher</u> concentration to an area of <u>lower</u> concentration).

2) At the same time lots of <u>oxygen</u> is being <u>made</u> as a waste product of photosynthesis. Some is used in <u>respiration</u>, and the rest diffuses <u>out</u> through the stomata (moving from an area of <u>higher</u> concentration to an area of <u>lower</u> concentration).

3) At <u>night</u> it's a different story — there's <u>no photosynthesis</u> going on because there's no <u>light</u>. Lots of carbon dioxide is made in <u>respiration</u> and lots of oxygen is used up. There's a lot of carbon dioxide in the leaf and not a lot of <u>oxygen</u>, so now it's mainly carbon dioxide diffusing <u>out</u> and oxygen diffusing <u>in</u>.

Leaf Structure

Leaves are **adapted** for **efficient photosynthesis**

1) Leaves are **broad**

This means that leaves have a large <u>surface area</u> exposed to <u>light</u>.

2) Leaves are **thin**

This means that <u>carbon dioxide</u> and <u>water vapour</u> only have to travel a <u>short distance</u> to reach the photosynthesising cells where they're needed.

3) Leaves have **air spaces**

There are <u>air spaces</u> in the <u>spongy mesophyll layer</u>. This lets gases like carbon dioxide and oxygen move easily between cells. It also means there's a large surface area for <u>gas exchange</u>.

4) Leaves contain **chlorophyll**

<u>Chlorophyll</u> is the pigment that absorbs light energy for photosynthesis. Chlorophyll is found in <u>chloroplasts</u>, and most of the chloroplasts are found in the <u>palisade layer</u> (see previous page). This is so that they're near the top of the leaf where they can get the most <u>light</u>.

5) Leaves have a **transparent epidermis**

The <u>upper epidermis</u> is <u>transparent</u> so that light can pass through it to the <u>palisade layer</u>.

6) Leaves have **stomata**

The lower surface is full of holes called <u>stomata</u>. They're there to let gases like <u>carbon dioxide</u> and <u>oxygen</u> in and out. They also allow <u>water</u> to escape — which is known as <u>transpiration</u>.

7) Leaves have **veins**

Leaves have a network of <u>veins</u> to <u>deliver water</u> and other <u>nutrients</u> to every part of the leaf and to take away the <u>food</u> produced by the leaf. They also help to <u>support</u> the leaf structure.

A plant's leaves are its organs for photosynthesis

Scientists know all this stuff because they've actually <u>looked</u> and seen the structures of leaves and the cells inside them. Not with the naked eye, of course — they used microscopes.

Warm-Up and Exam Questions

1) Name four factors that are needed for photosynthesis.
2) What is meant by a limiting factor for the rate of photosynthesis?
3) Describe four ways in which the structure of a leaf helps with photosynthesis.
4) How do carbon dioxide and oxygen get in and out of a leaf?

Exam Questions

1   Photosynthesis makes glucose. The glucose may then be converted to other substances.
    Some of these substances are listed below:

    cellulose   amino acids   sucrose   starch

    Match each of these substances to its correct function from the list below.

    - Making cell walls.   - Making fruit sweet.

    - Making enzymes.   - Storing energy.

    (4 marks)

2   The diagram shows part of the structure
    of a leaf as it looks under a microscope.

    (a) Name the parts labelled
         A, B and C.

    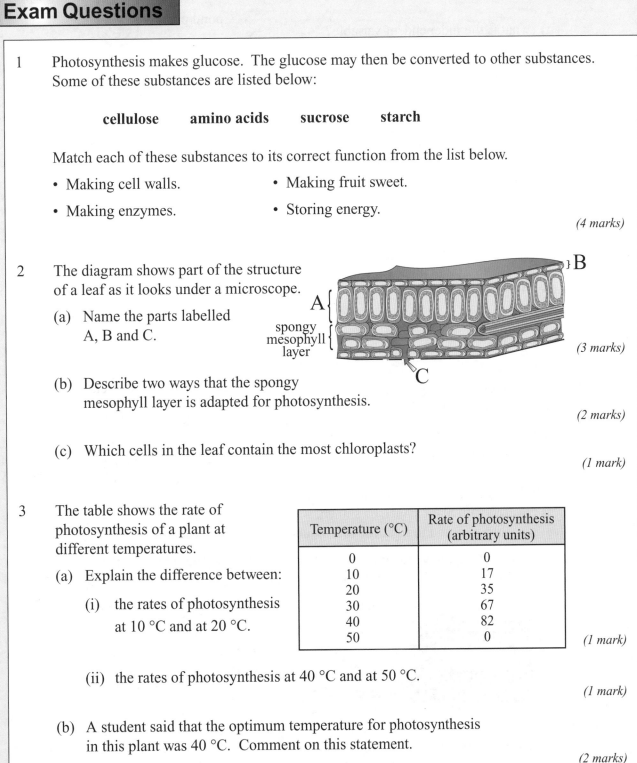

    (3 marks)

    (b) Describe two ways that the spongy
         mesophyll layer is adapted for photosynthesis.

    (2 marks)

    (c) Which cells in the leaf contain the most chloroplasts?

    (1 mark)

3   The table shows the rate of
    photosynthesis of a plant at
    different temperatures.

Temperature (°C)	Rate of photosynthesis (arbitrary units)
0	0
10	17
20	35
30	67
40	82
50	0

    (a) Explain the difference between:

         (i)   the rates of photosynthesis
               at 10 °C and at 20 °C.

    (1 mark)

         (ii) the rates of photosynthesis at 40 °C and at 50 °C.

    (1 mark)

    (b) A student said that the optimum temperature for photosynthesis
         in this plant was 40 °C. Comment on this statement.

    (2 marks)

Exam Questions

4 Jane did an experiment to see how the rate of photosynthesis depends on light intensity.
The diagram shows her apparatus.

   (a) How can Jane measure the rate of photosynthesis?

(1 mark)

   (b) In this experiment:

      (i) what is the dependent variable?

(1 mark)

      (ii) what is the independent variable?

(1 mark)

   (c) State one factor that should be kept constant during this experiment.

(1 mark)

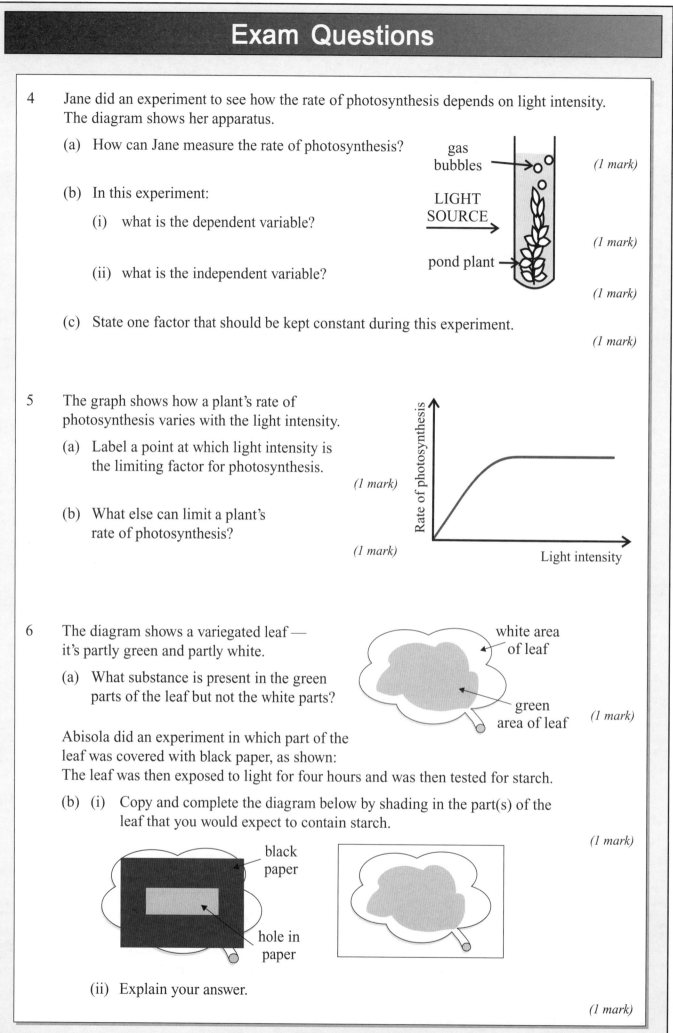

5 The graph shows how a plant's rate of
photosynthesis varies with the light intensity.

   (a) Label a point at which light intensity is
the limiting factor for photosynthesis.

(1 mark)

   (b) What else can limit a plant's
rate of photosynthesis?

(1 mark)

6 The diagram shows a variegated leaf —
it's partly green and partly white.

   (a) What substance is present in the green
parts of the leaf but not the white parts?

(1 mark)

Abisola did an experiment in which part of the
leaf was covered with black paper, as shown:
The leaf was then exposed to light for four hours and was then tested for starch.

   (b) (i) Copy and complete the diagram below by shading in the part(s) of the
leaf that you would expect to contain starch.

(1 mark)

      (ii) Explain your answer.

(1 mark)

Transpiration

If you don't water a house plant for a few days it starts to go all droopy. Plants need <u>water</u>.

Transpiration is the loss of water from the plant

1) Transpiration is caused by the <u>evaporation</u> and <u>diffusion</u> (see page 119) of water from inside the leaves.

2) This creates a slight <u>shortage</u> of water in the leaf, and so more water is drawn up from the rest of the plant through the <u>xylem vessels</u> (see page 172) to replace it.

3) This in turn means that more water is drawn up from the <u>roots</u>, and so there's a constant <u>transpiration stream</u> of water through the plant.

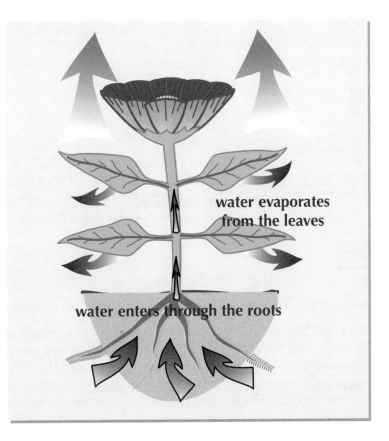

water evaporates from the leaves

water enters through the roots

Transpiration is just a <u>side-effect</u> of the way leaves are adapted for <u>photosynthesis</u>. They have to have <u>stomata</u> in them so that gases can be exchanged easily (see page 166). Because there's more water <u>inside</u> the plant than in the <u>air outside</u>, the water escapes from the leaves through the stomata.

The transpiration stream does have some <u>benefits</u> for the plants:

1) The constant stream of water from the ground helps to keep the plant <u>cool</u>.

2) It provides the plant with a constant supply of water for <u>photosynthesis</u>.

3) The water creates <u>turgor pressure</u> in the plant cells, which helps support the plant and stops it wilting (see page 171).

4) <u>Minerals</u> needed by the plant (see page 174) can be brought in from the soil along with the water.

Transpiration

The <u>rate</u> at which a plant loses water by transpiration depends on the external conditions.

Transpiration rate *is affected by* four main things

You need to learn what the <u>four</u> things are, and <u>how</u> they have an effect.

1) Light intensity

The <u>brighter</u> the light, the <u>greater</u> the transpiration rate.

This is because the <u>stomata</u> begin to <u>close</u> as it gets darker. Photosynthesis can't happen in the dark, so they don't need to be open to let <u>carbon dioxide</u> in. When the stomata are closed, very little water can escape.

2) Temperature

The <u>warmer</u> it is, the <u>faster</u> transpiration happens.

When it's warm the water particles have <u>more energy</u>. They're more likely to <u>evaporate</u> and they move about more when they do, so they <u>diffuse</u> out of the leaf more quickly.

3) Air movement

If there's <u>lots</u> of air movement (wind) around a leaf, transpiration happens <u>faster</u>.

If the air around a leaf is very still, the water vapour that diffuses out just <u>surrounds the leaf</u> and doesn't move away. This means there's a <u>high concentration</u> of water particles outside the leaf as well as inside it, so <u>diffusion</u> doesn't happen as quickly. If it's windy, the water vapour is <u>swept away</u>, maintaining a <u>low concentration</u> of water in the air outside the leaf. Diffusion then happens quickly, from an area of high concentration to an area of low concentration.

4) Air humidity

If the air around the leaf is very <u>dry</u>, transpiration happens more <u>quickly</u>.

This is like what happens with air movement. If the air is <u>humid</u> there's a lot of water in it already, so there's not much of a <u>difference</u> between the inside and the outside of the leaf. Diffusion happens <u>fastest</u> if there's a <u>really high concentration</u> in one place, and a <u>really low concentration</u> in the other.

Transpiration isn't so great if the plant is short of water

One good way to remember those <u>four factors</u> that affect the rate of transpiration is to think about drying washing. Then you'll realise there are far more boring things you could be doing than revision, and you'll try harder. No, only joking — it's the <u>same</u> stuff: sunny, warm, windy and dry.

Water Flow in Plants

Plants <u>can't</u> avoid transpiration if they want to carry out photosynthesis — but if they lose <u>too much</u> water they could be in trouble.

Plants need to **balance water loss** with **water uptake**

Transpiration can help plants in some ways (see page 169), but if it hasn't rained for a while and you're <u>short of water</u> it's not a good idea to have it rushing out of your leaves. So plants have <u>adaptations</u> to help <u>reduce water loss</u> from their leaves.

1) Leaves usually have a <u>waxy waterproof cuticle</u> covering the <u>upper epidermis</u>.

2) Most <u>stomata</u> are found on the <u>lower surface</u> of a leaf where it's <u>darker</u> and <u>cooler</u>. This helps to slow down <u>diffusion</u> of water out of the leaf.

3) The <u>bigger</u> the stomata and the <u>more</u> stomata a leaf has, the more <u>water</u> the plant will <u>lose</u>. Plants in <u>hot climates</u> really need to conserve water, so they have <u>fewer</u> and <u>smaller</u> stomata on the underside of the leaf and <u>no</u> stomata on the upper epidermis.

Turgor pressure supports plant tissues

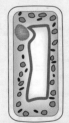

normal cell   turgid cell

1) When a plant is well watered, all its cells will draw water in by <u>osmosis</u> and become plump and swollen. When the cells are like this, they're said to be <u>turgid</u>.

2) The contents of the cell push against the cell wall — this is called <u>turgor pressure</u>. Turgor pressure helps <u>support</u> the plant tissues.

3) If there's no water in the soil, a plant starts to <u>wilt</u> (droop). This is because the cells start to lose water and so <u>lose</u> their turgor pressure. The cells are then said to be <u>flaccid</u>.

4) If the plant's really short of water, the <u>cytoplasm</u> inside its cells starts to <u>shrink</u> and the membrane <u>pulls away</u> from the cell wall. The cell is now said to be <u>plasmolysed</u>. The plant doesn't totally lose its shape though, because the <u>inelastic cell wall</u> keeps things in position. It just droops a bit.

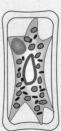

flaccid cell   plasmolysed cell

Water Flow in Plants

Plants have two separate types of <u>vessel</u> — xylem and phloem — for transporting stuff around. Both types of vessel go to <u>every</u> part of the plant, but they are totally <u>separate</u>.

Xylem vessels take **water** up from the roots to the rest of the plant

1) Xylem vessels are made of <u>dead cells</u> joined end to end.

2) There are <u>no</u> end walls between them and there's a hole (<u>lumen</u>) down the middle.

3) The thick side walls are strong and stiff, which gives the plant <u>support</u>.

4) The xylem vessels carry <u>water</u> and <u>minerals</u> from the <u>roots</u> up the shoot to the leaves in the <u>transpiration stream</u>.

Phloem vessels transport **food** around the plant

1) Phloem vessels are made of columns of <u>living</u> cells.

2) They have <u>perforated end-plates</u> to allow stuff to flow through.

3) They transport <u>food substances</u> (mainly <u>sugars</u>) made in the leaves to growing and storage tissues, in <u>both directions</u>.

4) This movement of food substances around the plant is known as <u>translocation</u>.

Xylem vessels carry water, phloem vessels carry sugars

You probably did that really dull experiment at school where you stick a piece of celery in a beaker of water with red food colouring in it. Then you stare at it for half an hour, and once the time is up, hey presto, the red has reached the top of the celery. That's because it travelled there in the <u>xylem</u>.

Warm-Up and Exam Questions

Transpiration, turgor pressure, plasmolysed — it's like a different language has been invented just to talk about plants and water. Here are some questions to help you get really fluent in it.

Warm-Up Questions

1) What is the transpiration stream?
2) Where are the main places that a plant: (a) absorbs water? (b) loses water?
3) Give four environmental conditions that can increase transpiration rate.
4) What does it mean if a plant cell is 'plasmolysed'?
5) Give the functions of the xylem and phloem in plants.

Exam Questions

1 Martin did an experiment to measure the effect of air currents on the rate of transpiration.

The graph shows his results.

rate of transpiration

wind speed

(a) Suggest what Martin should do to:

(i) check that his results are reliable.

(1 mark)

(ii) make sure that his experiment is a fair test.

(2 marks)

(b) Explain what Martin's results show.

(2 marks)

2 Describe how xylem vessels are different from phloem vessels:

(a) in their structure.

(2 marks)

(b) in their function.

(2 marks)

3 Explain the reasons for each of the following:

(a) In most plants, the lower surfaces of the leaves lose more water than the upper surfaces.

(1 mark)

(b) When a plant loses too much water, it wilts.

(1 mark)

(c) Cacti have thick cuticles covering their stems and leaves.

(1 mark)

Minerals for Healthy Growth

Plants are important in <u>food chains</u> and <u>nutrient cycles</u> because they can take minerals from the soil and energy from the Sun and turn it into food. And then, after all that hard work, we eat them.

Plants need **three** main **minerals**

Plants need certain <u>elements</u> so they can produce important compounds. They get these elements from <u>minerals</u> in the <u>soil</u>.

If there aren't enough of these minerals in the soil, plants suffer <u>deficiency symptoms</u>.

1) Nitrates

- Nitrates contain nitrogen for making <u>amino acids</u> and <u>proteins</u>.
- They are needed for <u>cell growth</u>.
- If a plant can't get enough nitrates it will be <u>stunted</u> and will have <u>yellow older leaves</u>.

2) Phosphates

- Phosphates contain phosphorus for <u>DNA</u> and <u>cell membranes</u>.
- They're needed for <u>respiration</u> and <u>growth</u>.
- Plants without enough phosphate have <u>poor root growth</u> and <u>purple older leaves</u>.

3) Potassium

- Potassium is needed by the <u>enzymes</u> that control <u>photosynthesis</u> and <u>respiration</u>.
- If there's not enough potassium in the soil, plants have <u>poor flower and fruit growth</u> and <u>discoloured leaves</u>.

Magnesium is also needed in **small amounts**

The three main minerals are needed in fairly <u>large amounts</u>, but there are other elements which are needed in much <u>smaller</u> amounts.

- <u>Magnesium</u> is one of the most significant as it's required for making <u>chlorophyll</u> (needed for <u>photosynthesis</u>).
- Plants without enough magnesium have <u>yellow leaves</u>.

Plants get minerals from the soil for healthy growth

When a farmer or gardener buys <u>fertiliser</u>, he or she is basically buying nitrates, phosphates and potassium. A fertiliser's <u>NPK label</u> tells you the relative proportions of nitrogen (N), phosphorus (P) and potassium (K) it contains, so you can choose the right one for your plants and soil.

Minerals for Healthy Growth

The roots of a plant, like most things in biology, are <u>adapted</u> for their function.

Root hairs *take in* minerals *and* water

1) The cells on plant roots grow into long 'hairs' which stick out into the soil.

2) Each branch of a root will be covered in <u>millions</u> of these microscopic hairs.

3) This gives the plant a <u>big surface area</u> for absorbing <u>minerals</u> and <u>water</u> from the soil.

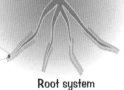
Root hair cell

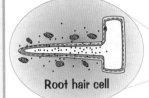
Root system

Minerals *are taken in by* active transport

1) The <u>concentration</u> of minerals in the <u>soil</u> is usually pretty <u>low</u>. It's normally <u>higher</u> in the <u>root hair cell</u> than in the soil around it.

2) So normal diffusion <u>doesn't</u> explain how minerals are taken up into the root hair cell. They should go the <u>other way</u> if they followed the rules of diffusion.

3) The answer is that a different process called '<u>active transport</u>' is responsible.

4) Active transport uses <u>energy</u> from <u>respiration</u> to help the plant pull minerals into the root hair <u>against the concentration gradient</u>. This is essential for its growth.

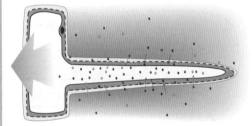

Water *is taken in by* osmosis

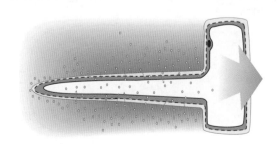

There's usually a <u>higher concentration</u> of water in the soil than there is inside the plant, so the water is drawn into the root hair cell by <u>osmosis</u>.

A big surface area helps speed up both active transport and osmosis

Here's an interesting fact — a biggish tree loses about a <u>thousand litres</u> of water from its leaves <u>every single day</u>. That's as much water as the average person drinks in a whole year, so the <u>roots</u> have to be very effective at drawing in water from the soil. Which is why they have all those root <u>hairs</u>, you see.

Warm-Up and Exam Questions

More questions already? You'll be getting spoilt if I'm not careful.

Warm-Up Questions

1) If a plant has purple leaves and poor root growth, which mineral is it likely to be lacking?
2) What does a plant look like if it's not getting enough magnesium?
3) Which process does a plant use to take mineral ions into its roots?
4) Which process allows a plant to absorb water into its roots?

Exam Questions

1   The diagram shows a root hair cell from a plant.

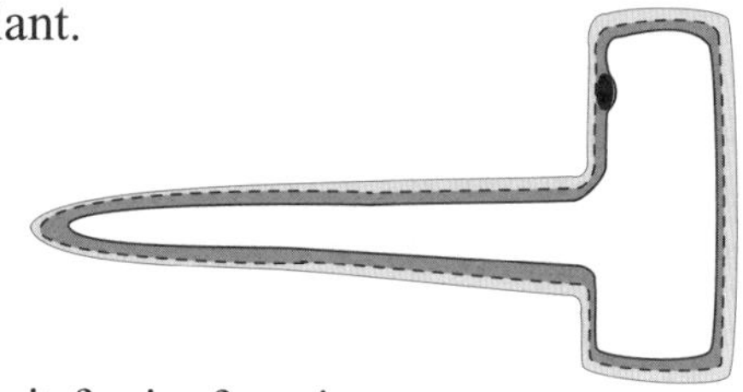

(a) What is the main function of this cell?

(1 mark)

(b) Explain how the shape of the cell adapts it for its function.

(1 mark)

2   Complete the table to show the main functions of different minerals in a plant.

Mineral	Function
	needed for making chlorophyll
	needed for making DNA and cell membranes and for healthy roots
potassium	
nitrate	

(4 marks)

3   Mrs Foyle often wins prizes for her plants, but this year some of them aren't growing very well. She thinks this is because of a mineral deficiency.

Which mineral could her plants be lacking if:

(a) they have yellow older leaves?

(1 mark)

(b) they have poor flower and fruit growth?

(1 mark)

(c) they have purple older leaves?

(1 mark)

Pyramids of Number and Biomass

For this page you should know that a <u>trophic level</u> is a <u>feeding level</u> in a food chain or web.

You need to be able to **construct pyramids** of **number**

Luckily it's pretty easy — they'll give you all the information you need to do it in the exam.

Here's an example:

<u>5000</u> dandelions... feed... <u>100</u> rabbits... which feed... <u>1</u> fox.

1) Each bar on a pyramid of numbers shows the <u>number of organisms</u> at that stage of the food chain.

2) So the '<u>dandelions</u>' bar on this pyramid would need to be <u>longer</u> than the '<u>rabbits</u>' bar, which in turn should be <u>longer</u> than the '<u>fox</u>' bar.

3) <u>Dandelions</u> go at the <u>bottom</u> because they're at the bottom of the food chain.

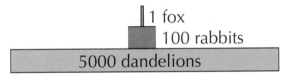

1 fox
100 rabbits
5000 dandelions

This gives a <u>typical pyramid of numbers</u>, where every time you go up a <u>trophic (feeding) level</u>, the number of organisms goes <u>down</u>. This is because it takes a <u>lot</u> of food from the level below to keep one animal alive.

But there are cases where a number pyramid is <u>not a pyramid at all</u>, e.g. one fox might feed 500 fleas.

fleas
fox
rabbits
dandelions

You'll have to **construct pyramids** of **biomass** too

1) Each bar on a <u>pyramid of biomass</u> shows the <u>mass of living material</u> at that stage of the food chain — basically how much all the organisms at each level would '<u>weigh</u>' if you put them <u>all together</u>.

2) So the one fox above would have quite a <u>big biomass</u> and the <u>hundreds of fleas</u> would have a <u>very small biomass</u>. Biomass pyramids are practically <u>always the right shape</u>:

fleas
fox
rabbits
dandelions

The species in an **environment** are **interdependent**

1) In the above food chain, if <u>rabbits</u> were wiped out, then the <u>foxes</u> would soon follow as they have <u>nothing to eat</u>. Foxes are said to be <u>dependent</u> on rabbits for survival.

2) Unfortunately life just isn't as simple as that. There are many different species within an environment, all <u>interdependent</u>. This means if one species changes, it <u>affects all the others</u>. For example, if lots of rabbits died, then:

foxes
rabbits
mice
dandelions

- There would be <u>less food</u> for the <u>foxes</u>, so their numbers might <u>decrease</u>.

- The number of <u>dandelions</u> might <u>increase</u>, because the rabbits wouldn't be eating them.

- The <u>mice</u> wouldn't be <u>competing</u> with the rabbits for food, so their numbers might <u>increase</u>.

Energy Transfer and Energy Flow

There's a reason why pyramids of biomass are almost always <u>pyramid-shaped</u>. Read on...

*All that **energy** just **disappears** somehow...*

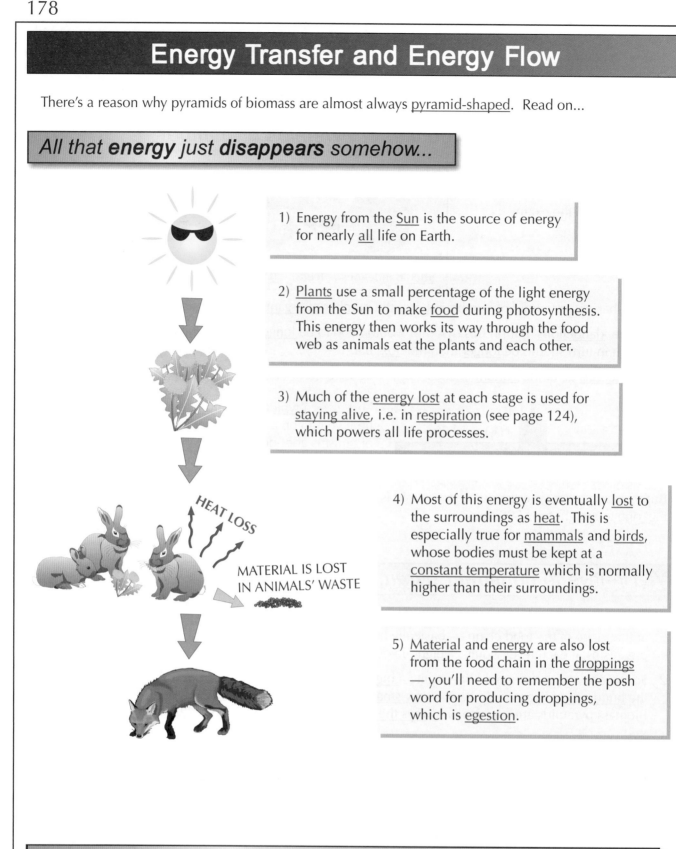

1) Energy from the <u>Sun</u> is the source of energy for nearly <u>all</u> life on Earth.

2) <u>Plants</u> use a small percentage of the light energy from the Sun to make <u>food</u> during photosynthesis. This energy then works its way through the food web as animals eat the plants and each other.

3) Much of the <u>energy lost</u> at each stage is used for <u>staying alive</u>, i.e. in <u>respiration</u> (see page 124), which powers all life processes.

HEAT LOSS

MATERIAL IS LOST IN ANIMALS' WASTE

4) Most of this energy is eventually <u>lost</u> to the surroundings as <u>heat</u>. This is especially true for <u>mammals</u> and <u>birds</u>, whose bodies must be kept at a <u>constant temperature</u> which is normally higher than their surroundings.

5) <u>Material</u> and <u>energy</u> are also lost from the food chain in the <u>droppings</u> — you'll need to remember the posh word for producing droppings, which is <u>egestion</u>.

*This **explains a lot** about **pyramids of biomass** and **food chains***

1) Material and energy are both <u>lost</u> at <u>every stage</u> of a food chain.

2) This explains why you almost always get pyramid-shaped <u>biomass pyramids</u>. Most of the biomass at each stage is <u>lost</u> and so does <u>not</u> become biomass in the <u>next level up</u>.

3) It also explains why you hardly ever get <u>food chains</u> with more than about <u>five trophic levels</u>. So much <u>energy</u> is <u>lost</u> at each stage that there's not enough left to support more organisms after four or five stages.

Energy Transfer and Energy Flow

Bit of maths here, but there's no need to panic — it's just some simple subtraction and one fairly harmless equation to learn.

You need to be able to *interpret data* on *energy flow*

Look at the typical food chain shown below.

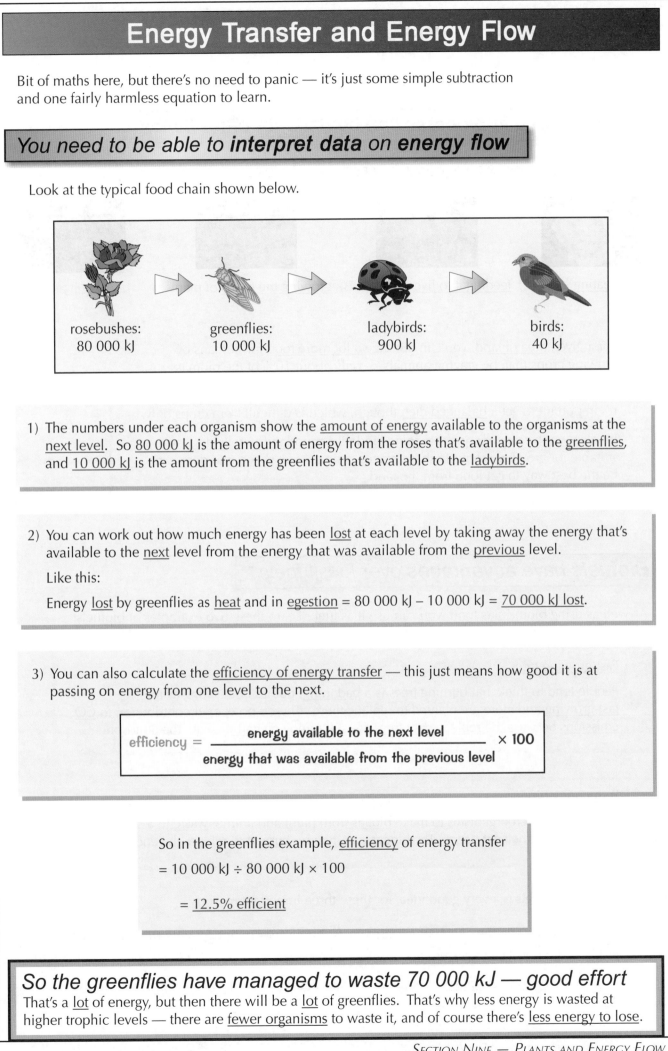

rosebushes: 80 000 kJ

greenflies: 10 000 kJ

ladybirds: 900 kJ

birds: 40 kJ

1) The numbers under each organism show the <u>amount of energy</u> available to the organisms at the <u>next level</u>. So <u>80 000 kJ</u> is the amount of energy from the roses that's available to the <u>greenflies</u>, and <u>10 000 kJ</u> is the amount from the greenflies that's available to the <u>ladybirds</u>.

2) You can work out how much energy has been <u>lost</u> at each level by taking away the energy that's available to the <u>next</u> level from the energy that was available from the <u>previous</u> level.

Like this:

Energy <u>lost</u> by greenflies as <u>heat</u> and in <u>egestion</u> = 80 000 kJ – 10 000 kJ = <u>70 000 kJ lost</u>.

3) You can also calculate the <u>efficiency of energy transfer</u> — this just means how good it is at passing on energy from one level to the next.

$$\text{efficiency} = \frac{\text{energy available to the next level}}{\text{energy that was available from the previous level}} \times 100$$

So in the greenflies example, <u>efficiency</u> of energy transfer

= 10 000 kJ ÷ 80 000 kJ × 100

= <u>12.5% efficient</u>

So the greenflies have managed to waste 70 000 kJ — good effort

That's a <u>lot</u> of energy, but then there will be a <u>lot</u> of greenflies. That's why less energy is wasted at higher trophic levels — there are <u>fewer organisms</u> to waste it, and of course there's <u>less energy to lose</u>.

Biomass and Fermentation

Biomass basically refers to <u>living</u> (or recently living) material. There are lots of ways we can use it.

Energy stored in biomass can be used for other things

There are many different ways to <u>release</u> the <u>energy</u> stored in <u>biomass</u> — including:

1) <u>eating</u> it   2) <u>feeding it to livestock</u>   3) <u>growing the seeds</u> of plants   4) using it as a <u>fuel</u>.

For a given <u>area of land</u>, you can produce <u>a lot more food</u> for humans by growing <u>crops</u> than by grazing <u>animals</u> — only about <u>10%</u> of the biomass eaten by beef cattle becomes useful meat for people to eat.

It's important to get a <u>balanced diet</u>, though, which is difficult from crops only.

It's also worth remembering that <u>some land</u>, like <u>moorland</u> or <u>fellsides</u>, isn't suitable for growing crops. In these places, animals like <u>sheep</u> and <u>deer</u> can be the <u>best way</u> to get food from the land.

Biofuels have advantages over fossil fuels

As well as using biomass as food, you can use it as <u>fuel</u>. Learn these two examples of <u>biofuels</u>:

1) <u>Fast-growing trees</u>

   People tend to think that burning trees is a <u>bad thing</u>, but it's not as long as they're <u>fast-growing</u> and more are planted to replace them. There's <u>no</u> overall contribution to <u>CO_2</u> <u>emissions</u> because the <u>replacement trees</u> are still <u>removing carbon</u> from the atmosphere.

2) <u>Fermenting biomass</u>

   You can use microorganisms to make <u>biogas</u> from plant and animal <u>waste</u> in a simple fermenter (see the next page). The biogas can then be <u>burned</u> to release the energy.

Developing biofuels is a very good idea, for these three important reasons:

* Unlike coal, oil and the like, biofuels are <u>renewable</u> — they're <u>not</u> going to run out one day.

* Using biofuels reduces <u>air pollution</u> — no <u>acid rain gases</u> are produced when wood and biogas burn.

* You can be <u>energy self-reliant</u>. Theoretically, you could supply all your energy from <u>household waste</u>.

Biomass and Fermentation

Mycoprotein is a very useful kind of <u>edible biomass</u>. The meat substitutes it is used to make tend to be lower in fat, so often healthier than meat itself. Some non-vege's even prefer it to meat 'cos of this.

Mycoprotein is made by fungi

1) <u>Mycoprotein</u> is protein from a fungus. It's used to make <u>meat substitutes</u> for <u>vegetarian</u> meals, for example <u>Quorn</u>™.

2) The fungus is grown in huge vessels called <u>fermenters</u>, using <u>glucose syrup</u> as food.

3) Microorganisms like fungi can <u>grow very quickly</u>... which is great if you're using them to make food.

4) They're also <u>easy to look after</u>. All that's needed is <u>something to grow them in</u>, <u>food</u>, <u>oxygen</u>, and the <u>right temperature</u>. So food can be produced whether the <u>climate is hot or cold</u>.

5) <u>Microorganisms</u> can use <u>waste products</u> from <u>agriculture</u> and <u>industry</u> as <u>food</u>.

6) This often makes using microorganisms <u>cheaper</u> than other methods.

Mycoprotein is grown in fermenters

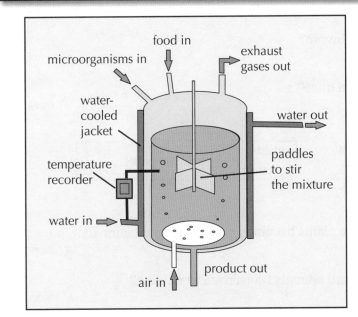

A fermenter is a big container full of <u>liquid</u> 'culture medium' in which microorganisms can <u>grow</u> and <u>reproduce</u>.

A typical example is shown in the diagram.

The microorganisms need the right conditions to <u>grow</u> and produce their <u>useful product</u>:

1) <u>Food</u> (e.g. carbohydrate, mineral ions, nitrates) is provided in the liquid culture medium.

2) Air is piped in to supply <u>oxygen</u> (if needed).

3) The medium needs to be kept at the right temperature and pH for optimum growth of the microorganisms. Fermenters can be cooled with a <u>water</u> jacket which cold water is pumped through.

4) <u>Sterile conditions</u> are needed to <u>prevent contamination</u>.

5) A <u>motorised stirrer</u> keeps the microorganisms from <u>sinking to the bottom</u>.

Learn the diagram and make sure you know what each bit is for

Microorganisms are really useful — as well making <u>biogas</u>, and producing <u>mycoprotein</u>, they're used to make <u>antibiotics</u>, AND we can genetically engineer them to make <u>human proteins</u> like insulin (see p.87).

Warm-Up and Exam Questions

Warm-Up Questions

1) What is a trophic level?
2) In most food chains, there are fewer carnivores than herbivores. Why?
3) Explain why all animals, even carnivores, depend on plants for their food.
4) What is biomass?
5) Give two examples of biofuels.

Exam Questions

1   Three pyramids of numbers are shown.
     Which is most likely to be:

     (a)   from a woodland?

     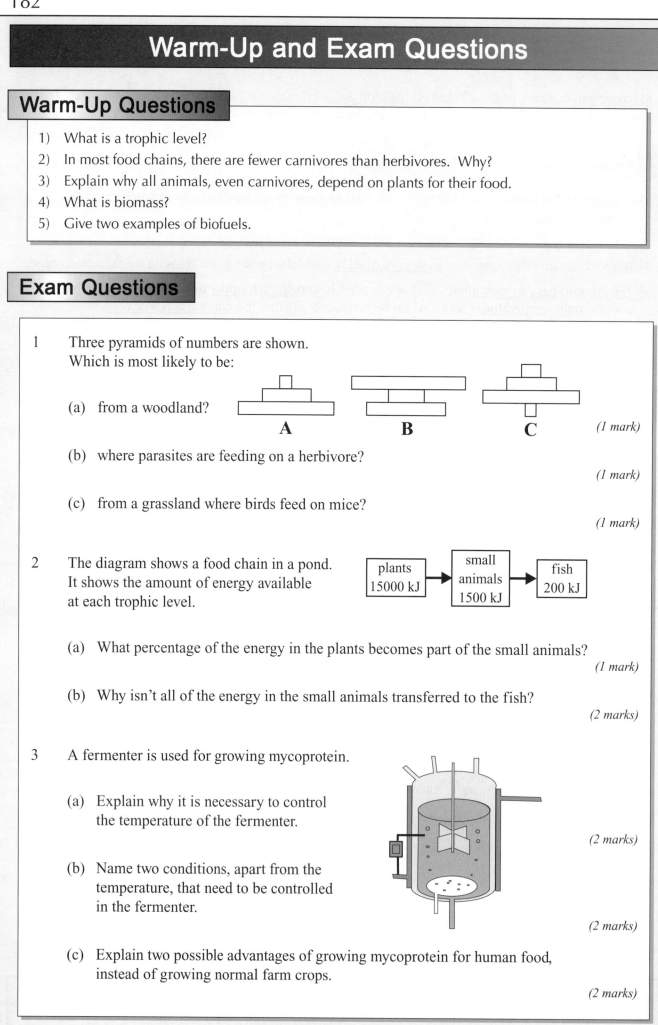

                                    A   **B**   **C**   *(1 mark)*

     (b)   where parasites are feeding on a herbivore?

                                                                                          (1 mark)

     (c)   from a grassland where birds feed on mice?

                                                                                          (1 mark)

2   The diagram shows a food chain in a pond.
     It shows the amount of energy available
     at each trophic level.

     plants 15000 kJ → small animals 1500 kJ → fish 200 kJ

     (a)   What percentage of the energy in the plants becomes part of the small animals?

                                                                                          (1 mark)

     (b)   Why isn't all of the energy in the small animals transferred to the fish?

                                                                                          (2 marks)

3   A fermenter is used for growing mycoprotein.

     (a)   Explain why it is necessary to control
           the temperature of the fermenter.

                                                                                          (2 marks)

     (b)   Name two conditions, apart from the
           temperature, that need to be controlled
           in the fermenter.

                                                                                          (2 marks)

     (c)   Explain two possible advantages of growing mycoprotein for human food,
           instead of growing normal farm crops.

                                                                                          (2 marks)

Managing Food Production

On page 179 you saw that a lot of energy tends to be <u>lost</u> from food chains. If you're producing food, you need to <u>limit</u> this as much as possible.

There are *four* main ways to *maximise food production*

The four main ways are:

1) increase the energy transfer,

2) reduce disease,

3) improve feeding/growing conditions,

4) control predators.

- If you <u>reduce</u> the number of <u>stages in the food chain</u>, you reduce the amount of energy lost. For a given area of land, you can produce <u>more food</u> for humans by growing <u>crops</u> than by grazing <u>animals</u>.

- Food production can also be made more efficient by <u>reducing the amount of energy</u> animals use, e.g. if you keep animals warm and still, they won't use as much energy and won't need to eat as much.

Fish farms reduce *energy loss*, *disease* and *predators*

Fish is an increasingly popular dish, but fish stocks are dwindling. '<u>Fish farms</u>' were set up to rear fish in a controlled way and increase their production. <u>Salmon farming</u> in Scotland is a good example:

1) The fish are kept in <u>cages</u> in a <u>sea loch</u>, to <u>stop them using as much energy</u> swimming about.

2) The cage also <u>protects</u> them from <u>predators</u> like birds and seals.

3) They're fed a <u>diet</u> of food pellets that's <u>carefully controlled</u> to <u>maximise</u> energy transfer and to avoid <u>pollution</u> to the loch.

4) Young fish are reared in <u>special tanks</u> to ensure as many survive as possible.

5) Fish kept in cages are more prone to <u>disease</u> and <u>parasites</u>. One pest is <u>sea lice</u>, which are normally killed off using <u>pesticides</u>.

To <u>avoid pollution</u> from chemical pesticides, <u>biological pest control</u> (see page 186) can be used instead, e.g. a small fish called a <u>wrasse</u> eats the lice off the backs of the salmon.

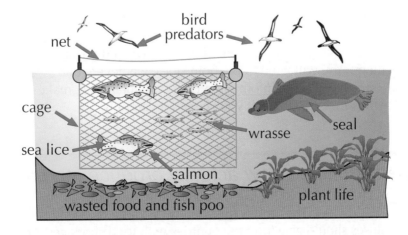

Section Nine — Plants and Energy Flow

Managing Food Production

Making food production more efficient has both disadvantages and advantages.
You need to be aware of <u>both sides</u> of the argument.

*Food production involves **compromises** and **conflict***

Improving the efficiency of food production is useful — it means
<u>cheaper food</u> for us, and <u>better standards of living</u> for farmers. But this
all comes at a <u>cost</u>.

Here are some examples of arguments <u>against</u> the <u>intensive farming
methods</u> used to increase the efficiency of food production:

1) Some people think that forcing animals to live in unnatural, overcrowded and
   uncomfortable conditions is <u>cruel</u>. There's a growing demand for <u>organic meat</u>,
   from animals which have <u>not</u> been intensively farmed.

2) The <u>crowded</u> conditions on factory farms create a favourable environment
   for the <u>spread of diseases</u>, like avian flu and foot-and-mouth disease.

3) To try to <u>prevent disease</u>, animals are given <u>antibiotics</u>. When the animals are eaten these
   can enter humans. This allows <u>microbes</u> that infect humans to develop <u>immunity</u> to those
   antibiotics — so the antibiotics become <u>less effective</u> as <u>human</u> medicines.

4) The environment where the animals are kept needs to be <u>carefully controlled</u>.
   The animals need to be kept <u>warm</u> to reduce the energy they lose as heat. This often
   means using power from <u>fossil fuels</u> — which wouldn't be used if the animals were
   grazing in their <u>natural</u> environment.

5) Our <u>fish stocks</u> are getting low. Yet a lot of fish is not eaten by humans but is instead
   fed to animals that are <u>intensively farmed</u> — these animals wouldn't usually eat fish.

In an exam, you might be asked to give an account of the <u>positive</u> and <u>negative</u>
aspects of food management. You will need to put <u>both sides</u>, whatever your
<u>personal opinion</u> is. If you're given some <u>information</u> on a particular case, make
sure you <u>use it</u> — they will want evidence that you've read it <u>carefully</u>.

Many developed countries now actually produce too much food

The world produces enough food to feed the Earth's population, but there are still millions of
<u>undernourished</u> people worldwide. The food is <u>not</u> equally distributed. Many people think that
countries with food surpluses should give food to countries with food shortages (or sell it cheaply).

Pesticides and Biological Control

Biological control (see next page) is growing <u>more popular</u>, as people get fed up with all the problems that are caused by <u>pesticides</u>.

Pesticides *disturb* food *chains*

1) <u>Pesticides</u> are sprayed onto crops to kill the creatures that <u>damage</u> them, but unfortunately they also kill lots of <u>harmless</u> (or even useful) animals such as bees and beetles.

2) This can cause a <u>shortage of food</u> for animals further up the food chain.

3) Pesticides also tend to be <u>toxic</u> to creatures that aren't pests and there's a danger of the poison <u>passing on</u> through the food chain to other animals. There's even a risk that they could harm <u>humans</u>.

Example — Otters and DDT

The dangers of a pesticide passing through a food chain are well illustrated by the case of <u>otters</u>, which were almost <u>wiped out</u> over much of crop-dominated southern England by a pesticide called <u>DDT</u> in the early 1960s.

The diagram below shows the <u>food chain</u> which ends with the <u>otter</u>. DDT can't be <u>excreted</u>, so it <u>accumulates</u> along the <u>food chain</u> and the <u>otter</u> ends up with <u>a lot</u> of the <u>DDT</u> collected by the other animals — enough to reach <u>toxic</u> levels.

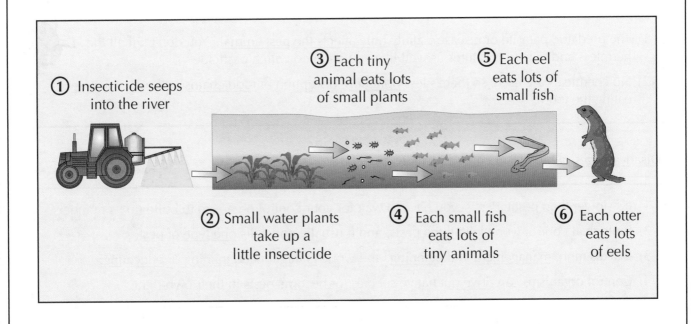

① Insecticide seeps into the river

② Small water plants take up a little insecticide

③ Each tiny animal eats lots of small plants

④ Each small fish eats lots of tiny animals

⑤ Each eel eats lots of small fish

⑥ Each otter eats lots of eels

DDT was banned in many countries, including the UK, in the 1970s

This benefited not just otters but many other creatures affected by DDT. But, as usual, there's a <u>conflict</u> — DDT was also the main <u>insecticide</u> used to fight disease-causing insects, like mosquitoes that spread malaria in many countries. So some people thought protecting <u>humans</u> should take priority.

Pesticides and Biological Control

Biological control means using <u>living things</u> instead of chemicals to control a pest.

You can use **biological control** instead of **pesticides**

There are various different types of biological control —
you could use a <u>predator</u>, a <u>parasite</u> or a <u>disease</u> to kill the pest.

For example:

1) <u>Aphids</u> are a pest because they eat <u>roses</u> and <u>vegetables</u>. <u>Ladybirds</u> are aphid <u>predators</u>, so people release them into their fields and gardens to keep aphid numbers down.

2) Certain types of <u>wasps</u> and <u>flies</u> produce <u>larvae</u> which develop on (or in, yuck) a <u>host insect</u>. This eventually <u>kills</u> the insect host. Lots of insect pests have <u>parasites</u> like this.

3) <u>Myxomatosis</u> is a <u>disease</u> which kills <u>rabbits</u>. The <u>myxoma virus</u> was released in <u>Australia</u> as a biological control when the rabbit population there grew out of control and ruined crops.

There are **advantages** and **disadvantages** of **biological control**

<u>Advantages</u> of biological control include:

1) The predator, parasite or disease usually <u>only affects the pest animal</u>. You don't kill all the harmless and helpful creatures as well like you often do with a pesticide.

2) No chemicals are used, so there's less <u>pollution</u>, disruption of <u>food chains</u> and risk to <u>people</u> eating the food.

<u>Disadvantages</u> of biological control include:

1) It's <u>slower</u> than pesticides — you have to wait for your control organism to build up its numbers.

2) Biological control won't kill <u>all</u> the pests, and it usually only kills <u>one type</u> of pest.

3) It takes more <u>management</u> and <u>planning</u>, and workers might need <u>training</u> or <u>educating</u>.

4) Control organisms can <u>drive out</u> native species, or become <u>pests</u> in their own right.

Remember that <u>removing</u> an organism from a food web, whether you use <u>biological control</u> or <u>pesticides</u>, can affect <u>all</u> the other organisms too. For example, if you remove a pest insect, you're removing a source of <u>food</u> from all the organisms that normally eat it. These might <u>die out</u>, and another insect that they normally feed on could <u>breed out of control</u> and become a pest instead. You have to be very careful.

Alternatives to Intensive Farming

Intensive farming methods are still used a lot. But people are also using other methods <u>more and more</u>.

Hydroponics *is where plants are grown* **without soil**

Most commercially grown <u>tomatoes</u> and <u>cucumbers</u> are grown in <u>nutrient solutions</u> (water and fertilisers) instead of in soil — this is called <u>hydroponics</u>.

There are <u>advantages</u> and <u>disadvantages</u> of using hydroponics instead of growing crops in soil:

Advantages

1) Hydroponics take up <u>less space</u> than conventional farming, so <u>less land</u> is required.

2) There is <u>no soil preparation</u> (e.g. ploughing) or <u>weeding</u> required, and <u>no herbicides</u> need to be used.

3) Plants can be grown anywhere, even in areas with <u>poor soil</u>.

4) Many <u>pest species</u> live in soil, so these are avoided without needing to use <u>pesticides</u>.

5) <u>Mineral levels</u> can be controlled more <u>accurately</u> and tailored exactly to the needs of the plant being grown, and the fertilisers can't be washed away to pollute rivers.

Disadvantages

1) It can be <u>expensive</u> to set up and run.

2) Specially formulated <u>soluble nutrients</u> have to be used.

3) Special <u>skills</u> are needed to use hydroponics — staff need to be properly <u>trained</u>.

4) There are no <u>roots</u> to <u>anchor</u> the plants so they usually need <u>extra support</u>.

Of course, hydroponics aren't the <u>only</u> alternative to intensive farming methods — in fact, rather than going all modern you can really get <u>back to basics</u> instead...

Organic farming *is still perfectly* **viable**

Modern intensive farming produces lots of <u>food</u> and we all appreciate it on the supermarket shelves. But traditional <u>organic farming</u> methods do still work (amazingly!), and they have their <u>benefits</u> too.

You need to know some organic farming <u>techniques</u> and there are several examples to learn on the next page.

Alternatives to Intensive Farming

Organic farmers <u>avoid</u> using chemicals, and their animals have to be reasonably <u>well-treated</u> too.

Learn these *five examples* of *organic farming techniques*

Organic farmers have to use <u>natural alternatives</u> to the chemical <u>pesticides</u>, <u>herbicides</u> and <u>fertilisers</u> used by intensive farmers.

1) <u>Use of organic fertilisers</u> (i.e. animal manure and compost).
   This <u>recycles</u> the nutrients left in plant and animal waste. It <u>doesn't</u> <u>work as well</u> as artificial fertilisers do, but it is better for the <u>environment</u>.

2) <u>Crop rotation</u>
   This means growing a cycle of <u>different crops</u> in a field each year. It stops the <u>pests</u> and <u>diseases</u> of one crop building up, and helps prevent <u>nutrients</u> running out (as each crop has slightly <u>different needs</u>). Most crop rotations include a <u>legume plant</u> like peas or beans, as they help put <u>nitrates</u> back into the soil (see page 174).

3) <u>Weeding</u>
   This means <u>physically removing</u> the weeds, rather than just spraying them with a <u>herbicide</u>. Obviously it's a lot more <u>labour-intensive</u>, but there are no nasty <u>chemicals</u> involved.

4) <u>Varying seed planting times</u>
   Sowing seeds later or earlier than usual in the season can <u>avoid</u> the <u>major pests</u> for that crop. This means the farmer <u>won't</u> need to use <u>pesticides</u>.

5) <u>Biological control</u> — this is covered on page 186.

As usual, there are both *pros* and *cons* of *organic farming*

You also need to be able to discuss the <u>advantages</u> and <u>disadvantages</u> of organic farming. Always try to give a <u>balanced</u> point of view, unless you're specifically asked to argue one way or another. You can always include your <u>own opinion</u> in a conclusion at the end.

Here are a few points you could mention:

1) Organic farming takes up <u>more space</u> than intensive farming — so more land has to be <u>farmland</u>, rather than being set aside for wildlife or for other uses.

2) It's more <u>labour-intensive</u>. This provides <u>more jobs</u>, but it also makes the food more <u>expensive</u>.

3) You can't grow <u>as much</u> food without artificial fertilisers — and also, some will always be lost to pests and weeds. But on the other hand, Europe <u>over-produces</u> food these days anyway.

4) Organic farming uses fewer <u>chemicals</u>, so there's less risk of toxic chemicals remaining on food.

5) It's better for the <u>environment</u>. There's less chance of <u>polluting rivers</u> with fertiliser. Organic farmers also avoid using <u>pesticides</u>, so don't disrupt food chains and harm wildlife.

6) For a farm to be classed as organic, it will usually have to follow guidelines on the <u>ethical treatment of animals</u>. This means <u>no</u> battery farming.

Warm-Up and Exam Questions

There's only one way to do well in the Exam — learn the facts and then practise lots of exam questions to see what it'll be like on the big day. We couldn't have made that easier for you — so do it.

Warm-Up Questions

1) Why are insecticides like DDT potentially harmful to predators like falcons and otters?
2) What is hydroponics?
3) Explain why crop rotation is a useful organic farming technique.
4) Organic produce tends to be a bit more expensive. Suggest why.

Exam Questions

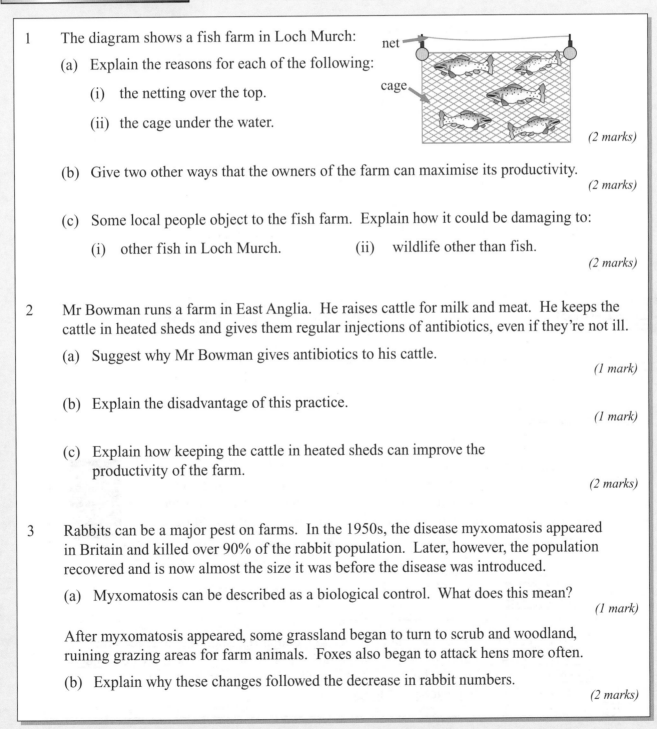

1   The diagram shows a fish farm in Loch Murch:

net

cage

(a) Explain the reasons for each of the following:

(i)   the netting over the top.

(ii)   the cage under the water.

(2 marks)

(b) Give two other ways that the owners of the farm can maximise its productivity.

(2 marks)

(c) Some local people object to the fish farm. Explain how it could be damaging to:

(i)   other fish in Loch Murch.   (ii)   wildlife other than fish.

(2 marks)

2   Mr Bowman runs a farm in East Anglia. He raises cattle for milk and meat. He keeps the cattle in heated sheds and gives them regular injections of antibiotics, even if they're not ill.

(a) Suggest why Mr Bowman gives antibiotics to his cattle.

(1 mark)

(b) Explain the disadvantage of this practice.

(1 mark)

(c) Explain how keeping the cattle in heated sheds can improve the productivity of the farm.

(2 marks)

3   Rabbits can be a major pest on farms. In the 1950s, the disease myxomatosis appeared in Britain and killed over 90% of the rabbit population. Later, however, the population recovered and is now almost the size it was before the disease was introduced.

(a) Myxomatosis can be described as a biological control. What does this mean?

(1 mark)

After myxomatosis appeared, some grassland began to turn to scrub and woodland, ruining grazing areas for farm animals. Foxes also began to attack hens more often.

(b) Explain why these changes followed the decrease in rabbit numbers.

(2 marks)

Recycling Nutrients

There is a limited amount of each of the materials that make up living things on planet Earth.

Nutrients are constantly recycled

1) Living things are made of materials they take from the world around them.

2) Plants take elements like carbon, oxygen, hydrogen and nitrogen from the soil or the air. They turn these elements into the complex compounds (carbohydrates, proteins and fats) that make up living organisms, and these then pass through the food chain.

3) These elements are returned to the environment in waste products produced by the organisms, or when the organisms die.

4) The materials decay because they're broken down (digested) by microorganisms — that's how the elements get put back into the soil.

5) Microorganisms work best in warm, moist conditions. Some also need oxygen.

6) All the important elements are thus recycled — they return to the soil, ready to be used by new plants and put back into the food chain again.

Detritivores and saprophytes help to recycle nutrients

Detritivores and saprophytes are both types of organism that are important in decay. They're grouped into those two types depending on how they feed.

Detritivores

Detritivores include earthworms, maggots and woodlice. They feed on dead and decaying material (detritus). As these detritivores feed on the decaying material, they break it up into smaller bits. This gives a bigger surface area for smaller decomposers to work on and so speeds up decay.

Saprophytes

Saprophytes feed on decaying material by extracellular digestion, i.e. they feed by secreting digestive enzymes onto the material outside their cells. The enzymes break down the material into smaller bits which can then be absorbed by the saprophyte. Most saprophytes are bacteria and fungi.

Recycling Nutrients

Carbon is constantly moving between the atmosphere, the soil and living things in the carbon cycle.

The *carbon cycle* shows how *carbon* is *recycled*

Carbon is an important element in the materials that living things are made from.
It's constantly recycled:

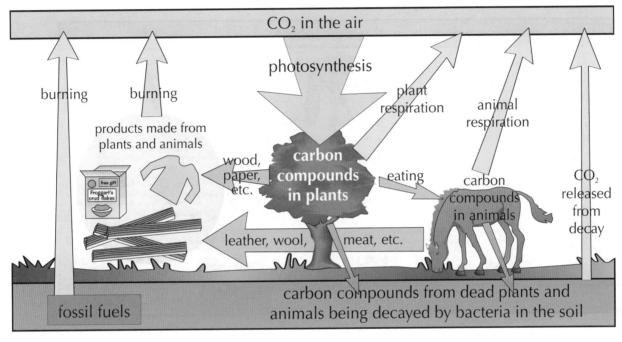

CO$_2$ in the air

photosynthesis

burning   burning   plant respiration   animal respiration

products made from plants and animals

free gift
Froggatt's crud flakes

wood, paper, etc.   carbon compounds in plants   eating   carbon compounds in animals   CO$_2$ released from decay

leather, wool,   meat, etc.

fossil fuels

carbon compounds from dead plants and animals being decayed by bacteria in the soil

Fossil fuels are made of decayed plant and animal matter.

This diagram isn't half as bad as it looks. Learn these important points:

1) There's only one arrow going down. The whole thing is 'powered' by photosynthesis. Green plants use the carbon from CO$_2$ in the air to make carbohydrates, fats and proteins.

2) Both plant and animal respiration while the organisms are alive releases CO$_2$ back into the air.

3) Dead plants and animals can go one of three ways:

   • be eaten
   • be decayed by microorganisms
   • be turned into useful products by humans.

4) Eating transfers some of the fats, proteins and carbohydrates to new fats, proteins and carbohydrates in the animals doing the eating.

5) Plant and animal products either decay or are burned (combustion) and CO$_2$ is released.

Some carbon cycles look a bit different, but the basics are the same

Carbon is a very important element for living things — it's the basis for all the organic molecules.

Recycling Nutrients

Nitrogen, just like carbon, is constantly being recycled. So the nitrogen in your proteins might once have been in the air. And before that it might have been in a plant.

Nitrogen is also recycled in the nitrogen cycle

Nitrogen is needed by living things to make proteins. Enzymes are proteins, and they're used to control all of an organism's reactions. So getting enough nitrogen is pretty important.

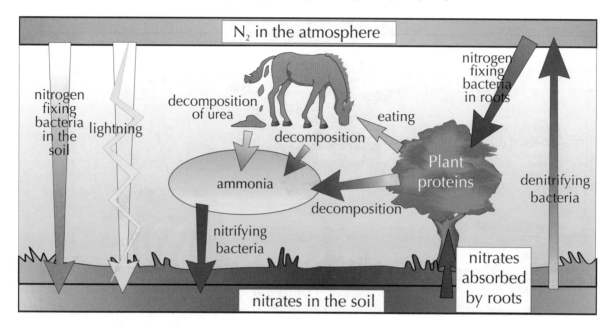

1) The atmosphere contains about 78% nitrogen gas, N_2. It's very unreactive and so it can't be used directly by plants or animals.

2) Plants get their nitrogen from the soil, so nitrogen in the air has to be turned into nitrogen compounds before plants can use it. Animals can only get proteins by eating plants (or each other).

3) Decomposers break down proteins in rotting plants and animals, and urea in animal waste, into ammonia. This can then be turned into nitrates in the soil, ready for plants to use (see the next page). So the nitrogen in these organisms is recycled.

4) Nitrogen fixation is the process of turning nitrogen gas from the air into nitrogen compounds in the soil which plants can use. There are two main ways that this happens:

   a) Lightning — there's so much energy in a bolt of lightning that it's enough to make nitrogen react with oxygen in the air to give nitrates.

   b) Nitrogen-fixing bacteria in roots and soil (see next page).

Recycling Nutrients

Microorganisms are vital in <u>any</u> nutrient cycle, and in the <u>nitrogen cycle</u> particularly.

Bacteria play a big part in the nitrogen cycle

There are <u>four</u> different types of <u>bacteria</u> involved in the nitrogen cycle.
You need to know their names and what each one does:

1) <u>DECOMPOSERS</u> —

   decompose <u>proteins</u> and <u>urea</u> and turn them into <u>ammonia</u>.

2) <u>NITRIFYING BACTERIA</u> —

   turn <u>ammonia</u> in decaying matter into <u>nitrates</u> that plants can use.

3) <u>NITROGEN-FIXING BACTERIA</u> —

   turn <u>atmospheric N_2</u> into <u>nitrogen compounds</u> that plants can use.

Leguminous plants like clover have nitrogen-fixing bacteria in root nodules.

4) <u>DENITRIFYING BACTERIA</u> —

   turn <u>nitrates</u> back into <u>N_2 gas</u>. This is of no benefit to living organisms.

Some <u>nitrogen-fixing bacteria</u> live in the <u>soil</u>. Others live in <u>nodules</u> on the roots of <u>legume plants</u> (like beans or clover). This is why legume plants are so good at putting nitrogen <u>back into the soil</u>. The plants have a <u>mutualistic relationship</u> with the bacteria — the bacteria get <u>food</u> (sugars) from the plant, and the plant gets <u>nitrogen compounds</u> from the bacteria to make into <u>proteins</u>.

A biosphere could be used to colonise Mars

1) Scientists have been able to create <u>artificial biospheres</u> — <u>sealed, self-contained environments</u> that aim to mimic the original biosphere — planet Earth. Everything in a biosphere has to be kept in <u>balance</u>, e.g. CO_2, O_2 and food. Scientists were able to live in an artificial biosphere in <u>Arizona</u> for two years, until the balance of <u>gases</u> in the biosphere was disrupted and oxygen levels fell.

2) <u>Mars</u> has a very <u>different environment</u> from Earth, so it's unlikely that organisms from Earth could survive there. However, it's been suggested that one way humans could survive on Mars is if they set up an <u>artificial biosphere</u> there — containing similar conditions to those found on Earth.

Colonies on Mars are still a very long way off

Firstly, nobody's ever even <u>landed</u> on Mars yet. And things would have to work a lot better than in Arizona if they did. It might seem a bit odd to put artificial biospheres with this stuff about cycles, but then that's what keeps any biosphere going — the ability to keep nutrients and gases in a constant, balanced <u>cycle</u>.

Warm-Up and Exam Questions

Warm-Up Questions

1) Explain what detritivores and saprophytes are.
2) Name three processes that release carbon dioxide into the atmosphere.
3) In what chemical form do plants usually absorb their nitrogen?
4) What chemical compounds containing nitrogen are present in animals and plants?

Exam Questions

1   The diagram shows the carbon cycle.

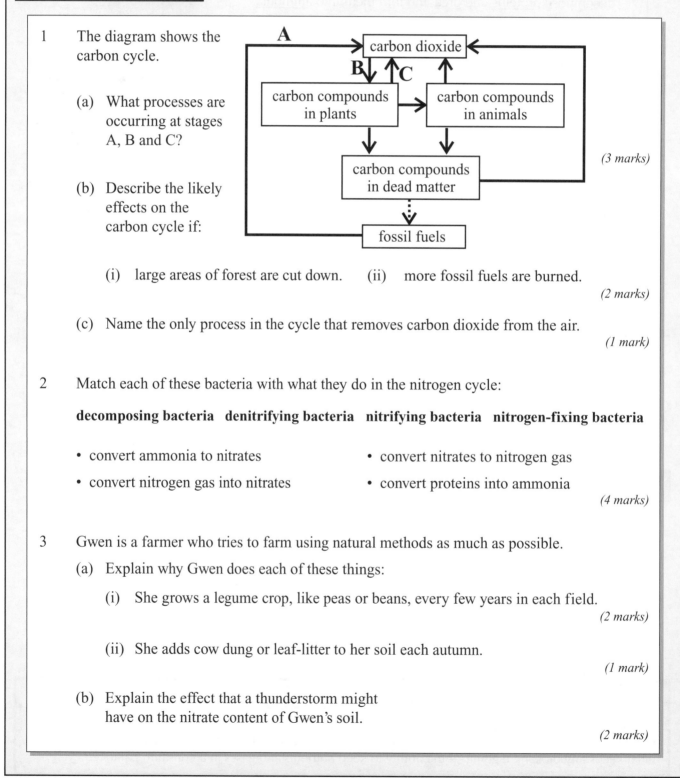

   (a)   What processes are occurring at stages A, B and C?

(3 marks)

   (b)   Describe the likely effects on the carbon cycle if:

      (i)   large areas of forest are cut down.   (ii)   more fossil fuels are burned.

(2 marks)

   (c)   Name the only process in the cycle that removes carbon dioxide from the air.

(1 mark)

2   Match each of these bacteria with what they do in the nitrogen cycle:

   decomposing bacteria   denitrifying bacteria   nitrifying bacteria   nitrogen-fixing bacteria

   • convert ammonia to nitrates   • convert nitrates to nitrogen gas

   • convert nitrogen gas into nitrates   • convert proteins into ammonia

(4 marks)

3   Gwen is a farmer who tries to farm using natural methods as much as possible.

   (a)   Explain why Gwen does each of these things:

      (i)   She grows a legume crop, like peas or beans, every few years in each field.

(2 marks)

      (ii)   She adds cow dung or leaf-litter to her soil each autumn.

(1 mark)

   (b)   Explain the effect that a thunderstorm might have on the nitrate content of Gwen's soil.

(2 marks)

Revision Summary for Section Nine

Here goes, folks — another beautiful page of revision questions to keep you at your desk studying hard until your parents have gone out and you can finally nip downstairs to watch TV. Think twice though before you reach for that remote control. These questions are actually pretty good — certainly more entertaining than 'Train Your Husband Like He's a Dog' or 'Celebrities Dance Around'. Question 14 is almost as good as an episode of 'Supernanny'. Question 4 is the corker though — like a reunion episode of 'Friends' but a lot funnier. Give the questions a go. Oh go on.

1) Write down the equation for photosynthesis.

2) Write down five ways that plants can use the glucose produced by photosynthesis.

3)* The graph shows how the rate of plant growth is affected by increasing the level of carbon dioxide. Look at the graph and answer the two questions below.

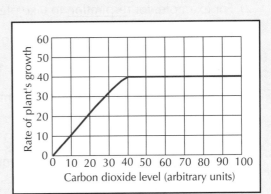

   a) At what level of carbon dioxide is the plant's growth limited by another factor?

   b) Suggest two possible limiting factors on the plant's growth above this level.

4) What happens to plant enzymes if the temperature is raised above 45 °C?

5) Why does carbon dioxide tend to move into leaves when they're photosynthesising?

6) How does being broad and thin help a leaf to photosynthesise?

7) Give three ways that the transpiration stream benefits a plant.

8) How is the transpiration rate affected by:

   a) increased temperature,   b) increased air humidity?

9) Stomata close automatically when a plant is short of water. How does this benefit the plant?

10) What is turgor pressure?

11) How are xylem vessels adapted to carry out their function?

12) Name the three main minerals plants need for healthy growth.

13) How can you tell by looking at a plant that it isn't getting enough phosphates?

14) What is active transport? Why is it used in the roots of a plant?

15) Explain why number pyramids are not always pyramid-shaped.

16) What is the source of all the energy in a typical food chain?

17) Why is it unusual to find a food chain with more than five trophic levels?

18) Give three reasons why developing biofuels is a good idea.

19) What is mycoprotein used for?

20) Give the four main ways in which it is possible to maximise food production.

21) Explain how fish farms reduce the following:

    a) energy loss,   b) disease,   c) threat of predators.

22) Give two advantages and two disadvantages of biological pest control.

23) What is meant by the term hydroponics?

24) Give an example of a detritivore.

25) How does carbon enter the carbon cycle from the air?

26) What important role do nitrogen-fixing bacteria play in the nitrogen cycle?

* Answers on page 293.

SECTION NINE — PLANTS AND ENERGY FLOW

Solute Exchange — Active Transport

The processes that keep organisms alive won't happen without the right <u>raw materials</u>. And the raw materials have to get to the right <u>places</u>.

Substances move by *diffusion*, *osmosis* and *active transport*

1) Life processes need <u>gases or other dissolved substances</u> before they can happen.

2) For example, for <u>respiration</u> to take place, glucose and oxygen both have to get inside cells.

3) <u>Waste substances</u> also need to move out of the cells so that the organism can get rid of them.

4) These substances move to where they need to be by <u>diffusion</u>, <u>osmosis</u> and <u>active transport</u>.

5) <u>Diffusion</u> is where particles move from an area of <u>high concentration</u> to an area of <u>low concentration</u> — see page 117.

6) <u>Osmosis</u> is similar, but it only refers to <u>water</u>. The water moves across a <u>partially permeable membrane</u> (e.g. a cell membrane) from an area of <u>high water concentration</u> to an area of <u>low water concentration</u> — see page 120.

7) Diffusion and osmosis both involve stuff moving from an area where there's a <u>high concentration</u> of it, to an area where there's a <u>lower concentration</u> of it. But sometimes substances need to move in the <u>other direction</u> — which is where <u>active transport</u> comes in...

We need *active transport* to stop us starving

<u>Active transport</u> is used in the digestive system when there is a <u>low concentration</u> of nutrients in the <u>gut</u>, but a <u>high concentration</u> of nutrients in the <u>blood</u>.

1) If there's a <u>higher concentration</u> of glucose and amino acids in the gut they <u>diffuse naturally</u> into the blood.

2) <u>BUT</u> — sometimes there's a <u>lower concentration</u> of nutrients in the gut than there is in the blood.

3) This means that the <u>concentration gradient</u> is the wrong way. The food molecules should go <u>the other way</u> if they followed the rules of diffusion.

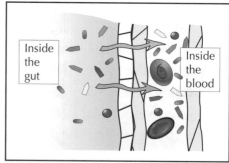

4) The answer is that a conveniently mysterious process called '<u>active transport</u>' is responsible.

5) Active transport allows nutrients to be taken into the blood, despite the fact that the <u>concentration gradient</u> is the wrong way. This is essential to stop us starving. But active transport needs <u>ENERGY</u> from <u>respiration</u> to make it work.

Plants take in minerals using *active transport*

The concentration of minerals is usually <u>higher</u> in the <u>root hair</u> cell of the plant than in the <u>soil</u> around it. So normal diffusion <u>doesn't</u> explain how minerals are taken up into the root hair cell. The same process used in the gut is used here... active transport.

The Respiratory System

You need to get <u>oxygen</u> from the air into your bloodstream so that it can get to your cells for respiration. You also need to get rid of <u>carbon dioxide</u> in your blood. This all happens inside the <u>lungs</u>. Breathing is how that air gets in and out of your lungs, so it's definitely a useful skill to have.

The lungs are in the *thorax*

1) The <u>thorax</u> is the top part of your 'body'. It's separated from the lower part by the <u>diaphragm</u>.

2) The lungs are like big pink <u>sponges</u> and are protected by the <u>ribcage</u>.

3) The air that you breathe in goes through the <u>trachea</u>. This splits into two tubes called '<u>bronchi</u>' (each one is 'a bronchus'), one going to each lung.

4) The bronchi split into progressively smaller tubes called <u>bronchioles</u>.

5) The bronchioles finally end at small bags called <u>alveoli</u> where the gas exchange takes place.

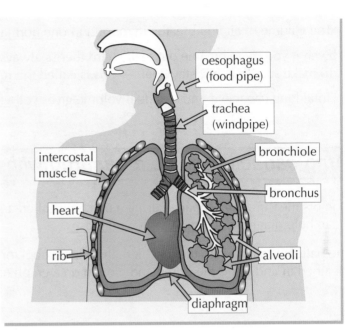

Breathing in...

1) <u>Intercostal muscles</u> and <u>diaphragm</u> contract.
2) Thorax volume <u>increases</u>.
3) This decreases the pressure, drawing air <u>in</u>.

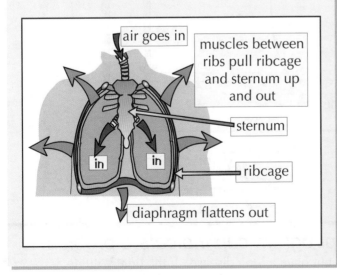

...and breathing out

1) <u>Intercostal muscles</u> and <u>diaphragm</u> relax.
2) Thorax volume <u>decreases</u>.
3) Air is forced <u>out</u>.

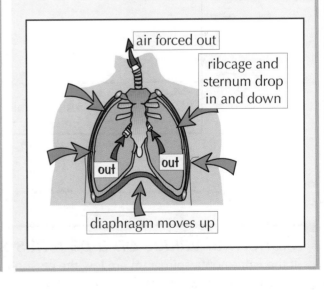

Lung Capacity and Disease

If you've ever blown into a white tube at the doctor's the chances are you were having your <u>lung capacity</u> measured — this gives the doctor an idea of how healthy your lungs are.

Lung capacity — the *total volume of air* in your lungs

1) The <u>total volume of air</u> you can fit in your lungs is your <u>total lung capacity</u> (usually about 6 litres).

2) The volume of air you breathe in (or out) in <u>one normal breath</u> is called your <u>tidal volume</u>.

3) Even if you try to breathe out really hard there's always <u>some air left</u> (just over a litre) in your lungs to make sure that they <u>stay open</u> — this is called the <u>residual volume</u>.

4) Total lung capacity minus residual volume gives you <u>vital capacity</u> — the amount of usable air.

Lung capacity can be *measured* with a *spirometer*

Doctors measure lung capacity using a machine called a <u>spirometer</u> — it can help <u>diagnose</u> and <u>monitor lung diseases</u>.

The patient breathes into the machine (through a tube) for a few minutes, and the volume of air that is breathed in and out is measured and plotted on a graph (called a <u>spirogram</u>) — like this one...

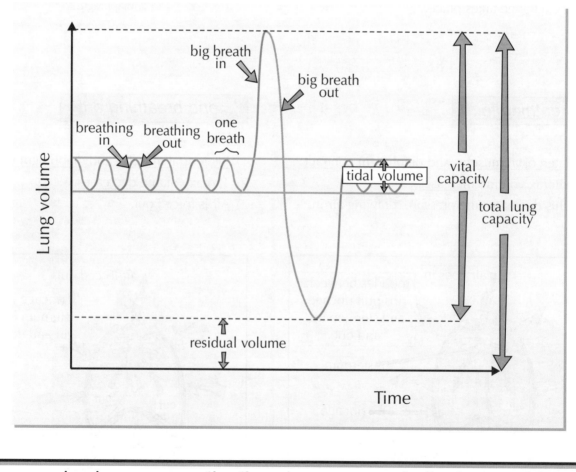

Abnormal values on a patient's spirogram can indicate a problem

If the values on a spirogram are <u>low</u> the person might have a lung disease. If the <u>tidal volume</u> <u>increases</u> (i.e. they're breathing more deeply), then they're probably exercising. A spirogram can also be used to calculate <u>breathing rate</u> (by counting the number of breaths in a minute). Simple really.

Lung Capacity and Disease

The lungs have various <u>defences</u> to help protect them from infection.
But unfortunately they can't prevent lung diseases altogether.

Cilia and mucus protect the lungs

1) The <u>respiratory tract</u> (trachea and bronchi) is lined with <u>mucus</u> and <u>cilia</u> (little hairs) which catch <u>dust</u> and <u>microbes</u> before they reach the lungs.

2) The cilia <u>beat</u>, pushing microbe-filled mucus out of the lungs as phlegm.

3) Sometimes the microbes get past the body's defences and cause infection. The lungs are particularly <u>prone</u> to <u>infections</u> because they're a <u>dead end</u> — microbes can't easily be flushed out.

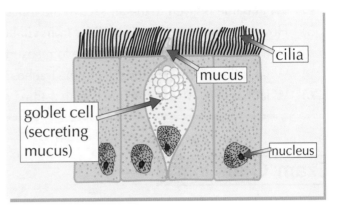

Lung disease can be caused by lots of things

1) Industrial materials

e.g. <u>asbestos</u>. Asbestos can cause cancers, as well as a disease called <u>asbestosis</u> (where lung tissue is scarred, causing breathlessness and even death). Asbestos used to be used as an insulator in roofs, floors, furnaces, etc. Its use is more tightly controlled now.

2) Genetic causes

e.g. <u>cystic fibrosis</u> is an inherited lung condition. A single defective gene causes the lungs to produce a really thick, sticky <u>mucus</u> that clogs up the lungs — this makes breathing difficult and can lead to life-threatening infections.

3) Lifestyle causes

e.g. <u>smoking</u> can cause <u>lung cancer</u> (see p.45). This is where <u>cells</u> divide <u>out of control</u>, forming a <u>tumour</u>. The abnormal cells can get into the blood and cause tumours elsewhere.

4) Asthma

Asthma affects around 1 in 12 adults in the UK. Asthmatics' lungs are <u>overly sensitive</u> to certain things (e.g. pet hair, pollen, dust, smoke...). When they encounter these things the <u>muscles</u> around the airways <u>constrict</u>, narrowing the airways and making it hard to breathe (an <u>asthma attack</u>).

Symptoms of an attack are <u>shortness of breath</u>, <u>coughing</u>, <u>wheezing</u> and a <u>tight chest</u>. When symptoms appear a muscle relaxant drug is inhaled (from an <u>inhaler</u>) to open up the airways. Some people also take drugs to stop attacks happening in the first place (but there's <u>no actual cure</u>.)

Warm-Up and Exam Questions

The hardest bit of those few pages was probably the stuff about lung capacity — there are a few new terms there that you really need to know. So here's some practice for you to help it sink in.

Warm-Up Questions

1) Give two differences between active transport and diffusion.
2) What name is given to the air sacs in the lungs where gas exchange happens?
3) How does total lung capacity differ from vital capacity?
4) Name the machine that doctors use to measure lung capacity.
5) What is the function of the cilia in the trachea?
6) What happens when someone has an asthma attack?

Exam Questions

1   The graph shows changes in the volume of air in a person's lungs over time.

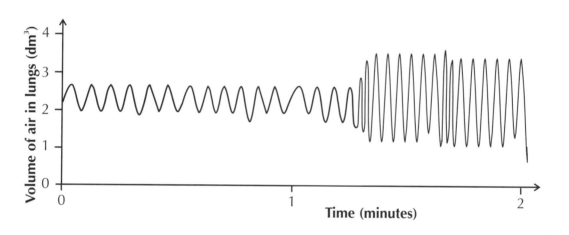

(a) Using a bracket (}) and the letter '**T**', mark the tidal volume on the diagram.

(1 mark)

(b) What is this person's breathing rate during the first minute?

(1 mark)

(c) (i)   What changes occur in this person's breathing over the next minute?

(2 marks)

(ii) Suggest a reason for these changes.

(1 mark)

2   Describe the changes that take place in the thorax when breathing air **into** the lungs. You should use the following words in your description:

diaphragm   **intercostal muscles**   **pressure**   **volume**

(4 marks)

The Circulatory System

There wouldn't be much point having lungs if you couldn't deliver the oxygen to where it needed to be. This is what the circulatory system is for — to get food and oxygen to every cell in the body.

The DOUBLE circulatory system, actually

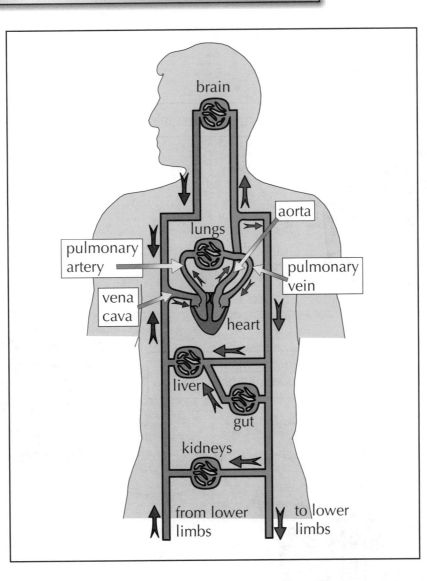

1) The heart is actually two pumps. The right side pumps deoxygenated blood to the lungs to collect oxygen and remove carbon dioxide. Then the left side pumps this oxygenated blood around the body.

2) Arteries carry blood away from the heart at high pressure.

3) Normally, arteries carry oxygenated blood and veins carry deoxygenated blood. The pulmonary artery and pulmonary vein are the big exceptions to this rule (see diagram).

4) The arteries eventually split off into thousands of tiny capillaries which take blood to every cell in the body.

5) The veins then collect the "used" blood and carry it back to the heart at low pressure to be pumped round again.

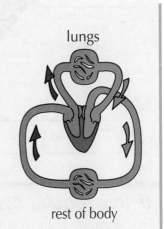

The Circulatory System

The heart doesn't just sit there, of course. It has to <u>beat</u> and push the blood around the body. To understand how the heart beats, you need to learn the <u>cardiac cycle</u>.

The **cardiac cycle** is how the **heart contracts**

The sequence of events in <u>one complete heartbeat</u> is called the <u>cardiac cycle</u>.

Learn the main stages shown below:

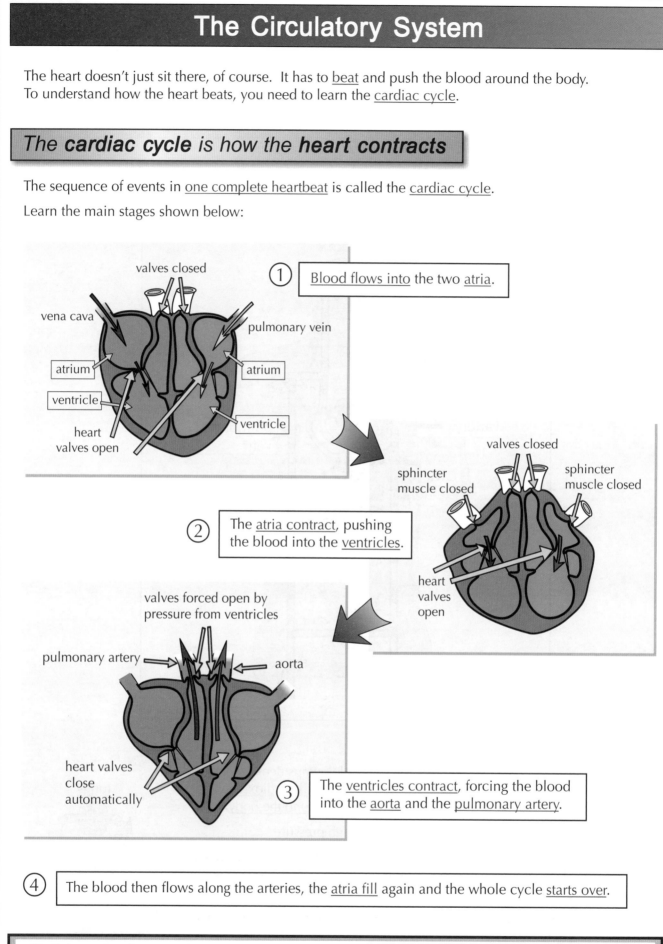

① <u>Blood flows into</u> the two <u>atria</u>.

② The <u>atria contract</u>, pushing the blood into the <u>ventricles</u>.

③ The <u>ventricles contract</u>, forcing the blood into the <u>aorta</u> and the <u>pulmonary artery</u>.

④ The blood then flows along the arteries, the <u>atria fill</u> again and the whole cycle <u>starts over</u>.

If this regular cycle is interrupted, it could lead to a heart attack

That diagram on the previous page only shows the <u>basic layout</u>. There's really zillions of blood vessels. If you laid all your arteries, capillaries and veins end to end, they'd go around the world about three times. These vessels vary from hose-pipe width arteries to capillaries that are too small to see.

The Heart and Heart Disease

The heart is pretty simple — just a <u>pump</u> that pushes blood around the body.
However, if something goes <u>wrong</u> the consequences can be dire.

The *heart* has a *pacemaker*

1) There are cells in the heart that <u>control how fast</u> the heartbeats — they act as a <u>pacemaker</u>.
They're found in an cluster called the <u>sino-atrial node</u> (SAN). These cells produce a small <u>electric current</u>, which spreads to the surrounding muscle cells, causing them to <u>contract</u>.

2) Another cluster of cells called the <u>atrio-ventricular node</u> (AVN) help to control how the heart beats.

3) In one complete heartbeat the SAN produces an electric current <u>first</u>, which spreads to the atria (making them contract). The current then passes through the AVN, which delays it a bit, and causes the ventricles to contract. This process ensures that the <u>atria always contract before the ventricles</u>.

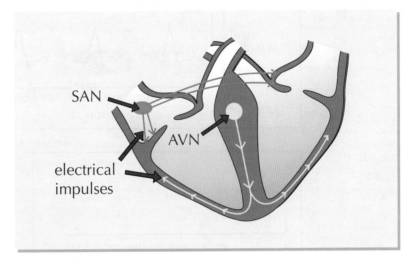

4) An <u>artificial pacemaker</u> can be used to control the heartbeat if the pacemaker doesn't work properly. It's a little device that's implanted under the skin and has a wire going to the heart. It produces an electric current.

Lifestyle affects the *health* of the *heart*

<u>Heart disease</u> is when the arteries that supply blood to the muscle of the heart get <u>blocked</u> by fatty deposits. This often results in a <u>heart attack</u>. There are several common lifestyle '<u>risk factors</u>' for heart disease...

1) <u>Unhealthy diet</u>

2) <u>Drinking alcohol</u>

3) <u>Smoking</u>

4) <u>Stress</u>

5) <u>Drugs</u>

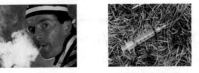

The Heart and Heart Disease

ECGs and echocardiograms measure the heart function

Doctors can measure how well the heart is working (<u>heart function</u>) in two main ways:

1) Electrocardiogram (ECG)

These measure the <u>electrical activity</u> of the heart. They can show:

- <u>heart attacks</u> — e.g. if you're having a heart attack, or are about to have one,
- <u>irregular heartbeats</u> and <u>general health</u> of the heart.

This is what a <u>healthy</u> person's ECG looks like...

...and here are some <u>unhealthy</u> ones.

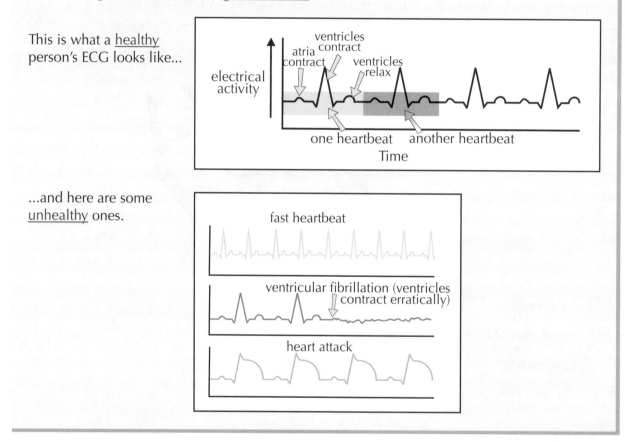

2) Echocardiogram

This is an <u>ultrasound scan</u> of the heart, which can show:

- <u>enlarged heart</u> — this could indicate <u>heart failure</u>,
- <u>decreased pumping ability</u> — this could indicate a disease called <u>cardiomyopathy</u>,
- <u>valve function</u> — torn, infected or scarred heart valves can cause problems.

Making sure of the diagnosis helps to ensure the right treatment

In the exam you might be asked to <u>interpret</u> an <u>ECG</u> — they can look scary but they're not too difficult. If a peak is <u>missing</u>, then that part of the heart isn't contracting. If the peaks are <u>close together</u>, the heart's beating faster. But if everything is going haywire, then it could be a heart attack or fibrillation.

Blood

If you get a cut, you don't want all your blood to drain away — this is why <u>clotting</u> is so handy.

Sometimes *blood doesn't clot* properly

1) When you're injured, your blood <u>clots</u> to <u>prevent too much bleeding</u>. <u>Platelets</u> clump together to 'plug' the damaged area. In a clot, platelets are held together by a mesh of a protein called <u>fibrin</u> (though this process also needs other proteins called <u>clotting factors</u> to work properly).

<u>PLATELETS</u>

These are small fragments of cells that help blood to clot.

---

2) Some substances in <u>food</u> and <u>drink</u> can have an effect on the way the blood clots:

- <u>Vitamin K</u> — this is needed for blood to clot properly. <u>Green vegetables</u> contain lots of vitamin K.

- <u>Alcohol</u> — a moderate intake of alcohol slows blood clotting.

- <u>Cranberries</u> — it's been suggested that they may slow blood clotting (but more research is needed).

---

3) Too little clotting could mean you bleed to death (well, you're more likely get loads of bruises anyway). Too much clotting can cause <u>strokes</u> and <u>deep vein thrombosis</u> (DVT).

4) People who are at a higher risk of strokes and DVT can take <u>drugs</u> to help 'thin' their blood. <u>Warfarin</u>, <u>heparin</u> and <u>aspirin</u> all help <u>prevent</u> the blood from clotting.

5) <u>Haemophilia</u> is a <u>genetic condition</u> where the blood <u>doesn't clot easily</u> because a <u>clotting factor</u> can't be made by the body — this missing clotting factor can be injected.

Blood needs to clot, but not too much

Clotting is incredibly useful — it means that when you cut yourself, your wounds heal really quickly and stop all your blood flowing out onto the floor. However, if your blood clots too much, you could be at risk of strokes and lots of other nasty things. It's a fine balance that your body has to maintain.

Blood

Sometimes injuries may be so bad that you lose too much blood and need to replace it — that's where <u>transfusions</u> come in. (The structures and functions of blood cells are covered on page 131.)

Blood type is important in transfusions

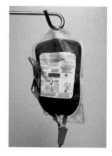

1) If you're in an accident or having surgery, you may lose a lot of blood — this needs to be replaced by a <u>blood transfusion</u> (using blood from a <u>blood donor</u>). But you can't just use any old blood...

2) People have different <u>blood groups</u> or <u>types</u> — you can be any one of:

> • <u>**A**</u>   • <u>**B**</u>   • <u>**O**</u>   • <u>**AB**</u>

3) These letters refer to the type of <u>antigens</u> on the surface of a person's red blood cells. (An antigen is a substance that can trigger a response from a person's <u>immune system</u>.)

4) Red blood cells can have <u>A or B antigens</u> (or <u>neither</u>, or <u>both</u>) on their surface.

5) And blood plasma can contain <u>anti-A or anti-B antibodies</u>. (Plasma's the pale liquid in blood that actually carries all the different bits — e.g. the blood cells, antibodies, hormones, etc.)

6) If an anti-A antibody meets an A antigen, the blood clots up and it all goes <u>hideously wrong</u>. The same thing happens when an anti-B antibody meets a B antigen.

7) This disastrous clotting is called <u>agglutination</u> — a fancy name for 'clumping together'. The <u>antibodies</u> are acting as <u>agglutinins</u> — or 'things that make stuff clump together'.

8) It's quite confusing at first, but this table should make everything clear...

Blood Group	Antigens	Antibodies	Can give blood to:	Can get blood from:
A	A	anti-B	A and AB	A and O
B	B	anti-A	B and AB	B and O
AB	A, B	none	only AB	anyone
O	none	anti-A, anti-B	anyone	only O

> For example, '<u>O-type blood</u>' can be given to <u>anyone</u> — there are <u>no antigens</u> on the blood cells, so any <u>anti-A</u> or <u>anti-B antibodies</u> have nothing to 'attack'.

You might need to spend some extra time on this page

You could be asked a question about who can <u>donate</u> blood to who (or <u>receive</u> from who) in the exam. Just look at what blood type the donor is and think about what <u>antigens</u> and <u>antibodies</u> they have in their blood. It's hard, and you need to think carefully about it (I do anyway), but it does make sense.

Warm-Up and Exam Questions

Here's some practice for you to see what went in and what needs looking at again.

Warm-Up Questions

1) What is unusual about the pulmonary artery, compared to other arteries in the body?
2) What is the cardiac cycle?
3) What are the functions of the SAN and the AVN in the heart?
4) What is an echocardiogram?
5) Name a genetic disease in which the blood fails to clot properly.

Exam Questions

1   The graph below shows part of an electrocardiogram (ECG) of the heartbeat of a patient in hospital.

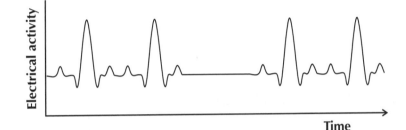

(a) How many heartbeats are shown?

(1 mark)

(b) On the graph, label one place where the ventricles are contracting.

(1 mark)

(c) The ECG shows one abnormal feature. Explain what this is.

(1 mark)

2   The bar chart shows the rates of coronary heart disease (CHD) in four different countries.

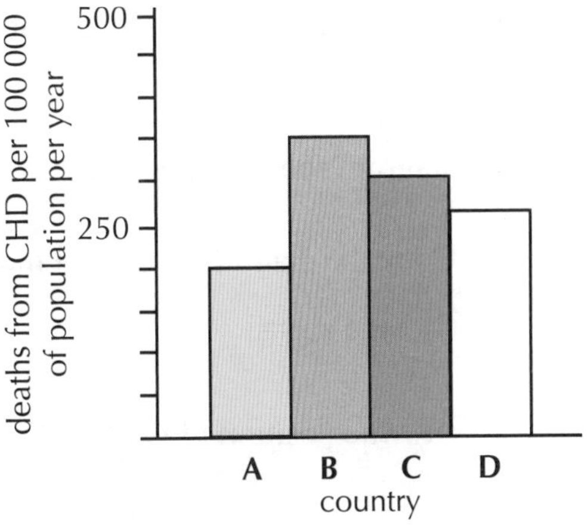

(a) (i) What is the difference between the rates of CHD in countries A and B?

(1 mark)

(ii) Suggest a possible reason for this difference.

(1 mark)

(b) Mr Singh is a patient in a hospital. He has had a small heart attack but is about to be discharged. Suggest three things that he could do to reduce his chances of another heart attack.

(3 marks)

Exam Questions

3 (a) Briefly explain what antigens are.

(1 mark)

(b) Mr Brown is of blood group B. In hospital, he receives a transfusion of blood from Mr Omar, who is of blood group O.

(i) People with blood group O are sometimes described as 'universal donors'. Explain what this means.

(1 mark)

(ii) If Mr Brown donated blood himself in the future, which blood groups could receive his blood?

(1 mark)

4 Amazing Airlines produced this passenger information card:

> **DEEP VEIN THROMBOSIS**
>
> During long flights, passengers may be at risk of deep vein thrombosis (DVT). To reduce the risk of DVT, we recommend that, during flights, passengers:
>
> • drink water regularly
> • get up and move around from time to time
>
> Passengers at high risk of DVT may be advised by their doctors to take aspirin before flying.

(a) What happens in the vein in DVT?

(1 mark)

(b) Suggest why it's a good idea for passengers to occasionally get up and move around.

(2 marks)

(c) Explain why aspirin is recommended.

(1 mark)

5 The diagram shows the human heart, seen from the front.

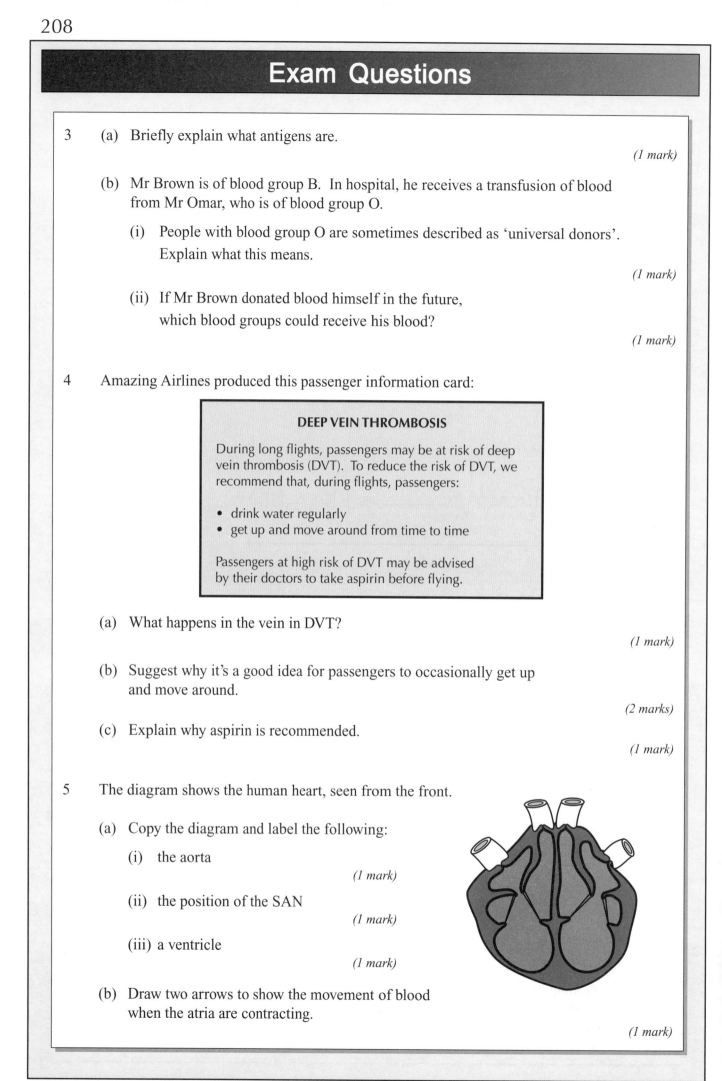

(a) Copy the diagram and label the following:

(i) the aorta

(1 mark)

(ii) the position of the SAN

(1 mark)

(iii) a ventricle

(1 mark)

(b) Draw two arrows to show the movement of blood when the atria are contracting.

(1 mark)

Waste Disposal — The Kidneys

The kidneys are really important organs. They get rid of <u>toxic waste</u> like urea as well as adjusting the amount of <u>dissolved ions</u> and <u>water</u> in the blood. The kidneys were introduced on page 137, but here's the rest of the stuff you need to know.

Nephrons are the filtration units in the kidneys

1) Ultrafiltration

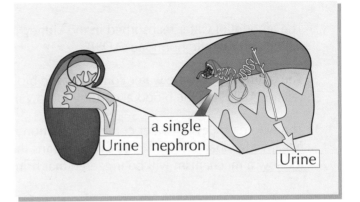

1) A <u>high pressure</u> is built up which squeezes <u>water</u>, <u>urea</u>, <u>ions</u> and <u>sugar</u> out of the blood and into the <u>Bowman's capsule</u>.

2) The membranes between the blood vessels and the Bowman's capsule act like <u>filters</u>, so <u>big</u> molecules like <u>proteins</u> and <u>blood cells</u> are <u>not</u> squeezed out. They stay in the blood.

Enlarged View of a Single Nephron

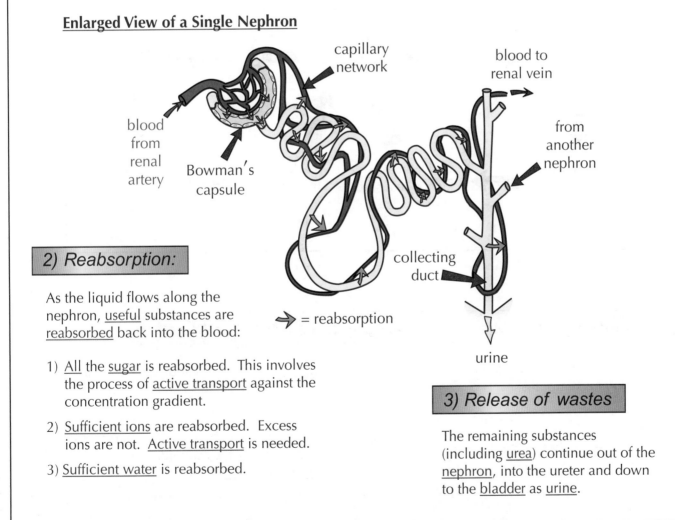

2) Reabsorption:

As the liquid flows along the nephron, <u>useful</u> substances are <u>reabsorbed</u> back into the blood:

1) <u>All</u> the <u>sugar</u> is reabsorbed. This involves the process of <u>active transport</u> against the concentration gradient.

2) <u>Sufficient ions</u> are reabsorbed. Excess ions are not. <u>Active transport</u> is needed.

3) <u>Sufficient water</u> is reabsorbed.

3) Release of wastes

The remaining substances (including <u>urea</u>) continue out of the <u>nephron</u>, into the ureter and down to the <u>bladder</u> as <u>urine</u>.

Each kidney contains about one million nephrons

The kidneys are pretty complicated organs as you can see. Luckily you won't have to reproduce that diagram on the last page in the exam, but you do have to make sure you know exactly what happens in each of the <u>three stages</u>. Learn what's filtered, what's reabsorbed and what's released as urine.

Waste Disposal — The Kidneys

The kidneys reabsorb enough water to make sure that the concentration of the blood is correct. This is controlled by a <u>hormone</u>.

Water content is controlled by the kidneys

1) The amount of water reabsorbed in the kidney nephrons is <u>controlled</u> by a hormone called <u>anti-diuretic hormone</u> (ADH).

2) The brain <u>monitors the water content of the blood</u> and instructs the <u>pituitary gland</u> to release <u>ADH</u> into the blood according to how much is needed.

3) The whole process of water content regulation is controlled by a mechanism called <u>negative feedback</u> (see page 20). This means that if the water content gets <u>too high</u> or <u>too low</u> a mechanism will be triggered that brings it back to <u>normal</u>.

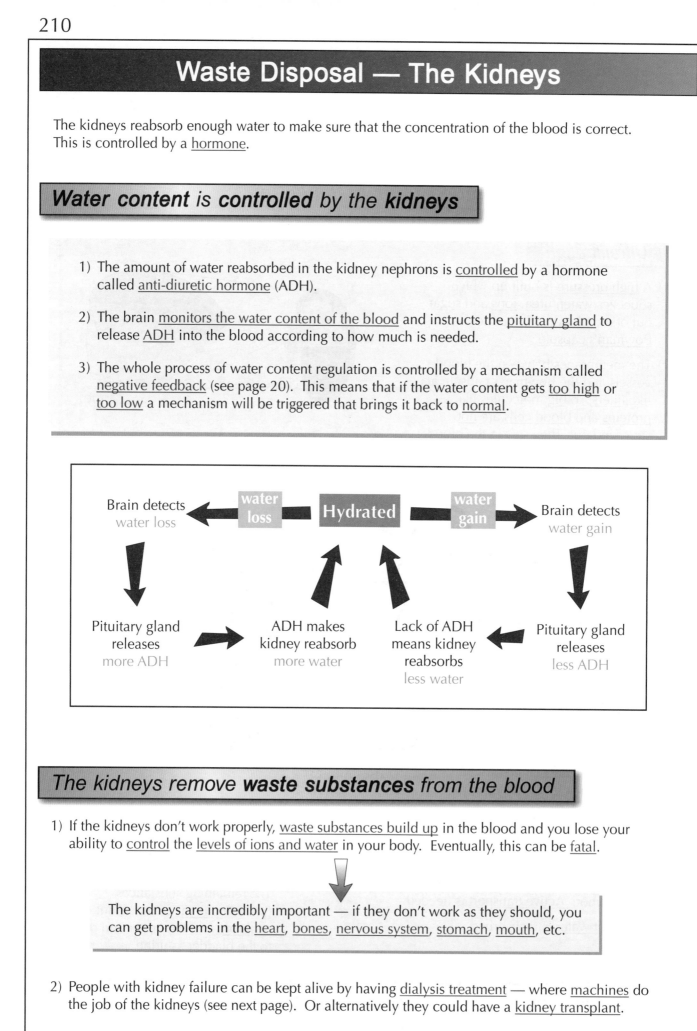

*The kidneys remove **waste substances** from the blood*

1) If the kidneys don't work properly, <u>waste substances build up</u> in the blood and you lose your ability to <u>control</u> the <u>levels of ions and water</u> in your body. Eventually, this can be <u>fatal</u>.

The kidneys are incredibly important — if they don't work as they should, you can get problems in the <u>heart</u>, <u>bones</u>, <u>nervous system</u>, <u>stomach</u>, <u>mouth</u>, etc.

2) People with kidney failure can be kept alive by having <u>dialysis treatment</u> — where <u>machines</u> do the job of the kidneys (see next page). Or alternatively they could have a <u>kidney transplant</u>.

Waste Disposal — The Kidneys

Dialysis machines can do the same job as the kidneys for a person whose own kidneys have failed.
They're certainly not as convenient as having your own working kidneys though.

Dialysis machines filter the blood

1) Dialysis has to be done regularly to keep the concentrations of dissolved substances in the
blood at normal levels, and to remove waste substances.

2) In a dialysis machine the person's blood flows alongside a selectively permeable barrier,
surrounded by dialysis fluid.

3) The barrier is permeable to things like ions and waste substances, but not to big molecules
like proteins (just like the membranes in the kidney).

4) The dialysis fluid has the same concentration of dissolved ions and glucose as healthy blood.

5) This means that useful dissolved ions and glucose won't diffuse out of the blood and into the
dialysis fluid during dialysis.

6) Only waste substances (such as urea) and excess ions and water diffuse across the barrier.

7) Many patients with kidney failure have to have a dialysis session three times a week.
Each session takes 3–4 hours — not much fun.

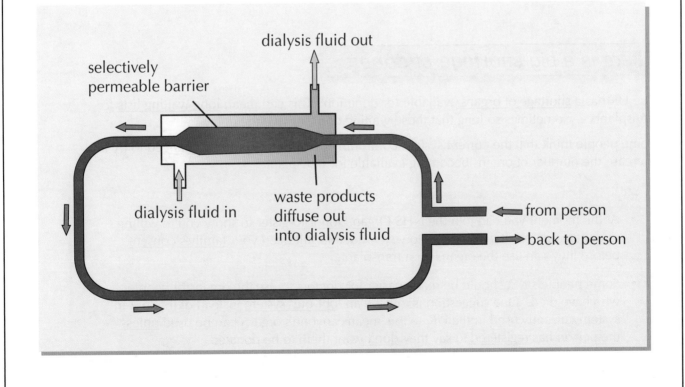

Patients have to spend hours each week having dialysis

Kidney failure patients often have high blood pressure because diseased kidneys can't control the
water content of the blood properly. The excess water is removed during dialysis — up to five litres
of fluid can be removed in a single session.

Organ Replacements and Donation

If an organ's severely damaged, it can be replaced by an <u>artificial</u> part or by a <u>donated</u> natural organ.

Organs can be **replaced** by **living** or **dead donors**

1) <u>Living donors</u> can donate whole (or parts of) certain organs. For example, you can live with just one of your two <u>kidneys</u> and donate the other, or you can donate a piece of your <u>liver</u>.

2) To be a living donor you must be <u>fit and healthy</u>, <u>over 18</u> years old, and usually a close family member (so that there's a good <u>tissue match</u>).

3) Organs from people who have recently <u>died</u>, or who are <u>brain dead</u>, can also be <u>transplanted</u>.

4) Any donor organ must by <u>relatively young</u>, the <u>right size</u> and a good <u>tissue match</u>.

5) <u>Success rates</u> of transplants depend on a lot of things — such as the type of organ (for example, the heart is riskier than a kidney), the age of the patient, the skill of the surgeon, etc.

6) But transplants involve <u>major surgery</u> — and even if all goes well, there can be problems with <u>rejection</u> or as a result of taking <u>immunosuppressive</u> drugs (see page 135).

There is a big **shortage** of **donors**

The UK has a <u>shortage of organs</u> available for donation. This can mean <u>long waiting lists</u> for transplants — sometimes so long that those waiting don't survive the delay.

Some people think that the current system controlling donations should be <u>changed</u> to try and increase the number of organs becoming available for transplant.

- At the moment you can join the <u>NHS Organ Donor Register</u> to show you're <u>willing</u> to donate organs after you die. However, doctors <u>still</u> need your <u>family's consent</u> before they can use the organs for a transplant.

- Some people say it should be made <u>easier</u> for doctors to use the organs of people who have died. One suggestion is to have an '<u>opt-out</u>' system instead of the 'opt-in' system currently used in the UK — this means anyone's organs can be used <u>unless</u> the person has <u>registered</u> to say they <u>don't</u> want them to be donated.

Some European countries, e.g. Spain, already use the opt-out system

Did you know that if you transplant a piece of a liver it can actually grow back to normal size within a few weeks? Impressive. Changing the subject slightly... <u>one donor</u> can donate <u>several organs</u> — e.g. their heart, kidneys, liver, lungs, pancreas... And on top of that, other tissues (e.g. skin, bone, tendons, corneas...) can also be donated. It's amazing really, when you think about it.

Organ Replacements and Donation

Transplants have saved a lot of lives, but not everyone is in favour of them.

There are **issues** surrounding **organ donation**

Like with lots of medical advances, there are <u>ethical</u> issues to take into account:

1) Some people think for religious reasons that a person's body should be <u>buried intact</u> (so <u>giving</u> organs is wrong). Others think that whether someone lives or dies is up to <u>God</u> and people shouldn't interfere (so <u>receiving</u> organs is wrong).

2) Some people are afraid that doctors might <u>not</u> try as hard to save them if they're critically ill and their organs are <u>needed</u> for transplant. There are <u>safeguards</u> in place that should prevent this though.

3) There are also worries that people may get <u>pressured</u> into being a '<u>living donor</u>' (for example, donating a kidney to a close relative). But doctors try to ensure that it's always the donor's <u>personal choice</u> through interviews and counselling.

Mechanical replacements can sometimes be used

1) <u>Mechanical</u> (artificial) replacements made from metal and plastic can also be used. These don't have the same problems with <u>rejection</u>.

2) However, mechanical replacements can have a whole <u>new</u> set of problems instead. For example, artificial <u>heart valves</u> need more major surgery and don't work as well as healthy natural ones.

3) Sometimes, <u>temporary</u> mechanical replacements are needed to keep someone <u>alive</u>. This could be for anything from a few <u>hours</u> (e.g. during an operation), to several <u>months</u> or even <u>years</u> (e.g. if they're waiting for a suitable organ donor). For example...

- A <u>heart-lung machine</u> keeps a patient's blood oxygenated and pumping during heart or lung surgery.

- A <u>kidney dialysis machine</u> can filter a patient's blood (e.g. while they wait for a kidney transplant). See page 211 for more info.

Warm-Up and Exam Questions

Warm-Up Questions

1) What is a nephron?
2) Where is ADH secreted?
3) Explain what is meant by a 'living organ donor'.
4) Give one advantage of receiving an artificial heart valve rather than having a transplant.

Exam Questions

1   The table shows the concentrations of some different substances in the fluid inside a nephron of a kidney — in the Bowman's capsule, and in the collecting duct.

Substance	Conc. in Bowman's capsule (g/100 ml)	Conc. in urine (g/100 ml)
water	99	96
protein	0	0
glucose	0.10	0
urea	0.04	2.0
salt	0.70	0.30

(a)   Explain why there is a difference in the concentrations of glucose.

(1 mark)

(b)   Explain why the liquid in the Bowman's capsule does not contain any proteins.

(2 marks)

2   Mary has kidney failure. She has dialysis three times a week.

(a)   (i)   Explain how the dialysis machine removes urea from Mary's blood.

(2 marks)

(ii)   Explain why Mary does not lose glucose from her blood during dialysis.

(2 marks)

(b)   Mary is hoping that she will soon have a kidney transplant.
Suggest one reason why this form of treatment may be preferable to dialysis.

(1 mark)

3   Mr Hooper has heart disease. He is hoping for a transplant.
Mr Chester dies in a car accident. His heart might be suitable for a transplant.

(a)   Suggest two reasons why Mr Chester's heart might **not** be suitable for Mr Hooper.

(2 marks)

(b)   Mrs Chester does not want her husband's heart to be used for transplantation.
Suggest a possible reason why not.

(1 mark)

(c)   There is a shortage of suitable donors for transplants. Suggest one way in which the supply of suitable organs might be increased.

(1 mark)

Bones and Cartilage

<u>Bones</u> and <u>joints</u> are pretty important — without them you wouldn't be able to move around at all. All you'd do is wobble around on the floor like a big squidgy thing.

*If you didn't have a **skeleton**, you'd be **jelly-like***

1) The job of a <u>skeleton</u> is to <u>support</u> the body and allow it to <u>move</u> — as well as to <u>protect</u> vital <u>organs</u>.

2) Fish, amphibians, reptiles, birds and mammals are all <u>vertebrates</u> — they all have a <u>backbone</u> and an <u>internal skeleton</u>. Other animals (e.g. <u>insects</u>) have their skeleton on the <u>outside</u>.

3) An <u>internal skeleton</u> has certain advantages:

- It can <u>easily grow</u> with the body.
- It's easy to <u>attach muscles</u> to it.
- It's <u>more flexible</u> than an external skeleton.

*Skeleton on the outside
Skeleton on the inside*

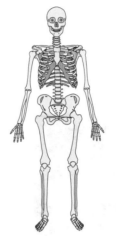

*Bones are **living tissues***

Bones are a lot cleverer than they might look...

1) <u>Bones</u> are made up of <u>living cells</u> — so they <u>grow</u>, and can <u>repair themselves</u> if they get damaged.

2) <u>Long bones</u> (e.g. the big one in your thigh) are actually <u>hollow</u> — this makes them <u>lighter</u> than solid bones of the same size (and <u>stronger</u> than solid bones of the same mass). This makes movement far more efficient.

3) The hole in the middle of some long bones is filled with <u>bone marrow</u>. Bone marrow is a spongy substance that makes new <u>blood cells</u> — meaning your bones are actually a kind of <u>blood factory</u>.

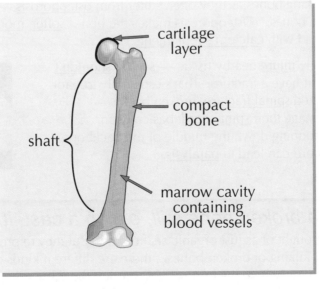

cartilage layer

compact bone

shaft

marrow cavity containing blood vessels

Bones and Cartilage

Bones are strong, but they can be <u>damaged</u>. Elderly people are at a particular risk of broken bones because bones get weaker with age. Doctors can use <u>X-rays</u> to check for damage to bones.

Bones begin life as **cartilage**

1) Bones start off as <u>cartilage</u> in the womb. (Cartilage is <u>living tissue</u> that looks and feels a bit <u>rubbery</u>.)

2) As you grow, cartilage is replaced by bone. Blood vessels deposit <u>calcium</u> and <u>phosphorus</u> in the cartilage, which eventually turns it into <u>bone</u>. This process is called <u>ossification</u>.

3) You can tell if someone is still <u>growing</u> by looking at how much <u>cartilage</u> is present — if there's a lot, they're still growing.

4) Even when you're fully grown, the ends of bones remain covered with <u>cartilage</u> (to stop the bones <u>rubbing</u> together at joints — see next page).

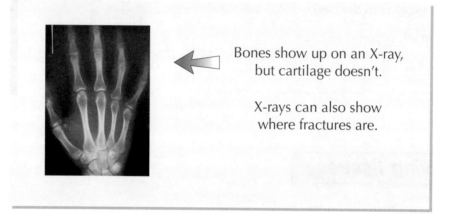

Bones show up on an X-ray, but cartilage doesn't.

X-rays can also show where fractures are.

Bones and cartilage can get **damaged**

1) Cartilage and bone are both made up of living tissue, and so can get <u>infected</u>. (The top of the ear is made of cartilage — if you get this pierced, you have to make sure no infection gets in. Not nice.)

2) Even though bones are really <u>strong</u>, they can be <u>fractured</u> (broken) by a sharp knock. <u>Elderly people</u> are more prone to breaking bones as they often suffer from <u>osteoporosis</u> — a condition where <u>calcium is lost</u> from the bones. (Osteoporosis makes the bones <u>softer</u>, <u>more brittle</u> and more likely to break — it can be treated with <u>calcium supplements</u>.)

3) A broken bone can easily <u>injure</u> nearby tissue — so you <u>shouldn't move</u> anyone who might have a fracture. That's especially true for someone with a suspected <u>spinal fracture</u> (broken back) — moving them could damage their <u>spinal cord</u> (basically an extension of the brain running down the middle of the backbone). Damage to the spinal cord can lead to <u>paralysis</u>.

If you can keep a broken bone still, e.g. in a cast, it will mend itself

Bones are all too easily thought of as just organic scaffolding. But they're pretty amazing really, and painful if you break one. Talking of broken bones... there are different kinds of break. You get <u>simple</u> fractures, <u>compound</u> fractures (where the bone pokes through the skin), <u>greenstick</u> fractures... and so on. But bones usually mend pretty easily — if you hold them still, a break will knit itself together.

Joints and Muscles

Like it says in the song, the knee bone's connected to the thigh bone. And it's done using a joint.

Joints allow the bones to move

1) The bones at a joint are held together with ligaments. Ligaments have tensile strength (i.e. you can pull them and they don't snap easily) but are pretty elastic (stretchy).

2) The ends of bones are covered with cartilage to stop the bones rubbing together. And because cartilage can be slightly compressed, it can act as a shock absorber.

3) Membranes at joints release oily synovial fluid to lubricate the joints, allowing them to move more easily.

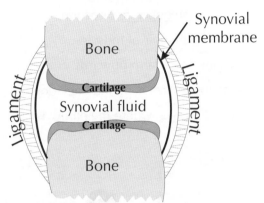

4) Different kinds of joints move in different ways. For example...

BALL AND SOCKET

The joint can move in all directions, and can also rotate.

...like the hip or shoulder.

HINGE

The joint can go backwards and forwards, but not side-to-side.

...like the knee or elbow.

There are other types of joint, but you only need to know those two

Different joints have different ranges of movement. And if you do something that makes the bone move further than its range of movement (like fall on it), then you could dislocate it. Painful.

Joints and Muscles

Your muscles move your bones about by pulling on them.

Muscles pull on bones to move them

1) Bones are attached to muscles by <u>tendons</u>.

2) Muscles move bones at a joint by <u>contracting</u> (becoming <u>shorter</u>).
They can only <u>pull</u> on bones to move a joint — they <u>can't</u> push.

3) This is why muscles usually come in <u>pairs</u> (called <u>antagonistic pairs</u>).

When one muscle in the pair contracts, the joint moves in one direction.
When the other contracts, it moves in the <u>opposite</u> direction.

4) The <u>biceps</u> and <u>triceps</u> are an antagonistic pair of muscles.

5) When the <u>biceps</u> contracts it pulls the lower arm <u>upwards</u>.

6) And when the <u>triceps</u> contracts the lower arm is pulled back <u>down</u>.

7) Together, they make the arm work as a <u>lever</u>, where the elbow is the pivot.

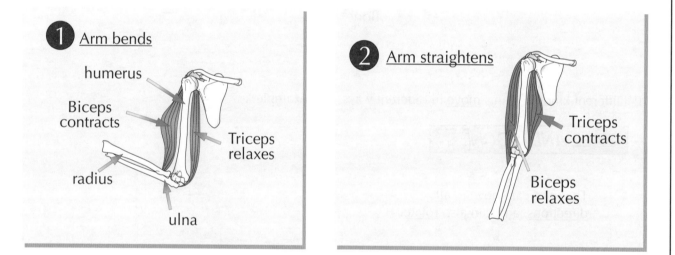

1 <u>Arm bends</u>

humerus

Biceps contracts

Triceps relaxes

radius

ulna

2 <u>Arm straightens</u>

Triceps contracts

Biceps relaxes

Joints can be replaced

If your <u>hip</u> or <u>knee joints</u> get damaged or diseased, they can be <u>replaced</u> with <u>artificial joints</u>.
Assuming all goes well, you'll be in <u>less pain</u> and discomfort, and will be <u>able to walk</u> better.
But there are <u>disadvantages</u>...

1) The surrounding tissue may become <u>inflamed</u> and <u>painful</u> — this is
caused by the body's reaction to the material the joint is made of.

2) <u>Hip dislocation</u> (ball comes out of its socket) is more common with artificial joints, as are <u>blood clots</u>.

3) There's a <u>risk of infection</u>, as with any surgery.

4) The <u>length of the legs</u> may be slightly different, causing difficulty walking.

5) Artificial joints <u>don't last forever</u> — they usually have to be replaced after 12–15 years.

Warm-Up and Exam Questions

You've nearly reached the end of the section — just these few simple Warm-Up Questions and a few slightly harder Exam Questions stand between you and the Revision Summary...

Warm-Up Questions
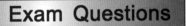

1) Give two functions of the human skeleton.
2) What is synovial fluid?
3) In the human body, where can you find: a) a hinge joint?   b) a ball and socket joint?
4) Why do skeletal muscles occur in antagonistic pairs?
5) What do ligaments do?

Exam Questions

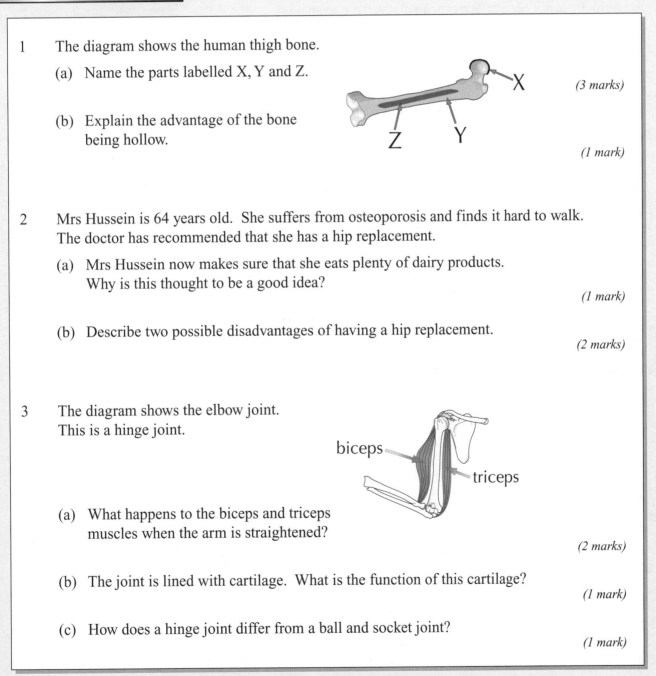

1   The diagram shows the human thigh bone.

(a) Name the parts labelled X, Y and Z.

(3 marks)

(b) Explain the advantage of the bone being hollow.

(1 mark)

2   Mrs Hussein is 64 years old. She suffers from osteoporosis and finds it hard to walk. The doctor has recommended that she has a hip replacement.

(a) Mrs Hussein now makes sure that she eats plenty of dairy products. Why is this thought to be a good idea?

(1 mark)

(b) Describe two possible disadvantages of having a hip replacement.

(2 marks)

3   The diagram shows the elbow joint. This is a hinge joint.

(a) What happens to the biceps and triceps muscles when the arm is straightened?

(2 marks)

(b) The joint is lined with cartilage. What is the function of this cartilage?

(1 mark)

(c) How does a hinge joint differ from a ball and socket joint?

(1 mark)

Revision Summary for Section Ten

It's no good just reading the section through and hoping you've got it all — it'll only stick if you've learned it <u>properly</u>. These questions are designed to really test whether you know all your stuff — ignore them at your peril. OK, rant over — I'll leave it to you...

1) Describe the differences between active transport and diffusion.

2) Give one example of where active transport happens in the human body.

3) Describe what happens to the intercostal muscles and diaphragm when you breathe in and out.

4) Why would you want to measure lung capacity?

5) List the four main causes of lung disease. Which of these is the most likely to result in lung cancer?

6) Describe the circulatory system of humans.

7) Describe the four stages that make up one complete heartbeat.

8) Which cluster of cells in the heart act as the pacemaker?

9) What does ECG stand for? Describe what a healthy person's ECG should look like.

10) List five lifestyle 'dangers' which may cause an increased likelihood of cardiovascular disease.

11) What exactly is happening when blood clots? How might your diet affect the way your blood clots?

12) Explain what would happen if a person with type A blood was given a transfusion of type B blood.

13) Explain how a kidney works.

14) Describe three things that affect the amount and concentration of urine produced.

15) Which hormone is responsible for controlling the amount of water reabsorbed in the kidneys?

16) How does a dialysis machine work? Which substances does it remove from the blood?

17) Give one example of an ethical concern surrounding organ donation.

18) Name two types of mechanical organ replacements. What do they do?

19) List three advantages of an internal skeleton compared to an external skeleton.

20) Why is it unwise to move someone who has a broken bone?

21) Describe how a ball and socket joint works.

22) What happens to the lower arm when the triceps contracts?

Bacteria

Bacteria are a type of microorganism. They're tiny — typically just a few <u>microns</u> (thousandths of a millimetre) wide. But despite their small size, they can have a mighty effect on humans...

Bacterial cells are usually **smaller** and **simpler** than animal cells

1) This table shows how bacterial cells <u>compare</u> to plant and animal cells.

2) Bacterial cells <u>don't</u> have a <u>proper nucleus</u> like plant and animal cells do. They have <u>bacterial DNA</u> to <u>control</u> the <u>cell's activities</u> and <u>replication</u>, but the DNA just floats about in the cytoplasm.

3) They <u>don't</u> have any <u>mitochondria</u>, <u>chloroplasts</u> or a <u>vacuole</u>.

4) They have a <u>cell wall</u> to <u>keep their shape</u> and <u>stop them bursting</u>. This isn't the same kind of cell wall found in a plant though.

Feature	Animal Cell	Plant Cell	Bacterial Cell
Nucleus	✓	✓	✗
Cell membrane	✓	✓	✓
Mitochondria	✓	✓	✗
Cell wall	✗	✓	✓
Chloroplasts	✗	✓	✗
Vacuole	✗	✓	✗
Extras	none	none	flagellum

5) They sometimes have a <u>flagellum</u> (like a tail) to help them <u>move</u>.

6) They come in <u>four shapes</u>: <u>rods</u>, <u>curved rods</u>, <u>spheres</u> and <u>spirals</u>.

7) Bacteria can <u>consume</u> a <u>huge range</u> of <u>organic nutrients</u> from their surroundings. This provides them with <u>energy</u>. Some types of bacteria can even make their own nutrients.

8) This means they can <u>survive</u> pretty much <u>anywhere</u> — in soil, water, air, in your house, in the human body and in food.

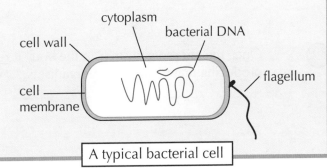

A typical bacterial cell

Bacteria **reproduce** *by* **asexual reproduction**

1) Bacteria reproduce by <u>asexual reproduction</u> — they're <u>clones</u> of each other. They reproduce by a process called <u>binary fission</u> (a posh way of saying 'they split in two').

2) Bacteria <u>reproduce very quickly</u>. If <u>disease-causing bacteria</u> enter your body, they can reproduce and <u>cause disease</u> before your body has a chance to respond.

3) Bacteria <u>reproduce more quickly</u> in <u>certain conditions</u>. Generally, if it's <u>warm</u> and they have a good source of <u>nutrients</u> then they will grow better. This is why it's important to <u>store food carefully</u>. If you leave some meat on a warm kitchen top, bacteria on the meat will reproduce very quickly and cause it to <u>spoil</u> (go off). But if you put the same meat in the fridge, then the <u>cold temperature</u> will <u>slow down</u> the bacteria's reproduction and it won't spoil as quickly.

Harmful Microorganisms

There are different kinds of microorganism, e.g. bacteria, viruses, fungi and protozoa. Some are useful, while others are pretty harmful if you get infected. This page focuses on the nasty ones...

There are **four stages** in an **infectious disease**

1 Firstly the microorganism has to get into the body to cause an infection. There are four main ways this can happen:

Drug users can be at risk of contracting diseases through needles.

- Through the nose, e.g. airborne microorganisms like the influenza virus are breathed in.

- Through the mouth, e.g. contaminated food and water causes food poisoning and cholera.

- Through the skin, e.g. cuts, insect bites and infected needles can introduce a pathogen into the body directly, or they can breach the skin and allow microorganisms on the skin to get in.

- Through sexual contact, e.g. the HIV virus that causes AIDS can get into the body this way.

2 Once the microorganism is in the body it reproduces rapidly, producing many more microorganisms.

3 The microorganisms then make toxins (poisonous substances) which damage cells and tissues.

4 The toxins cause symptoms of infection, e.g. pain, diarrhoea and stomach cramps. Your immune system's reaction to the infection can also cause symptoms, e.g. fever. The time between exposure to the microorganism and the development of symptoms is called the incubation period.

The body's defences do limit the number of microorganisms entering

The body has loads of different defence mechanisms to protect itself from microorganisms. There are things like the skin, mucus and cilia in the respiratory system and white blood cells (see p.46 for more).

Harmful Microorganisms

Good sanitation and hygiene are important factors in preventing disease. If you live in a place where these things are not available, you will be more at risk.

Poor sanitation is linked to a high incidence of disease

1) The incidence of a disease is the number of new cases that occurs in a population in a certain time.

2) Good sanitation and public health measures are linked to a low incidence of disease.
A clean water supply, good sewage works, public health education and clean hospitals prevent the spread of disease.

3) Poor sanitation is linked with a high incidence of disease. For example:

- A high incidence of food poisoning, dysentery and cholera might be caused by a lack of clean water or a run down sewage system.

- A high incidence of septicaemia (a bacterial blood infection) might be caused by poor hygiene in hospital operating theatres or a lack of education about cleaning cuts properly.

4) Developing countries are less likely to be able to afford good sanitation and public health measures than developed countries.

Diseases often spread rapidly after natural disasters

Natural disasters like earthquakes and hurricanes can damage the infrastructure of an area (i.e. the basic facilities like transport and communication links, water and power lines, schools, etc.) and completely disrupt health services. In these conditions disease can spread rapidly among the population.

1) Some natural disasters damage sewage systems and water supplies. This can result in contaminated drinking water containing the microorganisms that cause diseases like cholera and dysentery.

2) Transport systems can be damaged — making it difficult for health services to reach people in need.

3) Electricity supplies are also often damaged by natural disasters. This means that food goes off quickly because refrigerators can't work — this can lead to an increase in food poisoning.

Microorganisms and Food

Biotechnology ('bio' meaning life, and 'technology' meaning, well... technology) is nothing new. For years the food industry has been using microorganisms to produce cheese, yoghurt, chocolate, soy sauce, alcohol, etc. And more recently we've started using mycoproteins (see page 181).

Bacteria *ferment milk* to produce *yoghurt*

Fermentation is when microorganisms break sugars down to release energy — usually by anaerobic respiration. Yoghurt is basically fermented milk. Here's how it's made:

1) The equipment is sterilised to kill off any unwanted microorganisms.

2) The milk is pasteurised (heated up to 72 °C for 15 seconds) — again to kill any harmful microorganisms. Then the milk's cooled.

3) A starter culture of bacteria is added and the mixture is incubated (heated to about 40 °C) in a vessel called a fermenter (see p.181).

4) The bacteria ferment the lactose sugar in the milk to form lactic acid. This makes the milk clot and solidify into yoghurt (a sample is taken at this stage to make sure it's the right consistency).

5) Finally, flavours (e.g. fruit) and colours are sometimes added and the yoghurt is packaged.

Soy sauce *is made by* fermentation *too*

There are different kinds of soy sauce, and they're generally quite complicated to make. This is the process behind one particular kind of soy sauce — it involves three different kinds of microbes.

1) Cooked soy beans and roasted wheat are mixed together.

2) The mixture is fermented by the *Aspergillus* fungus.

3) The mixture is fermented again by yeasts.

4) The mixture is fermented yet again by the *Lactobacillus* bacterium.

5) The liquid is filtered to remove any gungy bits.

6) Then it's pasteurised to kill off the microorganisms, and finally put into sterile bottles.

Microorganisms and Food

As well as helping to make tasty foods like yoghurt and soy sauce, some bacteria can actually help to <u>improve</u> your <u>health</u>.

Functional foods *are* **marketed** *as having* **health benefits**

A <u>functional food</u> is one that has some kind of <u>health benefit</u> beyond basic <u>nutrition</u>. For example, it might <u>prevent</u> some kind of <u>disease</u>, or it might (as the marketing folk would put it) 'promote your well-being'.

Plant Stanol Esters

1) <u>Plant stanol esters</u> are chemicals that can <u>lower blood cholesterol</u> and reduce the risk of <u>heart disease</u>.

2) Some food manufacturers add them to <u>spreads</u> and some dairy products. People who are worried about their blood <u>cholesterol</u> levels may choose these spreads over the ordinary ones.

3) Stanols <u>occur naturally</u> in plants, but in very small quantities. Stanols are produced commercially by using <u>bacteria</u> to convert sterols (types of fat found in plants like the soya bean) into <u>stanols</u>.

Prebiotics

Some people take substances called <u>prebiotics</u> to promote the growth of <u>'good' bacteria</u> in the <u>gut</u>.

1) Prebiotics are <u>carbohydrates</u> such as <u>oligosaccharides</u>. They're a <u>food supply</u> for 'good' bacteria.

2) 'Bad' bacteria and humans can't digest the prebiotic — they don't have the right enzymes.

2) Prebiotics <u>occur naturally</u> in foods like leeks, onions and oats, but you can't get enough of them in a normal diet to cause a significant effect. This is why some people take <u>supplements</u>.

Not all bacteria cause disease if they get inside your body

We all have <u>bacteria</u> in our <u>guts</u>. The 'bad' bacteria can cause disease, but the 'good' bacteria help digestion. Don't get <u>prebiotics</u> and <u>probiotics</u> mixed up — probiotics are actually bacteria that you eat to 'top up' the levels in your gut. Interesting fact... there can be up to 2 kg of bacteria in your gut.

226

Microorganisms and Food

Unfortunately for you, the yoghurt and soy sauce on page 224 were just the tip of the iceberg — there are plenty of other ways that microorganisms are involved in producing foods.

Lots of *microbial products* are used in *food*

In the two examples on this page, the microbial product is used to produce a food.

Enzymes

1) Enzymes such as invertase are used in the manufacture of sweets and other foods.

2) Invertase converts sucrose (a sugar) into glucose and fructose (different types of sugar) which taste sweeter.

3) This means that less sugar is needed for the same sweetness — meaning manufacturers can save money and produce lower-calorie sweet foods.

4) Invertase is naturally produced by a yeast called *Saccharomyces cerevisiae*.

Chymosin

1) Cheese is made using a substance called rennet.

2) Rennet traditionally comes from the lining of a calf's stomach and contains an enzyme called chymosin, which clots the milk.

3) But vegetarians probably don't want to eat cheese made with rennet from animals, so vegetarian cheese is made using chymosin from genetically modified microorganisms (see page 87).

4) Basically, the genes responsible for chymosin were isolated from calf stomach cells and put into yeast cells. These were then grown on an industrial scale to produce chymosin.

SECTION ELEVEN — MICROORGANISMS AND BIOTECHNOLOGY

Microorganisms and Food

In these four examples on this page, the microbial product is <u>eaten directly</u>.

Vitamin C

1) Vitamin C is used as a <u>dietary supplement</u> (in vitamin pills). It's also added to <u>drinks</u> (and other things, e.g. bread) to stop them going off.

2) A bacterium called *Acetobacter* naturally produces a chemical easily converted to <u>vitamin C</u>.

3) It's used to produce vitamin C commercially, as it's <u>cheaper</u> and easier than extracting vitamin C from <u>fruit</u>.

Citric Acid

1) Citric acid is a <u>flavouring</u> and <u>preservative</u> added to fruit-flavoured fizzy drinks.

2) It's found naturally in <u>citrus fruits</u> — but since fizzy drinks <u>rarely</u> use <u>fresh</u> fruit, citric acid has to be <u>added</u> separately.

3) A fungus called *Aspergillus niger* is used to commercially produce <u>citric acid</u>.

Monosodium Glutamate (MSG)

1) <u>Monosodium glutamate</u> is a <u>flavour enhancer</u> added to loads of foods (including many Asian foods).

2) It's made from <u>glutamic acid</u>, which is produced by the bacterium *Corynebacterium glutamicum*.

3) The bacteria secrete glutamic acid (an <u>amino acid</u>) into the medium they're grown in.

4) The glutamic acid is then used to make monosodium glutamate (a <u>sodium salt</u>).

Carrageenan (produced from the seaweed Carrageen)

1) You also need to know about <u>carrageenan</u> — it's a <u>gelling agent</u> that's extracted from the seaweed <u>carrageen</u>.

2) It's also used as an <u>emulsifier</u> in ice cream, jellies, soups and confectionery.

Seaweeds are algae. Some algae are microbes, but others (e.g. seaweed) aren't. So this example is a bit different to the others — no microorganisms are involved.

Warm-Up and Exam Questions

You must have known you were due a set of questions, and hey presto, here they are.
It's a double pager, so you're in for an extra treat.

Warm-Up Questions

1) What is binary fission?
2) What causes the symptoms of a disease?
3) What are prebiotics?
4) Why might citric acid be added to fizzy drinks?
5) What does invertase do?

Exam Questions

1   The diagram shows a bacterial cell as it appears under a microscope.

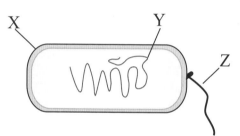

(a)   Name the parts labelled X, Y and Z.

(3 marks)

(b)   In the past, bacteria were classified by scientists as part of the plant kingdom.

    (i)   State two ways in which this cell is similar to a typical plant cell.

(2 marks)

    (ii)   State two ways in which it is different from a typical plant cell.

(2 marks)

2   Complete the table by giving an example of a disease that is transmitted by each method.

Typical method of transmission	Disease
insect bites	
contaminated food/water	
sexual contact	
droplet infection	

(4 marks)

3   Glenda Greene is a vegetarian. She likes cheese, but won't eat cheese that has been made using rennet.

(a) Rennet contains an enzyme.

(i)   Name this enzyme.

(1 mark)

(ii) How is this enzyme used during cheese production?

(1 mark)

(b) Suggest why Glenda won't eat cheese that contains rennet.

(1 mark)

(c) Explain how cheese can be made without using rennet.

(1 mark)

4   There was an earthquake in a city in Asia.
Shortly afterwards there was an outbreak of cholera.

The public health officer advised that, for the next few weeks,
people should boil any water before drinking it .

(a) Suggest why an outbreak of cholera occurred after the earthquake.

(2 marks)

(b) Explain the purpose of boiling the drinking water.

(1 mark)

(c) Suggest one other public health measure that could be helpful in controlling
the cholera outbreak.

(1 mark)

5   The BillyBio Company make health foods. One of their products is called
SuperSpread — 'The Succulent Spread that contains Super Stanols'.

(a) Describe the possible effect of eating 'super stanols' and explain why
this might be beneficial.

(2 marks)

(b) The BillyBio Company produce their stanols from soya bean extract.
Describe how this would be done.

(2 marks)

Yeast

This page is all about yeast — a pretty <u>useful</u> microorganism. It helps us to make wine and beer (see page 232), and bread too.

Yeast is a microorganism

1) Yeast is a type of <u>fungus</u>.

2) It reproduces <u>asexually</u> by a process called <u>budding</u>. A bulge forms on part of the cell and it eventually becomes a <u>daughter cell</u>, identical to the parent.

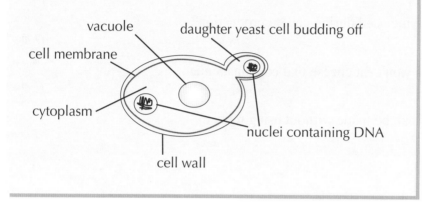

vacuole   daughter yeast cell budding off

cell membrane

cytoplasm

nuclei containing DNA

cell wall

3) Yeast can be <u>easily stored</u> in a <u>dry condition</u> — e.g. baker's yeast is dry granules.

*Yeast can respire **anaerobically** or **aerobically***

When yeast <u>respires anaerobically</u> (without oxygen) it produces ethanol, carbon dioxide and energy. This process is called <u>fermentation</u>. Here is the equation for fermentation:

> glucose → ethanol + carbon dioxide (+ energy)
>
> $C_6H_{12}O_6 \rightarrow 2C_2H_5OH + 2CO_2$ (+ energy)

Ethanol is a type of alcohol.

Yeast can also respire <u>aerobically</u> (with oxygen). This releases <u>more energy</u> than anaerobic respiration. Aerobic respiration is the same for yeast as it is for plants and animals:

> glucose + oxygen → carbon dioxide + water (+ energy)

Whether the yeast respire aerobically or anaerobically depends on <u>whether there is oxygen present</u>. If oxygen is present they respire aerobically. If <u>oxygen runs out</u> they <u>switch</u> to anaerobic respiration.

When yeast is used to make wine and beer, it respires anaerobically

Yeast releases more energy from <u>aerobic</u> respiration than from anaerobic respiration. This means that when there is a good <u>oxygen</u> supply, the yeast has more energy and so reproduces more.

Yeast

Yeast's *growth rate varies* depending on the *conditions*

The faster yeast <u>respires</u>, the faster it's able to <u>reproduce</u>. The <u>speed</u> (rate) that yeast respires and reproduces <u>varies</u> depending on factors like: the temperature, amount of glucose, level of toxins and pH.

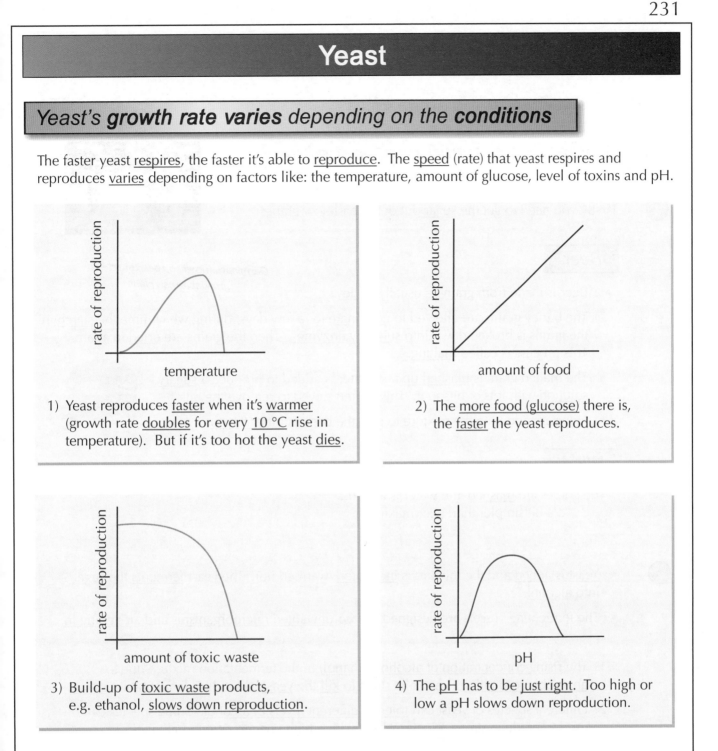

1) Yeast reproduces <u>faster</u> when it's <u>warmer</u> (growth rate <u>doubles</u> for every <u>10 °C</u> rise in temperature). But if it's too hot the yeast <u>dies</u>.

2) The <u>more food (glucose)</u> there is, the <u>faster</u> the yeast reproduces.

3) Build-up of <u>toxic waste</u> products, e.g. ethanol, <u>slows down reproduction</u>.

4) The <u>pH</u> has to be <u>just right</u>. Too high or low a pH slows down reproduction.

One way of <u>measuring</u> how fast the yeast is reproducing is to measure <u>how much glucose (sugar) it uses up</u>. The faster the yeast reproduces, the more glucose will be used up in a certain time.

Wastewater can be cleaned up with yeast

1) <u>Food-processing factories</u> need to get rid of <u>sugary water</u>. They can't just release it into waterways because it would cause pollution. <u>Bacteria</u> in the water would feed on the sugar and reproduce quickly, <u>using up</u> all the <u>oxygen</u> in the water. Other organisms in the water that <u>need oxygen</u> (like fish) would therefore <u>die</u>.

2) <u>Yeast</u> can be used to <u>treat the contaminated water</u> before it's released — it uses up the sugar in respiration.

Brewing

There's more to yeast than cleaning up sugar spills...

We use *yeast* for *brewing beer* and *wine*

(1) Firstly you need to get the <u>sugar out</u> of the barley or grapes:

Germination is when a seed starts to grow into a new plant.

Beer

1) Beer is made from <u>grain</u> — usually <u>barley</u>.

2) The barley grains are allowed to <u>germinate</u> for a few days, during which time the <u>starch</u> in the grains is broken down into <u>sugar</u> by <u>enzymes</u>. Then the grains are <u>dried</u> in a kiln. This process is called <u>malting</u>.

3) The malted grain is <u>mashed up</u> and water is added to produce a <u>sugary solution</u> with lots of bits in it. This is then sieved to remove the bits.

4) <u>Hops</u> are added to the mixture to give the beer its <u>bitter flavour</u>.

Wine

The grapes are <u>mashed</u> and water is added...
... a bit simpler than beer making.

(2)
- <u>Yeast</u> is <u>added</u> and the mixture is <u>incubated</u> (warmed up). The yeast <u>ferments</u> the <u>sugar</u> into <u>alcohol</u>.
- The fermenting vessels are designed to stop <u>unwanted microorganisms</u> and <u>air getting in</u>.

1) The <u>rising concentration of alcohol (ethanol)</u> in the fermentation mixture due to <u>anaerobic respiration</u> eventually starts to <u>kill</u> the <u>yeast</u>. As it dies, fermentation <u>slows</u>.

2) Different species of yeast can <u>tolerate different levels of alcohol</u>. Some species can be used to produce strong wine and beer with a <u>high concentration</u> of alcohol.

(3)
- The beer or wine produced is <u>drawn off</u> through a tap.
- Chemicals called <u>clarifying agents</u> may be added to <u>remove particles</u> and make it <u>clear</u>.

(4)
- <u>Beer</u> is then <u>pasteurised</u> — <u>heated</u> to <u>kill any yeast</u> left in the beer and stop fermentation. Wine isn't pasteurised — any yeast left in the wine carry on slowly fermenting the sugar. This <u>improves the taste</u> of the wine. Beer also tastes better if it's unpasteurised and aged in the <u>right conditions</u>. But big breweries pasteurise it because there's a <u>risk</u> that unpasteurised beer will <u>spoil</u> if it's not stored in the right conditions after it's sold.
- Finally the <u>beer</u> is <u>casked</u> and the <u>wine</u> is <u>bottled</u> ready for sale.

Brewing

To make stronger alcohols like spirits, the alcohol has to be <u>distilled</u>.

Distillation increases the alcohol concentration

1) Sometimes the products of fermentation are <u>distilled</u> to <u>increase</u> the <u>alcohol content</u>. This produces <u>spirits</u>, for example:

- If <u>cane sugar</u> is fermented and then distilled, you get <u>rum</u>.

- <u>Fermented malted barley</u> is distilled to make <u>whisky</u>.

- <u>Fermented potatoes</u> are distilled to make <u>vodka</u>.

2) Distillation is used to <u>separate</u> the alcohol out of the alcohol-water solution that's produced by fermentation.

3) The fermentation products are <u>heated to 78 °C</u>, the temperature at which the alcohol (but not the water) boils and turns into vapour.

4) The <u>alcohol vapour rises</u> and travels through a cooled tube which causes it to <u>condense</u> back into <u>liquid alcohol</u> and run down the tube into a <u>collecting vessel</u>.

5) Alcohol can only be <u>distilled</u> on <u>licensed premises</u> — you're not allowed to do it in your garden shed. (People can make their own beer and wine if they want to though.)

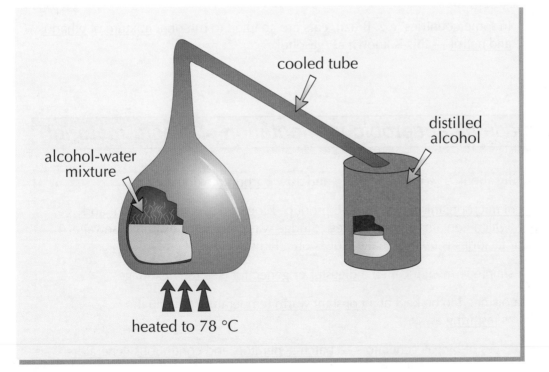

Really strong alcohols are sometimes distilled more than once

When you distil alcohol to separate it from water, there's always some water that evaporates and is recondensed with the alcohol. The more distillation steps, the less water gets through.

Fuels from Microorganisms

Food and booze aren't the only things microorganisms can be used for — the stuff they produce can also be used as <u>fuel</u>. And with the world's oil and gas supplies running low, other fuel sources such as this are going to become really important.

Fuels can be made by *fermentation*

1) Fuels can be made by <u>fermentation</u> of natural products — luckily enough, <u>waste</u> products can often be used.

2) Fermentation is when <u>bacteria</u> or <u>yeast</u> break sugars down by <u>anaerobic</u> respiration.

Anaerobic respiration does not use oxygen.

Ethanol is made by *anaerobic fermentation* of *sugar*

1) Yeast make <u>ethanol</u> when they break down <u>glucose</u> by <u>anaerobic respiration</u>.

2) <u>Sugar cane juices</u> can be used, or glucose can be derived from <u>maize starch</u> by the action of carbohydrase (an enzyme).

3) The ethanol is <u>distilled</u> to separate it from the yeast and remaining glucose before it's used.

4) In some countries, e.g. Brazil, <u>cars</u> are adapted to run on a <u>mixture</u> of <u>ethanol and petrol</u> — this is known as 'gasohol'.

This is the same as the reaction used in wine-making, see page 232.

Biogas is made by *anaerobic fermentation* of *waste material*

1) Biogas is usually about 70% <u>methane</u> (CH_4) and 30% <u>carbon dioxide</u> (CO_2).

2) Lots of <u>different microorganisms</u> are used to produce biogas. They ferment <u>plant and animal waste</u>, which contains <u>carbohydrates</u>. <u>Sludge waste</u> from, for example, <u>sewage works</u> or <u>sugar factories</u> is used to make biogas on a large scale.

3) It's made in a simple fermenter called a <u>digester</u> or <u>generator</u> (see the next page).

4) Biogas generators need to be kept at a <u>constant warm temperature</u> to keep the microorganisms <u>respiring</u> away.

5) There are two types of biogas generators — <u>batch generators</u> and <u>continuous generators</u>. These are explained on the next page.

6) Biogas <u>can't be stored as a liquid</u> (it needs too high a pressure), so it has to be used pretty much <u>straight away</u> — for <u>heating</u>, <u>cooking</u>, <u>lighting</u>, or to <u>power a turbine</u> and <u>generate electricity</u>.

Fuels from Microorganisms

Here's more than you could ever have wanted to know about that magic stuff, <u>biogas</u>.

Fuel production can happen on a *large* or *small scale*

1) <u>Large-scale</u> biogas generators are now being set up in a number of countries. Also, in some countries, <u>small biogas generators</u> are used to make enough gas for a <u>village</u> or a <u>family</u> to use in their <u>cooking stoves</u> and for <u>heating</u> and <u>lighting</u>.

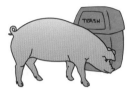

2) <u>Human waste</u>, waste from <u>keeping pigs</u> and other animals, and <u>food waste</u> (e.g. kitchen scraps) can be <u>digested</u> by <u>bacteria</u> to produce biogas.

3) By-products are used to <u>fertilise</u> crops and gardens.

Not all *biogas generators* are the same

There are two main types of biogas generator — <u>batch generators</u> and <u>continuous generators</u>.

Batch generators

<u>Batch generators</u> make biogas in <u>small batches</u>. They're <u>manually loaded up with waste</u>, which is left to digest, and the by-products are cleared away at the end of each session.

Continuous generators

<u>Continuous generators</u> make biogas <u>all the time</u>. Waste is <u>continuously fed in</u>, and biogas is produced at a <u>steady rate</u>. Continuous generators are more suited to <u>large-scale</u> biogas projects.

The diagram below shows a <u>simple biogas generator</u>. Any type of generator needs the following:

1) an inlet for <u>waste material</u> to be put in

2) an outlet for the <u>digested material</u> to be removed through

3) an outlet so that the <u>biogas</u> can be piped to where it is needed

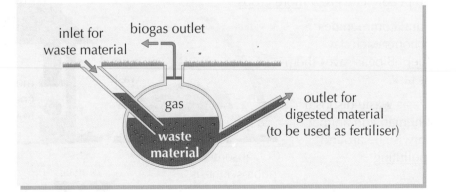

Fuels from Microorganisms

There are **four factors to consider** when designing a generator:

When biogas generators are being designed, the following factors need to be considered:

COST: Continuous generators are <u>more expensive</u> than batch ones, because waste has to be <u>mechanically pumped in</u> and digested material <u>mechanically removed</u> all the time.

CONVENIENCE: Batch generators are less convenient because they have to be regularly <u>loaded</u>, <u>emptied</u> and <u>cleaned</u> (rather than just topped up now and then).

EFFICIENCY: Gas is produced most quickly at about <u>35 °C</u>. If the temperature falls below this the gas production will be <u>slower</u>. Generators in some areas will need to be <u>insulated</u> or kept warm, e.g. by <u>solar heaters</u>. The generator shouldn't have any <u>leaks</u> or gas will be lost.

POSITION: The waste will <u>smell</u> during delivery, so generators should be sited <u>away from homes</u>. The generator is also best located fairly close to the <u>waste source</u>.

Using biofuels has **economic** and **environmental** effects

1) Biofuels are a '<u>greener</u>' alternative to fossil fuels. The <u>carbon dioxide</u> released into the atmosphere was taken in by <u>plants</u> which lived recently, so they're '<u>carbon neutral</u>'.

2) The use of biofuels <u>doesn't</u> produce significant amounts of sulfur dioxide or nitrous oxides, which cause <u>acid rain</u>.

3) <u>Methane</u> is a <u>greenhouse gas</u> and is one of those responsible for <u>global warming</u>. It's given off by <u>untreated waste</u>, which may be kept in farmyards or spread on agricultural land as fertiliser. Burning it as biogas means it's <u>not</u> released into the atmosphere.

4) The raw material is <u>cheap</u> and <u>readily available</u>.

5) The digested material is a <u>better fertiliser</u> than undigested dung — so people can grow <u>more crops</u>.

6) In some developing rural communities <u>people</u> have to spend hours each day <u>collecting wood for fuel</u>. Biogas saves them from having to do this task.

7) Biogas generators act as a <u>waste disposal system</u>, getting rid of human and animal waste that would otherwise lie around, causing <u>disease</u> and <u>polluting water supplies</u>.

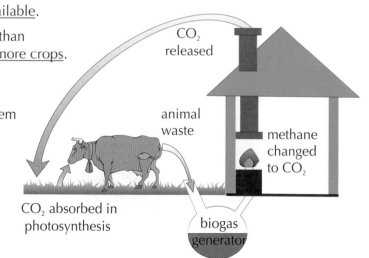

CO₂ released

animal waste

methane changed to CO₂

CO₂ absorbed in photosynthesis

biogas generator

Warm-Up and Exam Questions

Warm-Up Questions

1) How do yeast cells reproduce?
2) Why do brewers want their yeast to respire anaerobically, not aerobically?
3) What is the purpose of distilling alcoholic drinks?
4) What is gasohol?
5) Name the substance that is the chief component of biogas.

Exam Questions

1   Matthew did an experiment to measure the rate of growth of a yeast population at 25 °C. The graph shows his results.

   (a)   Name two conditions, apart from temperature, that Matthew should have kept constant in his experiment.

(2 marks)

   (b)   Suggest why the population stops growing at point X.

(1 mark)

   (c)   Sketch a graph showing how you would expect the population to grow if Matthew repeated his experiment at 35 °C.

(2 marks)

2   A brewery claims that 'Our beer contains only malted barley, water, hops and yeast'.
   (a)   Explain how barley is malted.

(2 marks)

   (b)   In the beer, what is the purpose of using: (i)   hops?

(1 mark)

                 (ii)   yeast?

(1 mark)

   (c)   Beer is sometimes pasteurised before it is bottled. Explain why.

(1 mark)

3   Some Chinese villages use biogas generators to provide energy.
   (a)   What sort of waste material can be used in a biogas generator?

(1 mark)

   (b)   Villagers usually site their generators some way from their houses and close to their agricultural fields. Suggest why:

      (i)   the generator is positioned away from the houses.

(1 mark)

      (ii)   the generator is sited close to the agricultural area.

(1 mark)

   (c)   Give two benefits of using a biogas generator instead of burning coal for energy.

(2 marks)

Enzymes in Action

Enzymes are molecules made of protein, which speed up (catalyse) chemical reactions in living organisms. Scientists know a good thing when they see one, and enzymes are now used for all sorts...

Enzymes are used in *biological washing powder*

1) Some stains are caused by soluble chemicals and so they wash out easily in water. Stubborn stains contain insoluble chemicals like starch, proteins and fats. They don't wash out with just water.

2) Non-biological washing powders (detergents) contain chemicals that break up stains on your clothes.

3) Biological washing powders contain the same chemicals as non-biological ones, but also contain a mixture of enzymes which break down the stubborn stains.

Stain	Sources of stain	Enzymes	Product
Carbohydrate	Jam, chocolate	Amylases	Simple sugars
Lipid (fats)	Butter, oil	Lipases	Fatty acids and glycerol
Protein	Blood, grass	Proteases	Amino acids

4) The products of the enzyme-controlled reactions are soluble in water and so can be easily washed out of the material.

5) Biological washing powders need a cooler wash temperature than non-biological powders because the enzymes are denatured (destroyed) by high temperatures (see page 114). However, some newer powders contain enzymes that are more resistant to heat and so can be used with a hotter water temperature.

6) The enzymes work best at pH 7 (neutral). Tap water is usually about pH 7, but in areas with very hard water (which contains high levels of calcium) it might be alkaline, which can damage the enzymes.

30°C

machine wash
in lukewarm water

7) You can buy special stain removers (e.g. for wine, blood or oil). Some of these are just special solvents, but some contain specific enzymes that will break down the stain.

Medical products often use enzymes

1) Diabetes (see page 23) is diagnosed by the presence of sugar in the urine. Many years ago, doctors actually used to taste patients' urine to test for sugar... yuk. Later they tested the urine for sugar using Benedict's solution. When it's heated, the solution changes colour from blue to orange if sugar is present. This test relies on chemical properties (not enzymes).

2) Nowadays, reagent strips (strips of paper with enzymes and chemicals in them) are used. They're dipped in urine and change colour if sugar is present.

3) This test is based on a sequence of enzyme reactions. The product of the enzyme-controlled reactions causes a chemical embedded in the strip to change colour.

4) There are similar strips which can be used to test blood sugar levels (see page 240).

Enzymes in Action

Not done yet, I'm afraid. These enzymes are too useful for their own good...

Enzymes are also used in the food industry

Low-calorie food

1) Table sugar (sucrose) is what you normally sweeten food with at home.

2) In the food industry an enzyme called invertase is used to break down sucrose into glucose and fructose. Glucose and fructose are much sweeter than sucrose.

3) This means you can get the same level of sweetness using less sugar. This helps to make low-calorie food sweeter without adding calories.

See page 226 for more about invertase.

Cheese

The enzyme rennet is used to clot milk in the first stages of cheese production.

Juice extraction

The enzyme pectinase is used in fruit juice extraction. It breaks down pectin (a substance found between plant cell walls), causing the cell to release its juice.

Immobilising enzymes makes them easier to remove

When enzymes are used to speed up reactions, they end up dissolved in the mixture with the substrates and products — and can be difficult to remove. One way to avoid this is to immobilise the enzymes.

1) Many industrial processes use immobilised enzymes, which don't need to be separated out from the mixture after the reaction has taken place.

enzyme molecule encapsulated within a bead of alginate

2) Immobilised enzymes are attached to an insoluble material, e.g. fibres (like collagen or cellulose), or silica gel. Or they are encapsulated in alginate beads (alginate is a gel-like substance).

3) The immobilised enzymes are still active and still help speed up reactions.

Advantages of Immobilising Enzymes

1) The insoluble material with attached enzymes can be washed and reused.

2) The enzymes don't contaminate the product.

3) Immobilised enzymes are often more stable and less likely to denature at high temperatures or extremes of pH.

Enzymes in Action

So <u>immobilised</u> enzymes sound even more useful than the regular kind.
And just to prove it, here are some examples of how they're used.

Immobilised enzymes can be used to make lactose-free milk

1) The sugar <u>lactose</u> is naturally found in <u>milk</u> (and yoghurt).
It's broken down in your digestive system by the <u>enzyme</u>
<u>lactase</u>. This produces <u>glucose</u> and <u>galactose</u>, which are then
<u>absorbed</u> into the blood.

2) Some people <u>lack the enzyme lactase</u>. If they drink milk the
lactose isn't broken down and gut <u>bacteria</u> feed on it, causing
<u>abdominal pain</u>, <u>wind</u> and <u>diarrhoea</u> — these people are
<u>lactose intolerant</u>.

3) <u>Cats</u> are also lactose intolerant (which is strange considering
how much they seem to like milk). They can't digest lactose
and have the same symptoms as humans if they drink it.

4) <u>Lactose-free milk</u> can be produced using <u>immobilised lactase</u>.
(Special <u>lactose-free cats' milk</u> is also produced using lactase.)

5) A method called <u>continuous flow processing</u> is often used for this:

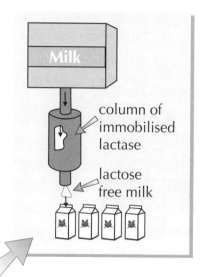

column of
immobilised
lactase

lactose
free milk

- The substrate solution (milk) is run through a <u>column of immobilised enzymes</u>.

- The enzymes convert the substrate (lactose) into the products (glucose and
galactose), but only the <u>products</u> emerge from the column. The enzymes stay
fixed in the column.

Immobilised enzymes are also used in reagent strips

1) People with <u>diabetes</u> use reagent strips to measure their <u>blood glucose concentration</u> on a
<u>daily basis</u>. They're <u>quick</u> and <u>convenient</u> to use. Before reagent strips diabetics had to
'guess' when they needed to inject insulin (e.g. before meals), because there was no quick
way of knowing what their glucose level was.

2) There are <u>immobilised enzymes</u> on the reagent strips.

3) A drop of blood from a finger prick is added to the strip. The enzymes in the strip cause it
to <u>change different colours</u> depending on the <u>glucose concentration</u>. The colour is then
compared to a <u>chart</u> to find out the level of blood sugar.

Around 5% of the population is lactose intolerant

Producing things like lactose-free milk and lactose-free ice cream is a pretty big industry. Make sure
you know how lactose-free products are made and all about immobilised enzymes.

Warm-Up and Exam Questions

You know what to do — get those brain cells working on these warm-up and exam questions.

Warm-Up Questions

1) What sort of substances do proteases break down?
2) What does the enzyme pectinase do?
3) Describe one way in which enzymes can be immobilised.
4) What is an advantage of using immobilisation in the extraction of an enzyme product?
5) What do people with diabetes use reagent strips for?

Exam Questions

1   The label from the side of a packet of washing powder says that the washing powder contains 'biological ingredients to help remove stains'.

    (a) What are these 'biological ingredients'?

(1 mark)

    (b) Explain briefly how they might help to remove grease from clothing.

(2 marks)

    (c) The washing powder works best at temperatures below 50 °C. Why is this?

(1 mark)

2   The graph shows how the rate of an enzyme-controlled reaction is affected by temperature when the enzyme is in solution and when it is immobilised on alginate beads.

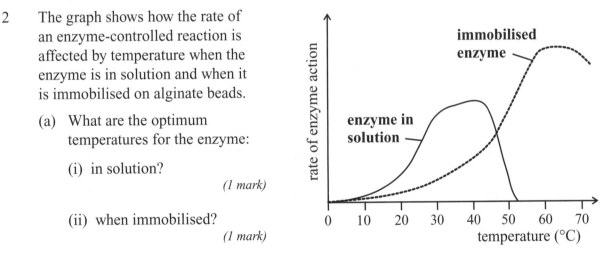

    (a) What are the optimum temperatures for the enzyme:

        (i) in solution?

(1 mark)

        (ii) when immobilised?

(1 mark)

    (b) Explain the difference between the rates of reaction at 60 °C.

(2 marks)

3   Purr-Fect Puss Cat Milk is made from cows' milk that has been treated with an enzyme. The manufacturers claim that "Purr-Fect Puss Cat Milk is easier for cats to digest", and that "cats prefer the taste of Purr-Fect Puss Cat Milk".

    (a) Name the enzyme that is used in making Purr-Fect Puss Cat Milk.

(1 mark)

    (b) Explain why the enzyme makes the milk suitable for cats.

(2 marks)

Genetically Modifying Plants

Genetic modification (another kind of biotechnology) is also on p.87. But you need more details now.

Genetically modifying plants is **different** to modifying bacteria

Genetically modified organisms (GMOs) are made by 'cutting and pasting' genes — you 'cut out' the gene for the characteristic you want, and 'paste' it into the organism you want it in. In reality, this cutting and pasting takes a bit of doing...

1) To make GM plants, scientists often use a bacterium called *Agrobacterium tumefaciens*. This naturally invades plant cells and inserts its genes into the plant's DNA.

2) If other genes are added to this bacterium, then those genes are taken along too. Works a treat.

3) For example, you could make a herbicide-resistant plant like this...

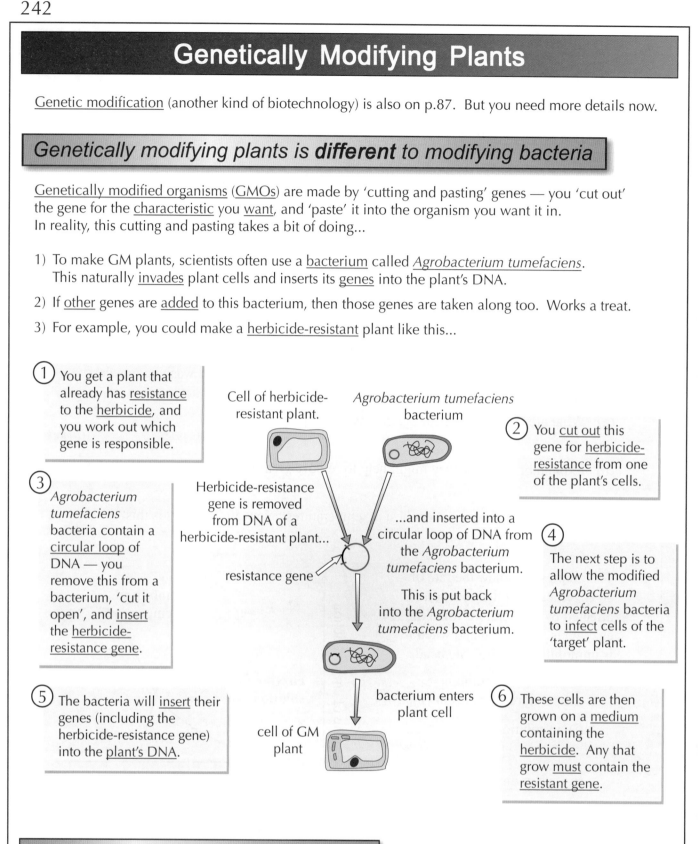

① You get a plant that already has resistance to the herbicide, and you work out which gene is responsible.

Cell of herbicide-resistant plant.

Agrobacterium tumefaciens bacterium

② You cut out this gene for herbicide-resistance from one of the plant's cells.

③ *Agrobacterium tumefaciens* bacteria contain a circular loop of DNA — you remove this from a bacterium, 'cut it open', and insert the herbicide-resistance gene.

Herbicide-resistance gene is removed from DNA of a herbicide-resistant plant...

resistance gene

...and inserted into a circular loop of DNA from the *Agrobacterium tumefaciens* bacterium.

This is put back into the *Agrobacterium tumefaciens* bacterium.

④ The next step is to allow the modified *Agrobacterium tumefaciens* bacteria to infect cells of the 'target' plant.

⑤ The bacteria will insert their genes (including the herbicide-resistance gene) into the plant's DNA.

cell of GM plant

bacterium enters plant cell

⑥ These cells are then grown on a medium containing the herbicide. Any that grow must contain the resistant gene.

GM crops **may** have **disadvantages**

There are lots of 'issues' around GM crops.

1) A big concern is that transplanted genes may get out into the natural environment. For example, the herbicide-resistance gene may be picked up by weeds, creating new 'superweeds'.

2) Some people say that growing GM crops may affect the number of weeds and flowers (and therefore wildlife) that usually lives in and around the crops — reducing farmland biodiversity.

3) Not everyone is convinced that GM crops are safe. People are worried they may develop allergies to the food — although no unexpected effects have been found in food currently on sale.

Developing New Treatments

Biotechnology can also be used when developing new <u>drugs</u> — talk about a finger in every pie. In the future studying <u>genes</u> could also be really important in developing new treatments.

Studying **genes** can lead to **development** of **new medicines**

The <u>study</u> of all the genes in an organism is called <u>genomics</u>. Genomics could have useful applications in various fields (for example, <u>medicine</u> and <u>agriculture</u>). It's the applications to <u>medicine</u> that you need to know about:

1) Determining which genes <u>predispose</u> people to diseases (make people <u>more likely</u> to get them) could lead to better <u>early diagnosis</u>, or even <u>prevention</u> of diseases.

2) Identifying defective genes and <u>what they do</u> can help scientists understand how a disease is <u>caused</u>, and so how to treat it. This might be with a <u>drug</u> or with <u>gene therapy</u> (see p.81).

3) Not everyone responds to the same drug in the <u>same way</u> because everyone has <u>different genes</u>. It may be possible in the future to <u>tailor</u> drugs to an <u>individual's genes</u> .

4) The more we know about the <u>pathogens' genes</u> and <u>what they do</u>, the more likely we are to be able to work out <u>new ways</u> to kill them.

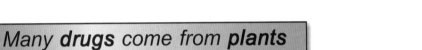

Many **drugs** come from **plants**

1) <u>Plants</u> and <u>animals</u> produce a variety of <u>chemicals</u>, some of which can be used as <u>drugs</u>. A lot of our current medicines were discovered by studying plants used in <u>traditional cures</u>.

2) Scientists identify promising plants, then look for the <u>active</u> <u>ingredient</u> (the chemical in the plant that <u>causes</u> the effect).

Scientists also 'screen' large numbers of plants to see if they contain anything useful.

Quinine

- <u>Quinine</u> comes from the South American <u>cinchona tree</u>.

- For years, it was the main treatment against <u>malaria</u> (though more effective drugs were produced in the 1930s).

Malaria is an infectious disease carried by mosquitoes. It kills over a million people a year.

Artemisinin

- One of the newer <u>anti-malarial</u> drugs is <u>artemisinin</u> — it comes from the plant *Artemisia annua*. It's an effective treatment, and it could help prevent <u>transmission</u> of the disease.

- It was used in <u>traditional Chinese medicine</u> to treat malaria and skin diseases.

- Chinese scientists isolated it in 1972. The rest of the world found out about it a bit later.

- Other, more powerful drugs have since been <u>derived</u> from artemisinin.

Developing New Treatments

Drug companies don't develop and produce new drugs just for the good of mankind —
they do it in order to make a profit. Sometimes this can lead to a conflict between
making money and saving lives.

Drug **development** costs a lot of **money**

1) Modern drugs can be very expensive to produce. When drug companies
   produce a new drug, they take out a patent on it — this means that only
   they can make it and sell it for a certain number of years.

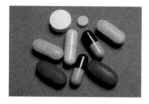

2) This allows the company to make back the huge amount of money needed
   to research and develop the drug (see page 37). But some people say that
   the patent means this company can basically charge what they like.

3) This is controversial — not everyone who needs them can afford treatments
   still under patent. Often it's people in developing countries who will suffer most.

Some people think

- Drug companies could charge less for their drugs and still make a profit.

- Making any profit from people's illnesses is unethical.

- Other companies should be allowed to copy the drugs and reproduce them cheaply.
  (They wouldn't have spent any money on research and development, so could afford
  to charge much lower prices.)

Other people think

- It'd be unfair if other companies could make and sell the treatment more cheaply
  when they haven't had to do any of the expensive research. Everyone would want
  to buy the cheaper version and the company that developed the drug might not be
  able to cover their costs.

- Profit from successful drugs has to cover the costs of research on drugs that are
  rejected during trials (which many are).

- There'd be no reason for a company to develop new treatments if they couldn't
  make a profit — so there would be no more new drugs.

Profit versus people — but it's not as simple as it might first sound

You might not have thought it but even making new drugs can be a bit of a controversial issue.
Make sure you know both sides of the argument — they could sneak a question about it into the exam.

Warm-Up and Exam Questions

Warm-Up Questions

1) What is a genetically modified organism?
2) What does a patent allow a company to do?
3) Give two possible benefits of genomics.
4) What is the drug artemisinin used for?

Exam Questions

1   A farmer is growing genetically modified tomato plants in his field. The plants have been modified to make them resistant to insect pests.

    (a)   The farmer claims that, by growing these crops, the farm actually does **less** damage to the environment than growing standard tomato plants. Explain why this may be so.

(1 mark)

    (b)   Some local residents object to the farmer growing these GM plants.
         Explain why they might object on the grounds of:

        (i)   danger to human health.   (ii)   danger to the environment.

(2 marks)

2   Herbicide-resistant soya bean plants can be produced by genetic modification.
     The stages involved in this process are shown below, but their order has been mixed up.

Resistance gene inserted into bacterial DNA loop.
Bacterium allowed to infect soya plant cells.
Resistance gene extracted from a wild bean plant. DNA loop removed from bacterium.
Modified DNA loop re-inserted into bacterium.
Modified soya cells grown in a medium containing herbicide.

    (a) List these processes in the correct order.

(2 marks)

    (b) Explain why the soya cells are grown in a medium containing herbicide.

(1 mark)

3   The Shareall Political Party says in its manifesto that it wants to control the prices that pharmaceutical companies charge for drugs. If elected, they plan to set a maximum price that companies can charge for drugs. And after ten years, other rival companies would be allowed to copy a new drug and sell it at a cheaper price.

    (a) Suggest an advantage of the Shareall Party's plan.

(1 mark)

    (b) The drugs companies say that this policy will be damaging in the long run.
        Explain why this might be so.

(2 marks)

Revision Summary for Section Eleven

I bet you thought you'd never get to the end of this book... well, you're not quite there yet, there's still a whole other section to come. I never knew how interesting microorganisms could be, they do so many different things — making yoghurt, causing disease, clearing up sugar spills, making booze and biogas. And as for those useful enzymes... they're a barrel of laughs.

1) State the function of the following parts of a bacterial cell:
   a) flagellum   b) cell wall   c) bacterial DNA.

2) How do bacteria reproduce?

3) Describe the four stages in an infectious disease.

4) Explain why natural disasters often cause rapid spread of disease.

5) Describe the process of making yoghurt.

6) Name the three types of microorganism used to make soy sauce.

7) Why are plant stanol esters added to spreads?

8) What are prebiotics? Why might some people choose to take them as a supplement?

9) How is chymosin traditionally obtained?
   Where does the chymosin used to make vegetarian cheese come from?

10) What is vitamin C used for? What species of bacterium helps to produce it?

11) How is MSG made? What is it used for?

12) What is carrageenan used for and where does it come from?

13) State the word equations for anaerobic respiration and aerobic respiration in yeast.

14) How is the rate of breakdown of sugar by yeast affected by temperature?

15) Describe the main stages in brewing beer.

16) How could you increase the alcohol concentration of a fermented product?

17) What are the two main components of biogas?

18)*Loompah is a small village. It's very hot in the summer but freezing cold in winter. The villagers keep goats and cows. They also try to grow crops, but the soil isn't very fertile, so it's difficult. The villagers currently rely on wood for fuel for heating and cooking. There's not much of this around, so they spend a lot of time collecting it.
   a)   How suitable do you think biogas would be for this village? Explain the advantages that using biogas would have for the village. What disadvantages or problems might there be?
   b)   Loompah starts using biogas and uses the digested material as fertiliser. They compare their crops with those grown by the village of Moompah, which uses normal manure as a fertiliser. Loompah's crops are bigger, so they conclude that the digested material is a better fertiliser than manure. What do you think of the conclusion they've drawn?

19) Which enzyme in biological powder would break down a stain made of: a) butter, b) grass?

20) Why do biological washing powders need a cool wash temperature and neutral pH?

21) Name an enzyme that breaks down sucrose. What is this enzyme used for in the food industry?

22) Give three advantages of immobilising enzymes.

23) Describe how *Agrobacterium tumefaciens* is used to genetically engineer plants, using the example of herbicide-resistant genes.

24) Describe three possible disadvantages of GM crops.

25) How might the study of genomics help develop new medicines?

26) Describe one way that a drug from a plant might be discovered.

27) Explain the arguments for and against pharmaceutical companies patenting their new drugs.

28) Why do some people think that drug company profits aren't fair?

* Answers on page 295.

Instinctive and Learned Behaviour

Behaviour is quite a complicated topic, but luckily it's pretty interesting too...

Behaviour is an **organism's response** to **changes** in its **environment**

1) Behaviour is how an organism <u>responds</u> to things going on in its environment — helping it to <u>survive</u>.

2) Behaviour can either be <u>inherited</u> or <u>learned</u>, but most behaviour relies on a <u>combination</u> of the two.

3) Both your <u>genes</u> and your <u>environment</u> play a part in influencing your behaviour and it's sometimes hard to decide what is inherited and what is learned. One example is <u>human speech</u>:

> Most humans are born with the <u>instinctive</u> ability to speak, but if a child is born <u>deaf</u>, or is brought up in <u>isolation</u> and doesn't hear people <u>speaking</u>, then it may not learn to speak properly. Humans have to <u>learn</u> language.

Some behaviour is **inherited**

1) Inherited behaviour is also known as <u>instinctive behaviour</u>.

2) Animals can respond in the <u>right way</u> to a stimulus <u>straight away</u>, even though they've never done it before, e.g. newborn mammals have an instinct to suckle from their mothers.

3) Instinctive behaviour can be a fairly simple <u>reflex</u>, or a <u>complicated</u> behaviour, like a courtship ritual.

Suckling is instinctive.

> <u>Reflex actions</u> are simple inherited behaviours, where a stimulus produces a fairly simple response. For example:
>
> • <u>sneezing</u>   • <u>salivation</u>   • <u>coughing</u>   • <u>blinking</u>
>
> They often protect us from <u>dangerous stimuli</u>. Reflexes are <u>automatic</u> actions — you don't have to think about them.

A stimulus is a detectable change in the environment.

> Some types of <u>reflex</u> are slightly more complex:
>
> 1) Earthworms show what's known as '<u>negative phototaxis</u>' — they <u>move away</u> from light.
>
> 2) <u>Sea anemones</u> wave their tentacles more when stimulated by <u>chemicals</u> emitted by their prey.

sea anemone

Instinctive and Learned Behaviour

The other main type of behaviour is <u>learned</u> behaviour. This develops over time, with experience.

*Some behaviour is **learned***

<u>Learned behaviour</u> isn't <u>inherited</u> — you have to learn it, obviously. It lets animals <u>respond</u> to <u>changing conditions</u>. Animals can learn from their previous <u>experiences</u> how to avoid predators and harmful food, and how to find food or a suitable mate.

Habituation

1) If you keep on giving an animal a stimulus that isn't <u>beneficial</u> or <u>harmful</u> to it, it quickly learns <u>not</u> to respond to it. This is called <u>habituation</u>.

2) This is the reason why crows eventually learn to <u>ignore scarecrows</u> (because they don't harm the bird or reward it).

3) It's also why you can often <u>sleep through</u> loud and familiar noises, like traffic, but might wake up instantly at a quiet but <u>unfamiliar</u> noise.

4) By <u>ignoring</u> non-threatening and non-rewarding stimuli, animals can spend their time and energy more <u>efficiently</u>.

5) This is an especially important learning process in <u>young animals</u> — they are born with an inherited tendency to be frightened by loud, bright, sudden stimuli and they must quickly learn which stimuli to ignore so they can concentrate on stimuli that are possibly dangerous.

*Behaviour learned **early in life** has a particularly **big impact***

<u>Experiences</u> in very <u>early</u> life, when the brain is actively <u>developing</u>, can massively affect later <u>behaviour</u>. Examples include:

1) <u>Pigs</u> removed from their <u>mothers</u> at an early stage become more <u>aggressive</u> adults.

2) Some birds never learn the proper <u>bird song</u> for their species if they are kept in <u>isolation</u> when they're young.

3) Babies whose parents <u>argue</u> a lot are thought to be more prone to suffering from attacks of <u>rage</u> when they get older.

In many animals, walking is instinctive — but in humans it's learned

<u>Habituation</u> happens <u>more often</u> than you'd think — e.g. you learn to ignore the stimuli produced by the weight of your clothes because you're used to wearing them. There is also a type of habituation nicknamed 'banner blindness' where internet users fail to notice advertising banners after a while.

Instinctive and Learned Behaviour

Habituation isn't the only type of learned behaviour. Another important type is conditioning, and there are two kinds of conditioning, classical and operant.

Classical conditioning was used in Pavlov's famous experiment

1) Classical conditioning happens when an animal learns passively (i.e. without actually trying) to associate a 'neutral stimulus' with an important one.

2) For example, a dog might learn to associate a bell ringing with the arrival of food (see below).

3) The response is automatic and reinforced by repetition.

Example: Ivan Pavlov — classical conditioning in dogs

Pavlov studied the behaviour of dogs and noticed that they would salivate (drool) every time they saw or smelled food. He began to ring a bell just before the dogs were given their food. After a while he found that the dogs salivated when the bell was rung even if he didn't give them any food.

Operant conditioning involves active learning

1) Operant conditioning is also known as 'trial and error learning'.

2) It happens where an animal learns actively to associate an action with a reward or a punishment (so the animal actually tries to work out what's going on.)

3) This happens in humans when children are rewarded or punished for specific behaviour.

Example: Burrhus Skinner — operant behaviour in pigeons and rats

Skinner trained rats and pigeons to obtain a food reward using a small cage that he invented (called a 'Skinner box'). The animal had a choice of buttons to press. When the animal pressed a particular lever or button, it was rewarded with food. He found that pigeons and rats used a system of trial and error to learn which button to press to get the reward.

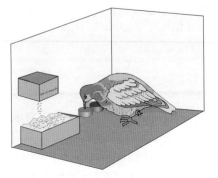

Instinctive and Learned Behaviour

Teaching animals to salivate when a bell rings or to peck a certain button may not be very helpful, but conditioning can be used to <u>train</u> animals and get them to behave in a way that's useful. Both <u>classical</u> and <u>operant conditioning</u> are used to train animals.

Operant conditioning is used most often to train animals

1) Training animals usually involves <u>operant conditioning</u> — giving <u>rewards</u> when the animal does what you want or <u>punishments</u> when it does something you don't want it to do.

2) Rewards like <u>food treats</u> work best, but sometimes just <u>praise</u> will do.

3) Punishments can be <u>physical</u> (for example, <u>choke chains</u> which pull around a dog's neck if it pulls on the lead) or <u>verbal</u> (like saying 'No!').

4) However, punishment <u>isn't recommended</u> any more for animal training — it's stressful for the animal and rewards work just as well.

Here are some examples of animal training using <u>operant conditioning</u>:

- Training <u>guide dogs</u> to <u>stop</u> at a roadside and <u>wait</u> for a command.
- Training police <u>sniffer dogs</u> to retrieve <u>drugs</u>.
- Training animals to 'act' in films, for example <u>horses falling down</u> as if they have been shot.

In certain situations, classical conditioning is needed too

Classical conditioning is used in <u>combination</u> with operant conditioning when the reward <u>can't</u> be given at the <u>exact</u> time the behaviour is carried out. For example:

1) A trainer can't always reward a performing <u>dolphin</u> with a fish at the exact moment it does a jump — it wouldn't be practical.

2) So the trainer gets the dolphin to learn to associate a <u>whistle</u> with getting fish, then whistles when the animal does the jump.

3) The whistle is, in a way, the reward, as it tells the dolphin that it will soon get a fish.

Reward good behaviour, punish bad — it's really just common sense

It's really important that you know the difference between classical conditioning and operant conditioning. Classical conditioning involves passive learning and operant conditioning involves active learning. The method used to train an animal will vary from situation to situation.

Social Behaviour and Communication

You thought it was only humans that had social lives and nice chats? Wrong!

Animals need to **communicate**

<u>Communication</u> between different animals in a group is <u>beneficial</u> in a number of ways. For example:

1) It can help keep the group <u>together</u>.

2) If any one animal sees a <u>predator</u>, it can <u>warn</u> all the others.

3) Communication of <u>mood</u> can avoid unnecessary <u>fighting</u>.

4) <u>Baby</u> animals can communicate their <u>needs</u> to their parents.

5) Communication can allow predators <u>hunting</u> in a pack to <u>coordinate</u> their attack.

Animals can communicate in **different ways**

Sound

Communication by <u>sound</u> is quite <u>common</u> in nature:

- <u>Whales</u> and <u>dolphins</u> can communicate over <u>long distances</u> using low-frequency sound.
- <u>Birds' calls</u> are used to declare their <u>territory</u>, attract a <u>mate</u> or warn others about <u>predators</u>.
- <u>Humans</u> communicate using sound too — through <u>language</u>.

Chemicals

Chemicals called <u>pheromones</u> can be released by animals to tell others <u>where it is</u> or <u>has been</u>:

- Many animals use chemical 'scents' to mark their <u>territory</u>, e.g. dogs pee on things.
- Other chemicals can act as <u>sexual attractants</u>. In some <u>moths</u>, the male can detect the female's pheromone even if he's several kilometres away from her.

Behaviour

Some animals use specific <u>behaviour signals</u> to communicate:

- <u>Honey bees</u> move in a certain way, called a '<u>waggle dance</u>', when they return to the hive to tell others where they've found <u>food</u>.
- Most <u>mammals</u> can communicate certain intentions through their <u>body posture</u> (how they hold themselves) and <u>gestures</u> (small movements). For example, many use behaviours to <u>threaten</u> others — to <u>intimidate</u> them and so avoid an actual fight. <u>Chimps</u> do this by <u>staring</u> or raising an <u>arm</u>.
- Just as behaviours are used to threaten, they're also used to <u>admit</u> <u>defeat</u> — e.g. a <u>dog</u> rolling on its back is showing <u>submission</u>.
- There are plenty of <u>courtship</u> behaviours in different species too — from funny <u>dances</u> to offering <u>gifts</u> to building elaborate <u>nests</u>.

Male peacocks display their tail feathers during courtship.

Social Behaviour and Communication

Humans have loads of different ways of communicating. It's <u>not</u> just about talking.

Humans *have* **complex** *ways of communicating*

There are loads of ways that you can <u>communicate</u> things to others, whether you <u>mean to</u> or not:

Language

1) <u>Language</u> is the most obvious form of human communication.

2) It can be <u>spoken</u>, <u>written</u> or <u>signed</u>, and is used to transmit knowledge of <u>past events</u>, <u>emotions</u> and <u>complex ideas</u> to other humans.

3) Language is <u>intentional</u> — you only use it when you <u>consciously</u> mean to communicate something.

4) It's also <u>symbolic</u> — words are used to <u>represent</u> objects or ideas. For example, we use the word 'carpet' to represent a soft covering for floors.

5) Complex language like this is <u>unique</u> to humans, although it is possible that animals such as some of the <u>great apes</u> have a very <u>simple</u> form of language.

6) The <u>way</u> we speak is important, too — the <u>volume</u> and <u>tone</u> of speech can indicate emotions like excitement, anger, fear, etc.

Non-verbal communication

<u>Non-verbal</u> communication in humans is also pretty <u>complex</u>. Some types of non-verbal communication are <u>intentional</u> and others <u>aren't</u>. The intentional, conscious types are <u>different</u> around the world, like languages are. For example, in Britain we indicate 'no' by shaking our heads, but in Greece they jerk their heads backwards. Other types of non-verbal communication are <u>automatic</u> (although they may be suppressed if we really try), and are the <u>same</u> all <u>around the world</u>:

<u>Unconscious facial expressions</u> are the same for everyone. We all raise our eyebrows in <u>surprise</u>, smile or laugh when we're <u>happy</u>, cry when we're <u>sad</u> and screw up our faces in <u>disgust</u>. These expressions are useful for telling others how we <u>feel</u> about things.

<u>Body language</u> is also a way in which we can <u>unconsciously</u> communicate our <u>feelings</u>, for example: pointing your leg or body towards someone may indicate your <u>interest</u> in them. Standing with your hands on your hips may indicate <u>aggression</u>. Showing your open palms may indicate <u>honesty</u>. Avoiding eye contact may indicate <u>shyness</u> or <u>deception</u>. There are loads of other examples.

All these forms of communication go on at the same time. Language is important, but research indicates that most people <u>react</u> far more to <u>non-verbal signals</u> than to what people are actually <u>saying</u>.

Social Behaviour and Communication

So stuff like frowning and smiling is the <u>same</u> whether you're Spanish or Japanese. But it's <u>not</u> the same whether you're a human or a chimpanzee...

Facial expressions are species-specific

We're all familiar with human expressions, but we shouldn't apply them to other animals. Facial expressions mean different things in different <u>species</u> — they're <u>species-specific</u>.

A <u>chimpanzee</u> that appears to be 'smiling' is really expressing <u>fear</u> if its teeth are exposed. And if its lips are closed it's actually <u>threatening</u> you, so you should probably stop doing whatever it is that you're doing pretty quick.

To us, this chimp looks like he's laughing, but really he's showing fear.

Some people think humans are more self-aware

Some scientists believe that one thing that distinguishes humans from other animals is <u>self-awareness</u>. The problem is, people don't all <u>define</u> self-awareness in the same way.

Here are two different definitions:

1 The most basic definition of <u>self-awareness</u> is being <u>aware</u> of your own <u>existence</u>. It's often tested by showing an animal its own image in a <u>mirror</u>. If it thinks it's seeing another animal, it isn't self-aware, but if it realises that what it's seeing is itself, it is <u>self-aware</u>. <u>Human</u> babies can do this at a very early age, but so do some other animals, like <u>chimps</u> and <u>dolphins</u>.

2 Some people think self-awareness is also about being <u>aware</u> of your own behaviour and feelings (<u>consciousness</u>), and the possible outcomes of your behaviour (<u>accountability</u>). For example, you know that if you watch your favourite programme on the TV, you will <u>enjoy</u> it. You also know that if you eat all your brother's sweets, he'll get <u>angry</u>.

It's hard to tell if <u>animals</u> have consciousness and accountability, because we can only see what they <u>do</u> — we can't tell what they're <u>thinking</u> when they do it. So the level of self-awareness in animals is <u>open to debate</u>, but we're pretty sure humans are <u>more self-aware</u> than other animals.

So spare a thought for all those 'smiling' chimps you see in films

If you've got a baby brother or sister, you can try the <u>self-awareness experiment</u> out at home. Stick a red dot on their forehead, leave them to forget about it, then sit them in front of the mirror. If they start feeling their forehead then it proves that they know their reflection is <u>them</u> and not a different baby.

Warm-Up and Exam Questions

Question time again — Warm-Up first, then Exam (or the other way round if you want to be different).

Warm-Up Questions

1) What is a reflex? Give an example.
2) How can operant conditioning be used to train a dog to sit?
3) Give three advantages of animals being able to communicate with others of their species.
4) How might you test whether an animal is self-aware?

Exam Questions

1 (a) What is meant by habituation?

(1 mark)

(b) Is habituation an example of learned or inherited behaviour? Explain your answer.

(2 marks)

(c) Explain the advantage to an animal of habituation.

(1 mark)

2 A rat is placed inside a Skinner box.
The box contains two different levers,
A and B. When the rat presses lever A,
it receives food. When it presses
lever B, nothing happens.

The graph shows the frequency with which
the rat pressed each lever over two days.

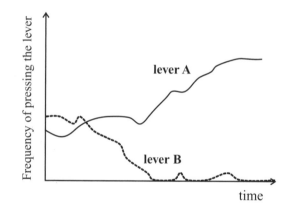

(a) Compare the frequency with which the rat pressed the levers over the two days.

(2 marks)

(b) What kind of learning process does this demonstrate?

(1 mark)

(c) What would you expect to happen if the rat was left in the box
but food was no longer supplied when it pressed lever A?

(1 mark)

3 Animals can communicate with other members of their species in several
different ways, such as by making sounds or using visual signals.

(a) Suggest which of these methods might be the more important for birds trying
to find a mate in the thick canopy of the Amazon rainforest.

(1 mark)

(b) Describe one other way in which animals can communicate (apart from through
sound and vision), and give an example of this method of communication.

(2 marks)

Exam Questions

4   Humans can communicate using language and non-verbal communication.

(a)   What is meant by non-verbal communication?

(1 mark)

(b)   Explain the usual meaning of these non-verbal signals to a Northern European:

A — screwing up the face   **B** — shaking the head   **C** — raising the eyebrows

(3 marks)

(c)   Which of behaviours A, B and C are learned and which are inherited?

(1 mark)

5   Karl von Frisch discovered that honey bees can communicate by performing a
'waggle-dance'. The same type of waggle-dance is performed by bees all over the world. A
bee that has found a source of nectar will dance in a figure-of-eight pattern. The speed and
orientation of the dance is related to the distance and direction of the nectar source.
Other bees, when they see the dance, can then fly straight to the source of nectar.

(a)   Is this an example of learned or inherited behaviour? Explain your answer.

(2 marks)

(b)   Explain the advantage to the bees of this behaviour.

(1 mark)

6   An experiment was done on
classical conditioning.
Dogs were conditioned to
salivate upon hearing a bell
by providing them with food
at the same time as the bell
was rung. The volume of
saliva secreted by the dogs was
measured. Later, the bell was
rung without food being provided
and the effect was measured.
The results are shown on the graph.

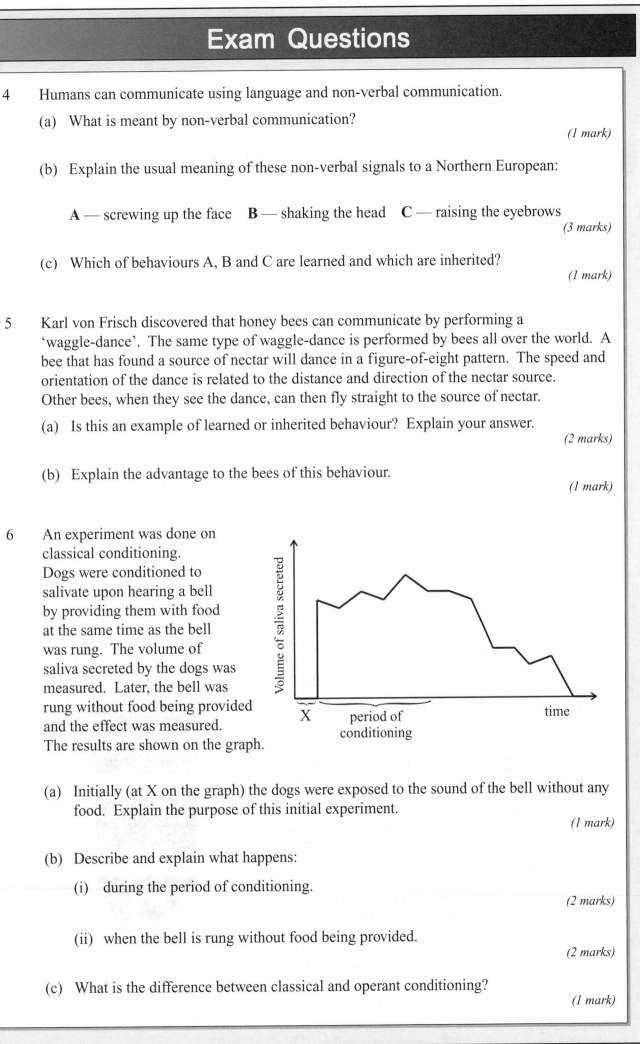

(a)   Initially (at X on the graph) the dogs were exposed to the sound of the bell without any
food. Explain the purpose of this initial experiment.

(1 mark)

(b)   Describe and explain what happens:

(i)   during the period of conditioning.

(2 marks)

(ii)   when the bell is rung without food being provided.

(2 marks)

(c)   What is the difference between classical and operant conditioning?

(1 mark)

Feeding Behaviours

Herbivores (plant-eaters) and carnivores (meat-eaters) have really different lifestyles —
and it's all because of their choice of food.

Feeding behaviour depends on what you eat

If you eat a certain type of food, you'll need to use a certain type of behaviour in order to get your
food in the most efficient way. This is why the feeding behaviour of herbivores and carnivores is
quite different.

This page focuses on the carnivores:

Carnivores

1) Carnivores are animals that eat meat, i.e. other animals.

2) Meat is a nutrient-rich food, so they don't need to spend long feeding compared to herbivores.

3) Carnivores like lions and tigers will eat a large amount of food when they catch prey, but then
may go several days without feeding at all.

Successful carnivores are adapted for detecting and catching their prey (predation):

- They have eyes at the front of their head, which helps them to judge distance
accurately when stalking and catching prey.

- They are usually quick and powerfully built, with sharp teeth and claws to help
them kill and eat their prey.

Some carnivores hunt in packs and others hunt on their own.

- Hunting in packs is useful for catching large animals
— e.g. lions hunt in packs to catch zebra and water
buffalo. Because the prey is large, it will be enough
to feed all the animals, and a lion probably couldn't
kill a buffalo alone.

- Carnivores that eat smaller animals tend to hunt
individually — what they catch only has to feed
themselves. E.g. foxes hunt individually for small
animals like rabbits (which they can catch fairly easily).

- Wolves hunt in packs for large animals like deer, but
also hunt individually for smaller prey such as
squirrels and mice.

Feeding Behaviours

Herbivores are very different to carnivores in <u>appearance</u> and <u>behaviour</u>.

There are advantages and disadvantages of being a **herbivore**

Herbivores are animals that <u>eat plants</u> and not other animals. Rabbits, cows, sheep, deer, horses and guinea pigs are all herbivores. Here are the main points about these guys:

Herbivores

1) Herbivores <u>don't</u> need to <u>catch</u> their food, which is a bonus.

2) However, because vegetation is <u>low</u> in some <u>essential nutrients</u> like amino acids (needed for growth), they need to eat a <u>lot</u> of plants to get enough nutrients.

3) Plants are also more <u>difficult to digest</u>, which makes it even harder to get those nutrients.

4) So, herbivores have to spend a lot of <u>time</u> eating in order to get enough nutrients. Donkeys, for instance, spend six to seven hours feeding every day.

5) Spending so long eating can be quite <u>dangerous</u> — it's hard to spot <u>predators</u> when you're eating.

6) <u>Vertebrate</u> herbivores like wildebeest and buffalo often feed in large groups or <u>herds</u> for <u>safety</u>. At any given time, there'll always be some of the group <u>not feeding</u> who may be able to <u>spot</u> predators and warn the herd.

7) Some members of the herd will probably still get <u>caught</u>, but the risk for any one individual is much <u>lower</u> when there's all those others in the group to choose instead.

8) The problem with feeding in a group is that the herd will quickly <u>eat up</u> all the food in one area, so they often have to <u>travel</u> large distances to get enough food.

As herbivores are the main food of most carnivores, herbivores have <u>evolved</u> methods of <u>spotting</u>, <u>avoiding</u>, <u>fleeing</u> from or <u>resisting</u> predation. <u>Antelopes</u>, for instance, are very <u>quick</u>. <u>Buffaloes</u> have strong <u>horns</u> which they use to defend themselves and the herd. And finally, most herbivores have <u>eyes</u> on the <u>sides</u> of their head rather than the front. This means that they can see almost all <u>around</u> them, making it easier to <u>spot</u> predators.

Animals are adapted to be herbivores or carnivores

Remember, these diets are what the animals <u>primarily</u> eat. Herbivores might eat bones if they have a nutritional deficiency, and carnivores eat plant matter in the stomachs of their prey. Carnivores often won't turn down sweet or milky food either. And don't forget <u>omnivores</u> — they eat plants <u>and</u> meat.

Feeding Behaviours

Now that you know <u>what</u> animals eat, it's time to consider <u>how</u> they do it. Knife and fork perhaps?

Mammals and birds **feed their young**

Mammals and birds show <u>parental care</u> — they look after and <u>feed</u> their young for some time after birth. Mammals feed their young on <u>milk</u>, whereas birds bring back food to the nest and then <u>regurgitate</u> it to feed their chicks.

Certain behaviours will <u>indicate</u> to the mother that her young <u>want to be fed</u>:

1) In mammals, this is usually the young <u>sucking</u> on the mother's teat — milk will be automatically <u>released</u> to feed the baby.

2) In birds, it's a bit more complex. The young birds may <u>call</u> to their parents in order to be fed, or open their <u>mouths</u> wide, showing off the <u>bright colour</u> inside their mouths. These <u>stimuli</u> cause the parents to <u>regurgitate</u> food into the mouths of their chicks.

Learn the following **example** *of a* **feeding behaviour**

Young <u>herring gulls</u> peck on a <u>red spot</u> on the mother's beak, and this <u>stimulates</u> the mother to <u>regurgitate</u> food. The young birds are 'programmed' to do this when they're hungry (i.e. it's instinctive behaviour). They will peck at <u>any</u> red spot when they're hungry — it doesn't have to be a real beak. Even a <u>red rubber</u> on the end of a pencil will be pecked at by hungry herring gull chicks.

Red spot

Feeding Behaviours

One of the more interesting types of feeding behaviour involves the use of <u>tools</u>.
It can be quite weird to see animals being so ingenious. Learn the four examples on this page.

Some animals use **tools** to get food

It used to be thought that <u>humans</u> were the only animals that used tools, but in recent years <u>monkeys</u>, <u>apes</u> and <u>birds</u> have also been seen to do the same thing.

<u>Chimpanzees</u> build tools from <u>twigs</u>, which they use to get <u>ants</u> out of their holes. They also use sticks to get <u>honey</u> from beehives, and to dig up edible <u>roots</u>. Chimps also use <u>leaves</u> to wipe dirt, blood and fruit from their fur.

The <u>woodpecker finch</u> uses a <u>spine</u> from a <u>cactus</u> to lever <u>grubs</u> out from tree bark. The finch uses the spine in its beak, then holds it under its foot while eating the grub. It then <u>carries</u> the spine to the next branch and <u>reuses</u> it.

<u>Hooded monkeys</u> in a lab were given a situation where yoghurt was available in narrow plastic tubes fixed to the table. The monkeys managed to get the yoghurt out by making '<u>spoons</u>' from pieces of wood which were available.

<u>Egyptian vultures</u> eat ostrich eggs, which have shells that are too hard to break open by pecking. The vultures have learned to throw <u>rocks</u> at them to break them instead. Other birds break eggs by throwing the <u>eggs</u> at rocks. This behaviour <u>isn't</u> considered to be tool use though, because to be classed as tool use, the rock must be used as an <u>extension</u> of the bird's own <u>body</u>.

Animals learn to use tools from parents or others in their social group

You find <u>different</u> sorts of tool use in different <u>populations</u> of the same species. E.g. some chimps might use an 'ant stick', and leaves as wet-wipes — but some other chimps fifty miles away will use a 'honey stick', and leaves as umbrellas. This proves that such behaviours are <u>learned</u>, not genetic.

Warm-Up and Exam Questions

Warm-Up Questions

1) What is a carnivore?
2) Why do carnivores often have both their eyes positioned on the front of their heads?
3) Why do herbivores have to spend so much of their time feeding?
4) Which two groups of animals show the most parental care?
5) Give an example of a bird using a tool to get food.

Exam Questions

1   Which of the following are examples of tool use by animals?

A — a thrush breaking open a snail's shell on a stone.
B — a monkey using a stick to remove edible insects from their burrows.
C — a dog using its teeth to kill its prey.

(1 mark)

2   The picture shows the head of a wildebeest.

(a) Describe one feature of this animal, visible in the diagram, that helps it to:

    (i)   detect the approach of a predator.

    (ii) defend itself against predators.
                  (2 marks)

(b) Wildebeest usually feed in large groups. Explain how this behaviour helps the wildebeest to avoid predators.

(1 mark)

3   Adult herring gulls have a red spot on their beaks. When a herring gull chick sees the red spot on its parent's beak, it pecks at the red area. When the parent bird is pecked at, it regurgitates food.

(a) In this behaviour:

    (i)   what is the stimulus for the parent bird to regurgitate food?

(1 mark)

    (ii) what is the stimulus for the chick to peck?

(1 mark)

(b) The behaviour of the chicks is thought to be instinctive.

    (i)   Explain what is meant by instinctive.

(1 mark)

    (ii) Why is it important that the chick's behaviour should be instinctive?

(1 mark)

Reproductive Behaviours

Ooh... mating and reproduction. No need to get all shy though, it's only about moths and lions doing it.

To **reproduce sexually** you need to **find** and **select a mate**

Finding a potential mate is fairly easy if an animal lives in a social group, but many animals live in isolation and only spend time with others during the mating season. They have to behave in a way that will allow them to find a mate. Here are a few common ways of attracting a mate:

1) Making a sound

A lot of animals make some sort of song or call to attract a mate — for example, many birds, whales and frogs do this. It is usually the males who make the call, to attract females to them.

2) Releasing chemicals

Some insects use chemicals called pheromones as sexual attractants, but here it's usually the female who produces the signal. In moths, the pheromone can be detected by a male several kilometres away, and he can follow the trail to find the female (see page 251).

3) Displays of aggression

Sometimes, males fight each other and only the winners get to mate, e.g. deer do this. However, in many species it's usually some kind of a display rather than an actual fight (certainly at first). These displays indicate strength and give the weaker male a chance to back away rather than risk injury or death.

4) Courtship displays

Courtship displays usually involve the male doing a special display to impress the female. They involve things like exaggerated posturing, dancing and showing brightly coloured parts of the anatomy.

Courtship displays are species-specific — so the female knows she is mating with a male of the right species. There is often a link between the impressiveness of the display and the fertility of the male. In the mandrill, a mammal with a very brightly coloured face and bum, the brightness of the colours is linked with the level of testosterone, the male sex hormone.

A male mandrill

Reproductive Behaviours

How come it's always the poor old <u>male</u> that's got to be colourful and dance around singing and beating up other males? Well, there's a very good reason actually...

Females usually *invest more* in the *young* than males do

1) Often it's the <u>female</u> that's responsible for most of the <u>parental care</u> — usually involving lots of effort and risk on her part. Even in species where <u>both</u> or <u>neither</u> of the parents care for their young, females invest more in their <u>eggs</u> (which are <u>massive</u> compared to sperm and contain a <u>food source</u> to nourish the young — provided by the female).

2) So it's important that the female doesn't mate with a male of a <u>closely related species</u> by mistake. If she did, she'd produce <u>infertile</u> offspring (or none at all) and all her efforts to pass on her genes would be wasted. That's why males often have these intricate dances and songs that are <u>unique</u> to their species.

3) The female also needs to make sure that the male she chooses is as <u>strong</u> and <u>fertile</u> as possible, as this ensures that her young will have the best possible chance of <u>survival</u>.

4) This is why <u>females</u> tend to <u>select</u> a mate, and males have to show that they're <u>worthy</u> of selection. It's not so important for males to be choosy — usually they simply try to mate with as <u>many</u> females as they can, giving themselves an investment in <u>several</u> sets of offspring.

Most animals have **more than one mate**

<u>Monogamy</u> (staying with just <u>one</u> mate) occurs mostly in <u>birds</u>. It's pretty <u>rare</u> in the rest of the animal kingdom. <u>Most</u> animals have <u>more than one</u> mate, but mating patterns <u>vary</u> between species:

1) In most species, the male takes <u>no part</u> in the birth or care of the young, so there's no reason for him to stick around. Instead he'll go off and mate with <u>other females</u> during the <u>same</u> mating season.

2) In some species (some birds, for instance), he'll mate with <u>one</u> female <u>each</u> season, though not necessarily the same one from year to year.

3) In some mammals (e.g. the lion), a male may have a <u>group</u> of females which he stays with, but mates with <u>all</u> of them. These females are known as his '<u>harem</u>'.

4) The few animals that are <u>monogamous</u> include the following:

Male sea lion with his harem

- Birds — albatross, bald eagle, swan, mallard, raven, penguins and parrots
- Mammals — gibbons and prairie voles

Females of many species will often mate with several males too...

So then... what about humans? Some cultures are <u>not</u> monogamous. In these it's fine for men to have more than one wife. Other cultures have a kind of '<u>enforced monogamy</u>', where society or religion say that you should have one partner only. In these cultures you find that there's a lot of secret infidelity.

Reproductive Behaviours

Our parents often look after us for out first eighteen years (at least)
— that's a crazy length of time compared to most animals.

Some animals **look after** their **young**

1) Most animals give birth to their young and then leave them to <u>fend for themselves</u>.

2) If they lay eggs, they may <u>incubate</u> and protect the eggs until they are hatched, and then <u>leave</u>.

3) However, in some species, one or both parents <u>look after</u> the young in a variety of ways for different lengths of time.

4) The care may involve <u>protecting</u> them, <u>feeding</u> them and <u>teaching</u> them basic skills.

5) This level of care is mostly seen in <u>birds</u> and <u>mammals</u>, although <u>crocodiles</u> and some <u>fish</u> also care for their young.

Protection

Protection may just involve one parent <u>staying</u> with the young to keep them together and to fend off <u>predators</u>. In some cases, protection is helped by the construction of elaborate <u>nests</u> to enclose the young.

The <u>weaver bird</u> weaves strands of leaves and twigs into a ball, sometimes with a long tube attached, which makes it difficult for predators to take, or even notice, the young.

Feeding

Some feeding behaviours have been covered on pages 256–259 (have a look). If a species both <u>feeds</u> and <u>protects</u> its young, this usually means that <u>both parents</u> need to be involved — one to stay with the young, the other to go and find food (unless it's a <u>mammal</u>, of course, where the mother provides milk made in her own body).

Teaching Skills

Certain behaviours are <u>instinctive</u> and baby animals will learn them without being taught — e.g. <u>walking</u> in mammals, and <u>flying</u> in birds. Other skills need to be <u>taught</u>.

Birds called <u>oystercatchers</u> get food by <u>opening mussels</u>, a difficult task which an experienced bird can do in less than a minute, but one that takes months for the young to learn.

<u>Human</u> babies need to be taught a whole range of skills from how to get dressed to eating with a knife and fork (or chopsticks). Apart from in humans, where <u>language</u> is very useful in teaching, babies usually learn by simply <u>imitating</u> their parents' behaviour.

Reproductive Behaviours

Parents don't do all this just because they like their young (although they may do) and it's not so there's someone to carry on the family name. Parental behaviour is ultimately due to <u>genes</u>, and if these genes mean you raise <u>six</u> babies successfully instead of just one, the genes (and therefore the <u>behaviour</u>) will <u>spread</u> quickly through the population. Basically, it's good old Darwin again.

Looking after young increases their survival

Looking after the young puts the mother (in particular) at <u>risk</u>. <u>Food</u> has to be <u>shared</u>, and a lot of <u>time</u> has to be spent with the eggs and baby animals. If the parents protect the young from predators, they <u>decrease</u> their own chances of <u>escaping</u>.

Here are three of the main reasons why they bother:

1) More of the young survive

Parental care greatly <u>increases</u> the proportion of the young that <u>survive</u>. In birds that care for their eggs and young, about <u>25%</u> of the eggs will produce adult birds. This is high compared to most animals — for example, fewer than <u>one in a million</u> cod eggs survive to become adult fish.

2) It's less risky than pregnancy

Looking after young is <u>less risky</u> for the mother than being <u>pregnant</u>, which puts <u>strain</u> on her body and makes it more difficult to <u>escape predators</u>. If animals <u>care</u> for their young, it means they can give birth to a <u>less developed</u> baby, and so have a <u>shorter pregnancy</u> and spend less time at risk. This only applies to <u>mammals</u> though, as the embryos in birds' eggs are undeveloped when laid.

3) They share their parents' genes

Ensuring offspring survive also ensures the parents' genes survive (because offspring contain half of each parent's genes). So it is really the survival of an animal's <u>genes</u> that is important, rather than the survival of the animal itself. This may be why an animal will <u>risk death</u> (and the loss of <u>one</u> copy of its genes) to protect, for example, <u>four</u> offspring, which all contain its genes.

Still, most insects, reptiles, amphibians and fish just don't bother

Think about all the things that <u>human</u> parents and carers do — they keep their kids well-fed, clean, warm, happy, healthy and safe, and they <u>keep</u> doing it for years. They most likely hold down a job in order to pay for all the things that kids need too. And all a cod does is lay some eggs and leave. Pah.

Warm-Up and Exam Questions

Warm-Up Questions

1) Give an example of an animal that uses a sound to help it attract a mate.
2) Give two other methods that animals use to attract mates.
3) Parents may provide food for their young. Give two other ways that parents care for offspring.
4) Give two advantages of providing parental care.

Exam Questions

1   (a)   What is meant by monogamy?

(1 mark)

(b)   In some species, two adults will only mate after an elaborate courtship display. Suggest two advantages of this courtship display.

(2 marks)

2   The table shows the average number of fertilised eggs produced by one pair of adults in their lives in different animal species.

Species	No. of fertilised eggs produced per adult pair
Adder	60
Blackbird	10
Fox	15
Frog	200
Herring	500 000

(a)   Assuming that the population size for each species **remains constant**:

(i)   What is the probability of a fertilised frog's egg surviving to adulthood?

(2 marks)

(ii)   In which species would you expect an individual egg to have the lowest chance of survival?

(1 mark)

(b)   Which species would you expect to provide most parental care?
Explain your answer.

(2 marks)

3   Sticklebacks are common freshwater fish. During the breeding season, males develop a red underbelly. They also set up a territory and defend it against other males.

(a)   Suggest why it might be an advantage for a male stickleback to defend a territory and keep other males out.

(1 mark)

(b)   The males only have a red belly during the breeding season. What other function might the red colour have, apart from acting as an aggressive signal to other males?

(1 mark)

Living in Soil

Soil is made up of bits of rock, dead material (like dead leaves and animals), living things, air and water. Soil is teeming with <u>life</u> — insects, bacteria, worms and loads more icky creepy crawlies... eugh.

Soil is *full* of *living things*

1) Soil may not look all that exciting, but it's pretty important to us. Plants need it for <u>anchorage</u> (to stop them falling over) and for a <u>supply of minerals</u> and <u>water</u>. And animals need plants for food and oxygen.

2) Soil is an ecosystem in itself, containing complex <u>food webs</u>. <u>Herbivores</u> (plant-eaters), <u>carnivores</u> (meat-eaters) and <u>detritivores</u> (which feed on dead organisms) are all found in the soil.

3) There are several other types of organism that live in the soil — <u>microscopic protozoans</u>, <u>fungi</u>, <u>nematode worms</u> and <u>bacteria</u>.

4) In order for a soil to support life, it must contain <u>water</u> and <u>oxygen</u>. All living things need water to <u>carry out reactions</u> in their cells, and cannot survive without it. Almost everything needs <u>oxygen</u> too, for <u>respiration</u> (see page 124). For example, the roots of plants need to get oxygen from the soil so they can respire.

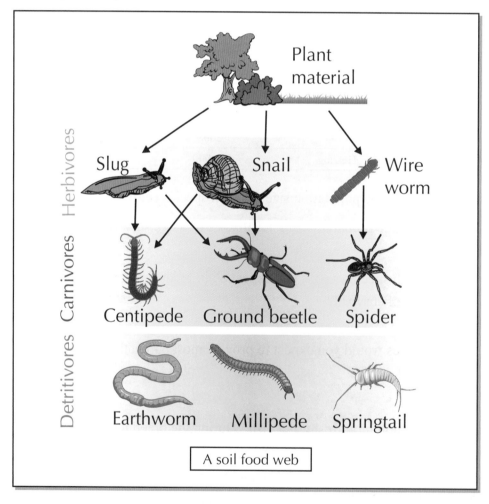

A soil food web

The food web above is just one typical example

In the exam you might get a question on <u>soil food webs</u>, e.g. 'What happens if you remove centipedes from the soil?' Well, the number of slugs and snails will increase (because fewer are being eaten) and the number of detritivores will go down (because they've got fewer dead centipedes to feed on).

Living in Soil

Some of the living things in a soil food web are <u>particularly important</u> for keeping the soil healthy. Without them, none of the other organisms in the food web could survive.

Earthworms help keep soil healthy and fertile

Charles Darwin

<u>Charles Darwin</u>, more famous for his theory of natural selection, spent an awful lot of his time <u>studying worms</u>. He observed them closely and experimented on them to see what sort of food they ate and how they behaved. He discovered these <u>reasons</u> why worms are <u>good for soil</u>:

earthworm

1) Earthworms <u>bury leaves</u> and other <u>organic material</u> in the soil, where <u>bacteria</u> can <u>decompose them</u>.

2) Their <u>burrows</u> allow <u>air to enter the soil</u> and <u>water to drain through it</u>. Aeration provides the soil organisms with <u>oxygen</u>, but drainage is important, too — if the soil is <u>waterlogged</u>, there is <u>less oxygen</u> available.

3) They <u>mix up</u> the <u>soil layers</u>, <u>distributing</u> the <u>nutrients</u> more <u>equally</u> through them.

4) Soil in earthworm poo is <u>less acidic</u> than the soil they eat. This can help to <u>neutralise soil acidity</u>, although worms tend to avoid very acidic soils. Acidic soils are <u>less fertile</u> than neutral or alkaline soils.

<u>Farmers</u> and <u>gardeners</u> can <u>buy earthworms</u> (from worm farms) and add them to their soil to improve it.

Bacteria are involved in recycling elements

1) Some elements are very important to living organisms, such as <u>nitrogen</u>, <u>sulfur</u> and <u>phosphorus</u>. Farmers sometimes add <u>fertiliser</u> (containing these elements) to the soil of their fields. But in the natural environment, there is no outside supply of these nutrients, so it's <u>essential</u> that they're <u>recycled</u>. If they weren't, they would <u>run out</u> and the plants would die... not good.

2) <u>Bacteria</u> are important in the recycling of elements, as many of them can change chemicals into other more useable ones. Different bacteria are involved in recycling different elements. E.g. in the <u>nitrogen cycle</u>, the following bacteria play a key part:

- <u>Saprophytic bacteria</u> in the soil start to <u>decompose dead material</u> into <u>ammonium compounds</u>.

- <u>Nitrifying bacteria</u>, such as <u>Nitrosomonas</u> and <u>Nitrobacter</u>. Nitrosomonas converts ammonium compounds into <u>nitrite</u>, and nitrobacter converts nitrite into <u>nitrate</u> (which plants can use).

- <u>Nitrogen-fixing bacteria</u> like <u>Azotobacter</u>, <u>Clostridium</u> and <u>Rhizobium</u>, convert <u>atmospheric nitrogen</u> into useful <u>nitrogen compounds</u>.

See page 192 for more on the nitrogen cycle.

Living in Water

Life in <u>water</u> is very <u>different</u> from life on land. The biggest challenge is regulating water content.

Living in water has its advantages...

1) One advantage of living in water is that there's a <u>plentiful supply</u> of <u>water</u>... unsurprisingly. There shouldn't be any danger of <u>water shortage</u> or <u>dehydration</u> (unless a drought makes streams dry up).

2) In water, there's <u>less variation</u> in <u>temperature</u>. Water doesn't heat up or cool down as quickly as air, so you don't normally get <u>sudden temperature changes</u> — which living things can find difficult to withstand.

3) Water provides <u>support</u> for plants and for animals that have <u>no skeletal system</u>. For example, <u>jellyfish</u> are umbrella-shaped in water (so they can swim) but if they get washed up on a beach they end up as quivering blobs, because there's not enough support.

4) <u>Waste disposal</u> is <u>easier</u>. Poo and wee are easily dispersed. The loss of water in wee doesn't matter because there's plenty of water about to make up for it.

...and its disadvantages

1) Water is <u>more resistant to movement</u> than air, so animals living in water have to use <u>more energy</u> to move about. Think how much effort it takes to walk in the sea compared to walking on the beach.

2) Aquatic animals have to be able to <u>control</u> the amount of water in their bodies (<u>water regulation</u>). This is because the <u>water</u> an animal lives in has a <u>different concentration of solutes</u> from the <u>animal's cells</u>. If the animal <u>couldn't regulate water</u>, water molecules would <u>enter or leave</u> the animal's cells by <u>osmosis</u> to <u>even up</u> the <u>solute concentrations</u>. This could <u>damage</u> the cells. See the next page for more on this.

Living in Water

As you learnt on the last page, regulating their water content is one of the biggest challenges for aquatic animals.

If an aquatic animal *can't* regulate its water content, it's doomed

Animals that live in the sea obviously have very different problems with water regulation than animals that live in freshwater lakes and rivers.

- If the animal lived in saltwater its cells would probably contain a lower solute concentration than the surrounding water. If the animal wasn't able to regulate water, then water molecules would leave its cells by osmosis, causing them to shrivel and die.

- If the animal lived in freshwater, its cells would probably contain a higher solute concentration than the surrounding water. If the animal wasn't able to regulate water, then water molecules would enter its cells by osmosis, causing them to swell and burst.

Water content *is* regulated in different ways

1) The kidneys of fish are specially adapted to either saltwater or freshwater to ensure that the concentration of water in the blood remains constant. Some types of fish move between saltwater and freshwater environments and need further adaptations, for example:

> Salmon live in the sea but move into freshwater rivers to breed.
> Their hormones adjust their bodies to cope with the different environments.

2) Single-celled organisms, like amoebas, only have a cell membrane between them and the surrounding water. They use a different method of water regulation:

> Amoebas regulate water with a contractile vacuole which collects the water that diffuses in by osmosis. The vacuole then moves to the cell membrane and contracts to empty the water outside the cell.

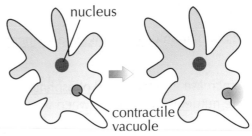

nucleus

contractile vacuole

Some animals can manage to live both in water and on land

Some organisms (mainly insects and amphibians) spend part of their life cycle in water and part on land to exploit both habitats. The two environments provide different challenges, so the different parts of the life cycle often have different body forms (e.g. tadpole and frog).

Living in Water

There are monsters in the water. Millions of them. They're only tiny, mind...

Plankton are microscopic organisms that live in water

1) Plankton are <u>microscopic</u> organisms that live in <u>fresh</u> and <u>salt water</u>. There are <u>two</u> types:

- <u>Phytoplankton</u> are microscopic <u>plants</u>.
- <u>Zooplankton</u> are microscopic <u>animals</u>. Zooplankton <u>feed on</u> phytoplankton.

2) Phytoplankton <u>photosynthesise</u> and are the main <u>producers</u> in <u>aquatic food webs</u>, so they're very important in both freshwater and saltwater ecosystems.

3) Plankton <u>can't move far</u> by themselves and so rely on <u>water currents</u> to carry them to new places.

4) <u>Phytoplankton</u> populations usually <u>increase</u> between late <u>spring</u> and late <u>summer</u>. This is called an <u>algal bloom</u> (phytoplankton are a type of algae). An algal bloom turns the water all green and murky.

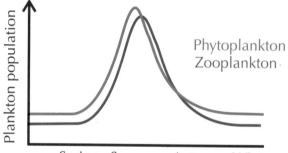

The increase in phytoplankton numbers is due to <u>longer, sunnier days</u> in summer:

- <u>More light</u> is available for <u>photosynthesis</u> and the energy is used for <u>growth</u>.
- <u>Temperatures increase</u>, causing both <u>photosynthesis</u> and <u>growth rates</u> to increase.

The population of <u>zooplankton</u> also <u>increases</u> because there is <u>more phytoplankton</u> to <u>feed on</u>.

5) An increase in <u>nitrates</u> and <u>phosphates</u> also causes algal blooms because the phytoplankton have <u>more nutrients</u>. It happens when water is <u>polluted</u> by <u>fertilisers</u> or <u>sewage</u>.

> You might be asked to <u>interpret marine food webs</u> in the exam.
> Think about how other organisms in the food chain will be affected by an <u>increase or decrease in plankton numbers</u>. If their food source decreases, so will their population. Keep your eye on what <u>season</u> it is too.

Living in Water

Animals that live on land use their <u>lungs</u> for gas exchange, and simply breathe in and out to take in oxygen and get rid of their carbon dioxide. Animals that live in <u>water</u> often do things a bit differently.

Animals can be adapted for gaseous exchange in water

Animals that live in water still need to exchange oxygen and carbon dioxide.
Some animals, such as <u>amphibians</u> and <u>fish</u>, have adapted different ways of doing this...

Amphibians

1) <u>Adult</u> amphibians have simple <u>lungs</u>, but their <u>skin</u> also plays an important part in <u>gaseous exchange</u>.

2) <u>Oxygen</u> moves into the animal and <u>carbon dioxide</u> moves out through the <u>skin</u> (as well as via the <u>lungs</u>). To help with this, an adult amphibian's skin has to be kept <u>moist</u>.

3) However, this means the skin can't be <u>waterproof</u>. This lack of waterproofing means the amphibian would <u>lose</u> too much water if it lived in a <u>dry</u> environment.

Fish

1) In <u>fish</u>, <u>gas exchange</u> occurs at the <u>gills</u> (slits near the side of the head).

2) A constant supply of <u>oxygen-rich</u> water flows through the open mouth of the fish, and is then forced through the <u>gill slits</u> (which are <u>highly folded</u> to increase the <u>surface area</u>).

3) Water helps <u>support</u> the gills — it keeps the gill folds separated from each other.

4) If fish weren't in water their gills would stick together and they would suffocate (which is why <u>fish</u> can <u>only</u> breathe when they're <u>in water</u>).

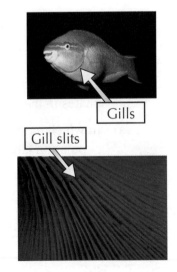

Gills

Gill slits

Whales and dolphins have to keep going to the surface to breathe

Different animals do gaseous exchange in different ways, though the basic aim is always the same — to get oxygen into the blood and carbon dioxide out. But all these methods can <u>restrict</u> animals (including us) to a certain kind of <u>habitat</u>. Learn this stuff, or you'll be a fish out of water on exam day.

Warm-Up and Exam Questions

It's time for the usual drill to test your progress — warm-up questions and practice exam questions. Remember, if you don't know it, go back and learn.

Warm-Up Questions

1) What are detritivores?
2) Give one advantage and one disadvantage of living in water.
3) How do frogs exchange gases?
4) How are fish gills adapted for breathing underwater?

Exam Questions

1   (a)   Explain the role of saprophytic bacteria in the nitrogen cycle.

(1 mark)

(b)   Some types of bacteria that live in soil are known as nitrifying bacteria. Explain what this means.

(1 mark)

2   It is important for aquatic animals to be able to regulate their water content.

(a)   Explain why an animal living in **fresh** water needs to regulate its water content.

(2 marks)

(b)   Explain why an animal living in **salt** water needs to regulate its water content.

(2 marks)

(c)   Amoebas regulate their water content using a contractile vacuole. Explain how a contractile vacuole works.

(2 marks)

3   The graph shows how the population of phytoplankton in a lake changed over one year. The graph also shows the concentration of phosphates in the water.

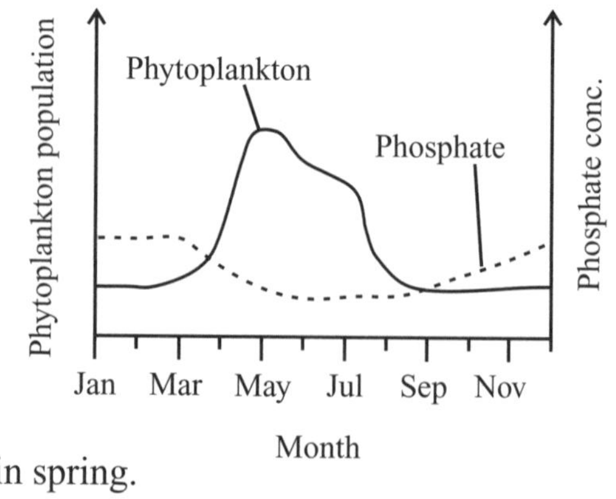

(a)   In which month is the phytoplankton population largest?

(1 mark)

(b)   Suggest why:

(i)   the population of phytoplankton increases in spring.

(1 mark)

(ii)   the phosphate concentration decreases during the summer.

(1 mark)

(c)   On the graph, mark the point at which you would expect the population of **zooplankton** in this lake to be biggest.

(1 mark)

Human Evolution and Development

We humans have come a long way since our ancestors were swinging about in trees...

Humans and great apes share **common ancestors**

Pygmy chimps (bonobos) are our closest living relatives. DNA studies suggest that humans and chimps shared a common ancestor that lived in the African rainforest 5–6 million years ago. This ancestral species evolved into two groups — one of which gave rise to modern chimpanzees, the other to humans:

1) The oldest human ancestor is thought to be *Australopithecus afarensis* (though some disagree), from 3.5 million years ago. It could walk on two legs but still spent a lot of time in the trees.

2) About 2 million years ago, *Homo erectus* had appeared in Africa — the first species that could be regarded as really human. *Homo erectus* was a hunter-gatherer living in small family groups. About 1.9 million years ago, they began to leave Africa and migrated to Asia and then into Europe.

3) *Homo erectus* evolved into *Homo heidelbergensis* and lived in Europe about 800 000 years ago. The discovery of spears and other artefacts show that these humans hunted animals. Hunting requires cooperation, so there must have been some social organisation.

4) Meanwhile, *Homo erectus* survived for a long time in the Far East. 'Java Man' was an example found in Indonesia.

5) About 200 000 years ago, human evolution branched, giving rise to Neanderthal man, or *Homo neanderthalensis*, in Europe, and *Homo sapiens* (modern humans) in Africa.

6) *Homo sapiens* were the more successful species, and when they arrived in Europe about 40 000 years ago, the neanderthals gradually became extinct, dying out about 28 000 years ago.

How we think the human family tree might look:

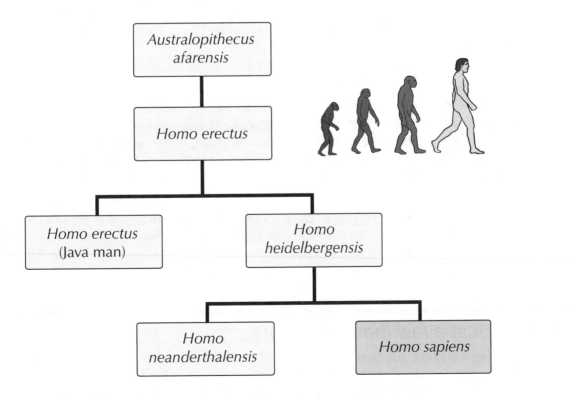

Human Evolution and Development

Although we are still the <u>same species</u>, human society has developed considerably since 190 000 years ago.

Tools helped humans to develop a complex society

1) A major factor in this development is the use of <u>tools</u>, and in particular being able to <u>create</u> tools for a specific purpose — something which we humans are really good at.

2) Tools enabled us to <u>modify</u> our environment — <u>farming</u>, <u>clearing land</u> and <u>building</u>.

3) This has led to an even more <u>complex society</u>, with people having <u>specific occupations</u> within it. You can achieve a <u>lot more</u> when the work is shared out and you have only <u>one thing</u> to concentrate on.

Humans also developed by exploiting animals

Humans have a long history of <u>exploiting</u> other animals:

1) <u>Dogs</u> were domesticated about 14 000 years ago, probably initially to help with <u>hunting</u>.

2) As the human population grew after the last ice age, it was difficult to supply all the food needed just by hunting and gathering. Humans developed a <u>farming</u> system with captive herds supplying a ready source of meat. Farming is known to have taken place in some parts of the world 10 000 years ago, although it might have started even earlier, alongside hunting and gathering.

3) <u>Tools</u> allowed people to <u>cultivate</u> land and grow <u>crops</u>. Early farmers also started using <u>animals</u> to actually help them with the <u>farm work</u>, as well as providing meat. For example, there is evidence that humans were <u>riding horses</u> 6000 years ago, and <u>sheep</u> and <u>goats</u> were certainly domesticated in the Middle East 9000 years ago.

4) Over the years, <u>selective breeding</u> has resulted in domestic animals that are <u>safer</u> to handle and more <u>productive</u>. For example, <u>cattle</u> have been bred to provide either <u>meat</u> or <u>milk</u>, and to be docile (calm and easy-going).

All this in just a few thousand years...

Modern <u>farming</u> has come a long way since the old days of hunter-gathering. Having said that though, don't make the mistake of saying that <u>all</u> humans use modern farming practices. There are plenty of tribal communities out there who still hunt and gather and don't fancy changing their ways.

Human Behaviour Towards Animals

Exploiting animals is a controversial issue, and you need to know both sides of the story.

Humans **exploit animals**

Animals obviously provide <u>meat</u> and <u>farm labour</u>, as mentioned on the previous page, but humans have also used them in many other ways:

Clothing and domestic materials

Animal hides are used for <u>clothing</u> and <u>upholstery</u>. For example, cow hides (<u>leather</u>) are used to make shoes, bags, jackets and to cover furniture like sofas. The skins from furry animals are sometimes used to make <u>fur coats</u>. <u>Wool</u> from sheep, goats and even rabbits is used to make woolly clothes, carpets and other furnishings.

Entertainment

Horses, dogs and even snails are used for <u>racing</u> — people enjoy <u>betting</u> on which one will win. <u>Bullfighting</u> and <u>cock-fighting</u> are spectator sports in some parts of the world, and again they are used for <u>gambling</u>. Animals also provide entertainment in <u>circuses</u>, <u>zoos</u> and <u>wildlife parks</u>, either by performing <u>tricks</u> or just by being <u>watched</u> by the visitors. Animals are also <u>hunted</u> for fun — deer, foxes and game birds are all hunted, and sometimes <u>dogs</u> are used to track them down and kill them.

Companionship

People enjoy keeping lots of different types of animals as <u>pets</u>. <u>Dogs</u> and <u>cats</u> are probably the most common pets — they can keep people <u>company</u>, and can be <u>loyal</u> and <u>affectionate</u>.

Medicinal uses

Animals can be used to produce <u>antibodies</u> for use in vaccines, and genetic engineering has enabled us to breed animals that will produce certain <u>drugs</u> for human use (normally in their <u>milk</u>). Scientists are researching the possibility of <u>transplanting organs</u> from animals such as pigs into humans if an appropriate human organ isn't available. Animals are also widely used for <u>testing drugs</u> before they are released for human use.

Human Behaviour Towards Animals

Animals are incredibly <u>useful</u> to humans — life would be pretty hard if we <u>weren't</u> allowed to exploit them any more. But some people think that the way humans treat animals goes much too far.

Some people are **unhappy** about the way **animals** are **treated**

People who believe that animals should have the same <u>rights</u> as humans might <u>protest</u> about the following:

1) The use of animals in <u>medical</u> or <u>cosmetic</u> <u>research</u> that causes them any pain or discomfort.

2) <u>Hunting</u>, particularly for <u>sport</u>, but also for <u>food</u> where it's considered cruel or unnecessary.

3) Using animals for <u>entertainment</u> in circuses etc. Some people are also against <u>zoos</u>.

4) Using animals to provide <u>unnecessary luxuries</u>, for example, fur coats and ivory ornaments.

5) <u>Intensive farming</u>, where animals are mistreated or suffer due to the unnatural conditions.

Others feel that making life better for **people** is most important

Of course, there's an answer for most of the points raised above:

1) If drugs weren't <u>tested</u> on animals, potentially <u>unsafe</u> drugs could get onto the human market.

2) Some say hunting is a humane way to keep foxes <u>under control</u> so they don't kill farm animals.

3) Circus owners claim that the animals are treated <u>kindly</u> and actually <u>enjoy performing</u>.

4) Zoos <u>educate</u> people and many have <u>breeding programmes</u> aimed at helping <u>endangered species</u>.

5) Where do we <u>draw the line</u>? Should we not kill things that carry <u>disease</u>? Is using <u>fly spray</u> cruel?

Just enough time left for one more big word...

We often attribute human feelings to animals (this is called <u>anthropomorphism</u>), but is it right to? Just because we might feel afraid or stressed in a situation doesn't mean an animal would. On the other hand, we shouldn't assume it <u>wouldn't</u>, either — humans and animals do have behaviours in common.

Warm-Up and Exam Questions

Would you believe it, this is the last page of questions in the book — well done you!
(Unless for some reason you started with this section, in which case, welcome along!)

Warm-Up Questions

1) About how long ago did *Homo sapiens* evolve?
2) What did humans probably use dogs for most when they first domesticated them?
3) Give two examples of the use of animals in making clothing.
4) Apart from drug testing, how can animals be used in medicine?
5) Why might animal rights activists object to intensive farming techniques?

Exam Questions

1   Which of the following is thought to be the earliest human ancestor?

   A *Homo sapiens*   **B** *Homo neanderthalensis*

   C *Homo heidelbergensis*   **D** *Australopithecus afarensis*

(1 mark)

2   Primitive humans developed partly by exploiting other animal species.

   (a) Describe one way in which early humans are thought to have exploited horses.

(1 mark)

   (b) Name one other type of animal that was exploited by early humans and explain
        how that animal was used.

(2 marks)

3   The Nu-Pharm Pharmaceuticals Company makes a drug called Slimmo. Nu-Pharm claims
    that Slimmo helps people to lose weight. Slimmo is tested on animals before being
    sold to the public.

    Some local people have formed a protest group against Nu-Pharm. They say that drugs
    like Slimmo should not be tested in this way.

   (a) Explain why Slimmo is tested on animals.

(1 mark)

   (b) Suggest two reasons why some people might object to Slimmo being
        tested on animals.

(2 marks)

   (c) Some members of the protest group agree with the testing of certain drugs
        on animals, but not others (such as Slimmo). Suggest a possible reason
        for this opinion.

(1 mark)

Revision Summary for Section Twelve

What an interesting topic. I don't know about you, but I'm fascinated by this sort of stuff. There are so many things for you to try out at home — conditioning your pets to salivate when you ring a bell, checking if your brothers and sisters are self-aware, habituating your parents to loud music...

There are also a lot of issues in this topic, so make sure you know both sides of the argument when it comes to animal testing, hunting and suchlike. It doesn't matter what your own opinion is — you've got to show that you're aware of other people's viewpoints too.

Anyway, I digress. Back to the important issue of finding out how much of this stuff you've taken in.

1) Define 'behaviour'.
2) Name three reflex actions. What are reflexes for?
3) Explain what negative phototaxis is and name one animal that displays it.
4) What name is given to the process by which birds learn to ignore scarecrows?
5) Which type of conditioning did Ivan Pavlov study? Describe the experiment he did.
6) Give a definition of classical conditioning. Make sure you use the word 'passively'.
7) Who trained rats and pigeons to press levers for rewards in a special type of box?
8) Name three species that communicate through sound.
9) What are pheromones? Name one animal that uses them to attract a mate.
10) What is the 'waggle dance'? Name two other behaviour signals used by animals.
11) Which species of animal uses complex language to communicate?
12) Name two types of non-verbal communication that can be automatic and unconscious.
13) Give two different definitions of self-awareness.
14) Describe two ways in which herbivores have adapted so that they avoid being caught by predators.
15) How are carnivores generally adapted for a life of hunting?
16) Which tend to hunt individually — animals that eat large prey or animals that eat small prey?
17) Why do adult herring gulls have a red spot on their beaks?
18) Name two species that use tools (apart from humans, of course). What tools do they use?
19) Why do females tend to be selective when it comes to choosing a mate?
20) Why are courtship displays species-specific?
21) Describe some of the mating patterns found in the animal kingdom. How common is monogamy?
22) Describe how weaver birds protect their young.
23) Give one example of parents teaching their offspring skills that improve their chances of survival.
24) Briefly explain the evolutionary argument for why mammals care for their young.
25) Describe four ways in which earthworms improve soil fertility.
26) What water-related problem faces salmon? How do they overcome it?
27) How do amoebas regulate their water content?
28) Explain what an algal bloom is.
29) Why do algal blooms normally occur in late spring and summer?
30) Explain why the skin of an amphibian can't be waterproof.
31) What is thought to be the oldest known human ancestor? When does this organism date from?
32) Name five animals that humans have exploited during their development into modern man.
33) Give arguments in favour of zoos, hunting and animal-testing.
34) What is anthropomorphism? How is this applicable to the animal-rights debate?

Answering Experiment Questions (i)

You'll definitely get some questions in the exam about experiments. They can be about any topic under the Sun — but if you learn the basics and throw in a bit of common sense, you'll be fine.

Read the question *carefully*

The question might describe an <u>experiment</u>, e.g. —

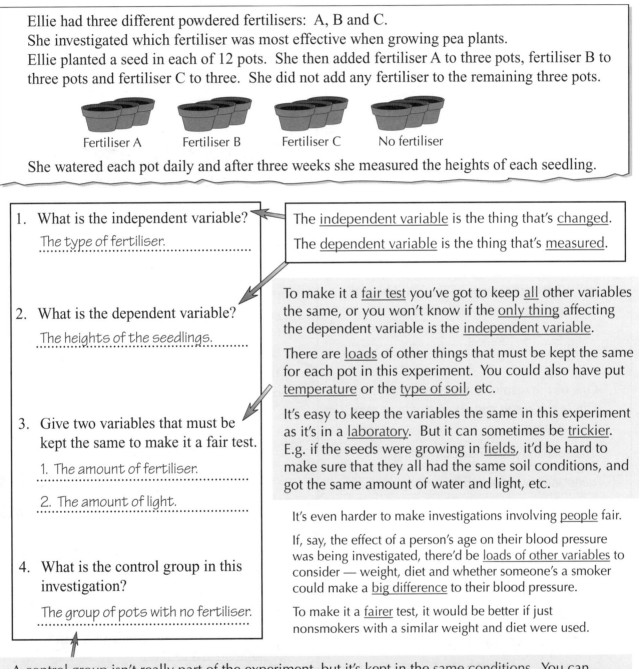

Ellie had three different powdered fertilisers: A, B and C.
She investigated which fertiliser was most effective when growing pea plants.
Ellie planted a seed in each of 12 pots. She then added fertiliser A to three pots, fertiliser B to three pots and fertiliser C to three. She did not add any fertiliser to the remaining three pots.

Fertiliser A   Fertiliser B   Fertiliser C   No fertiliser

She watered each pot daily and after three weeks she measured the heights of each seedling.

1. What is the independent variable?
   The type of fertiliser.

The <u>independent variable</u> is the thing that's <u>changed</u>.
The <u>dependent variable</u> is the thing that's <u>measured</u>.

2. What is the dependent variable?
   The heights of the seedlings.

To make it a <u>fair test</u> you've got to keep <u>all</u> other variables the same, or you won't know if the <u>only thing</u> affecting the dependent variable is the <u>independent variable</u>.

There are <u>loads</u> of other things that must be kept the same for each pot in this experiment. You could also have put <u>temperature</u> or the <u>type of soil</u>, etc.

It's easy to keep the variables the same in this experiment as it's in a <u>laboratory</u>. But it can sometimes be <u>trickier</u>. E.g. if the seeds were growing in <u>fields</u>, it'd be hard to make sure that they all had the same soil conditions, and got the same amount of water and light, etc.

3. Give two variables that must be kept the same to make it a fair test.
   1. *The amount of fertiliser.*
   2. *The amount of light.*

It's even harder to make investigations involving <u>people</u> fair.

If, say, the effect of a person's age on their blood pressure was being investigated, there'd be <u>loads of other variables</u> to consider — weight, diet and whether someone's a smoker could make a <u>big difference</u> to their blood pressure.

4. What is the control group in this investigation?
   The group of pots with no fertiliser.

To make it a <u>fairer</u> test, it would be better if just nonsmokers with a similar weight and diet were used.

A <u>control group</u> isn't really part of the experiment, but it's kept in the <u>same conditions</u>. You can compare changes in the experiment with those that happened to the control group, and see if the changes might have happened <u>anyway</u>. Control groups make results <u>more meaningful</u>.

In this experiment the seeds might <u>grow better</u> without any fertiliser — with a control group you can check for this.

Control groups are used when <u>testing drugs</u>. People can feel better just because they've been given a drug that they <u>believe</u> will work. To rule this out, researchers give one group of patients <u>dummy pills</u> (called placebos) — but they <u>don't tell them</u> that their pills aren't the real thing. This is the control group. By doing this, they can tell if the real drug is actually working.

Answering Experiment Questions (ii)

5. Why was each type of fertiliser added to three pots, instead of just one?

To check for anomalous results and make the results more reliable.

Sometimes <u>unusual results</u> are produced — <u>repeating</u> an experiment gives you a better idea what the <u>correct result</u> should be.

6. The table below shows the heights of the seedlings in each pot.

	First pot	Second pot	Third pot	Mean
Fertiliser A	4.4 cm	5.2 cm	4.2 cm	
Fertiliser B	8.3 cm	7.9 cm	8.7 cm	8.3 cm
Fertiliser C	6.7 cm	5.7 cm	(0 cm)	6.2 cm
No fertiliser	2.4 cm	1.9 cm	2.6 cm	2.3 cm

When an experiment is <u>repeated</u>, the results will usually be <u>slightly different</u> each time.

The <u>mean</u> (or average) of the measurements is usually used to represent the values.

The more times the experiment is <u>repeated</u> the <u>more reliable</u> the average will be.

To find the mean:

Add together all the data values and divide by the total number of values in the sample.

The <u>range</u> is how far the data <u>spreads</u>.

You just work out the <u>difference</u> between the <u>highest</u> and <u>lowest</u> numbers.

a) Calculate the mean height of the seedlings grown with fertiliser A.

Mean = (4.4 + 5.2 + 4.2) ÷ 3 = 4.6 cm

b) What is the range of the heights of the seedlings grown with fertiliser A?

5.2 – 4.2 = 1.0 cm

If one of the results doesn't seem to fit in, it's called an <u>anomalous</u> result. You should usually <u>ignore</u> an anomalous result. It's been <u>ignored</u> when the mean was worked out.

This is a <u>random error</u> — it only happens occasionally.

7. One of the results in the table is anomalous. Circle the result and suggest why it may have occurred.

The seed may have had something genetically wrong with it.

If the same mistake is made every time, it's a <u>systematic error</u>, e.g. if you measured from the very end of your ruler instead of from the 0 cm mark every time, meaning <u>all</u> your measurements would be a <u>bit small</u>.

8. What conclusion can you draw from these results?

Fertiliser B makes pea plants grow taller over the first three weeks than fertilisers A or C given daily watering.

Be careful that your conclusions <u>match</u> the data you've got, and <u>don't</u> go any further.

You can't say that fertiliser B will always be better than fertilisers A or C, because:

- The results may be <u>totally different</u> with <u>another type of plant</u>.

- After four weeks, the plants grown with fertiliser B may all <u>drop dead</u>, while the others <u>keep growing</u>. Etc.

Mistakes happen...

NASA made a bit of a mistake once. They muddled up measurements in pounds and newtons and caused the Mars Climate Orbiter to burn up in the Martian atmosphere. It just goes to show that anyone can make a mistake, even a bunch of clever scientists. So always double-check everything.

Answering Experiment Questions (iii)

Use **sensible measurements** for your **variables**

Pu-lin did an experiment to see how the mass of a potato changed depending on the sugar solution it was in. She started off by making potato tubes 5 cm in length, 1 cm in diameter and 2.0 g in mass. She then filled a beaker with 500 ml of pure water and placed a potato tube in it for 30 minutes. She repeated the experiment with different amounts of sugar dissolved in the water. For each potato tube, she measured the new mass. She did the experiment using Charlotte, Desiree, King Edward and Maris Piper potatoes.

Before she started, she did a trial run, which showed that most of the potato tubes shrunk to a minimum of 1 g (in a really strong sugar solution) or grew to a maximum of 3 g (in pure water).

1. What kind of variable was the list of potatoes?

   A A continuous variable ☐

   B A categoric variable ✓

   C An ordered variable ☐

   D A discrete variable ☐

> Categoric variables are variables that can't be related to size or quantity — they're <u>types</u> of things.
> E.g. <u>names of potatoes</u> or <u>types of fertiliser</u>.

<u>Continuous data</u> is <u>numerical data</u> that can have <u>any value</u> within a range — e.g. length, volume, temperature and time.

Note: You <u>can't</u> measure the <u>exact value</u> of continuous data. Say you measure a height as 5.6 cm to the nearest mm. It's not <u>exact</u> — you get a more precise value if you measure to the nearest 0.1 mm or 0.01 mm, etc.

<u>Ordered variables</u> are things like <u>small</u>, <u>medium</u> and <u>large lumps</u>, or <u>warm</u>, <u>very warm</u> and <u>hot</u>.

<u>Discrete data</u> is the type that can be counted in chunks, where there's no in-between value. E.g. <u>number of people</u> is discrete, not continuous, because you can't have half a person.

2. Pu-lin should add sugar in intervals of...

   A a pinch ☐

   B a teaspoon ✓

   C a cupful ☐

   D a bucketful ☐

> It's important to use <u>sensible values</u> for variables.
>
> It's no good using <u>loads</u> of sugar or <u>really small amounts</u> like a pinch at a time cos you'd be there <u>forever</u> and the results wouldn't show any <u>significant difference</u>. (You'd get different amounts of sugar per pinch anyway.)

3. The balance used to find the mass of the potato should be capable of measuring...

   A to the nearest 0.01 gram ✓

   B to the nearest 0.1 gram ☐

   C to the nearest gram ☐

   D to the nearest 10 grams ☐

> A balance measuring only to the nearest gram, or bigger, would <u>not</u> be <u>sensitive enough</u> — the changes in mass are likely to be quite small, so you'd need to measure to the <u>nearest 0.01 gram</u> to get the <u>most precise</u> results.

The <u>sensitivity</u> of an instrument is the <u>smallest change</u> it can detect, e.g. some balances measure to the nearest <u>gram</u>, but very sensitive ones measure to the nearest <u>hundredth of a gram</u>.

For measuring <u>tiny changes</u> — like from 2.00 g to 1.92 g — the more sensitive balance is needed.

You also have to think about the <u>precision</u> and <u>accuracy</u> of your results.

Measurements (of the same thing) that are very precise are all really close together (small range). Really accurate results are those that have an <u>average value</u> that is <u>really close</u> to the <u>true answer</u>. It's possible for results to be precise but not very accurate, e.g. a fancy piece of lab equipment might give results that are precise, but if it's not calibrated properly those results won't be accurate.

Answering Experiment Questions (iv)

Once you've collected all your data together, you need to analyse it to find any relationships between the variables. The easiest way to do this is to draw a graph, then describe what you see...

Graphs are used to show relationships

These are the results Pu-lin obtained with the King Edward potato.

Number of teaspoons of sugar	0	2	4	6	8	10	12	14	16	18	20
Mass of potato tube (g)	2.50	2.40	2.23	2.10	2.02	1.76	1.66	1.25	1.47	1.3	1.15

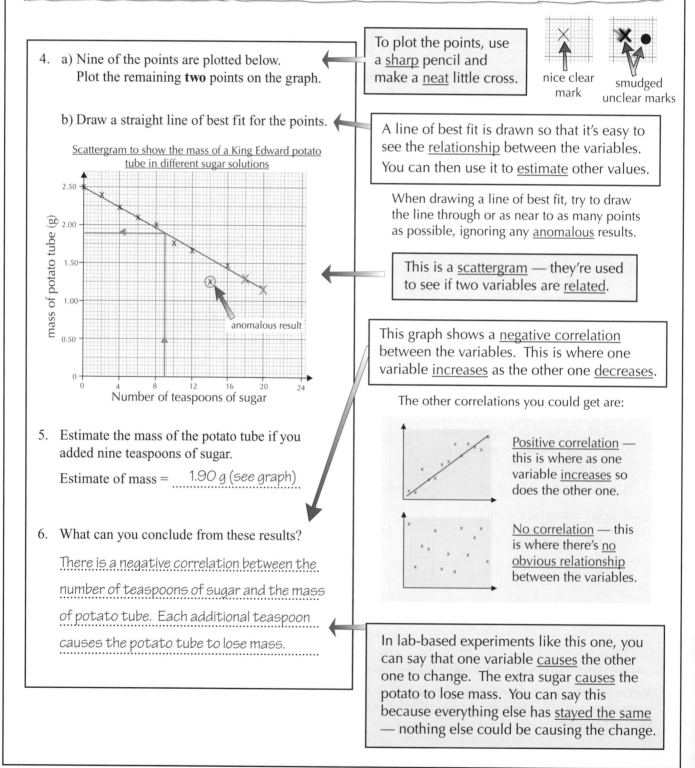

4. a) Nine of the points are plotted below.
   Plot the remaining **two** points on the graph.

To plot the points, use a <u>sharp</u> pencil and make a <u>neat</u> little cross.

nice clear mark

smudged unclear marks

b) Draw a straight line of best fit for the points.

A line of best fit is drawn so that it's easy to see the <u>relationship</u> between the variables. You can then use it to <u>estimate</u> other values.

Scattergram to show the mass of a King Edward potato tube in different sugar solutions

mass of potato tube (g)

Number of teaspoons of sugar

anomalous result

When drawing a line of best fit, try to draw the line through or as near to as many points as possible, ignoring any <u>anomalous</u> results.

This is a <u>scattergram</u> — they're used to see if two variables are <u>related</u>.

This graph shows a <u>negative correlation</u> between the variables. This is where one variable <u>increases</u> as the other one <u>decreases</u>.

5. Estimate the mass of the potato tube if you added nine teaspoons of sugar.

   Estimate of mass = ...1.90 g (see graph)....

The other correlations you could get are:

<u>Positive correlation</u> — this is where as one variable <u>increases</u> so does the other one.

<u>No correlation</u> — this is where there's <u>no</u> obvious relationship between the variables.

6. What can you conclude from these results?

   There is a negative correlation between the number of teaspoons of sugar and the mass of potato tube. Each additional teaspoon causes the potato tube to lose mass.

In lab-based experiments like this one, you can say that one variable <u>causes</u> the other one to change. The extra sugar <u>causes</u> the potato to lose mass. You can say this because everything else has <u>stayed the same</u> — nothing else could be causing the change.

Answering Experiment Questions (v)

Not all experiments can be carefully controlled in a laboratory. Some have to be done in the real world.

Relationships do NOT always tell you the cause

Melanomas are a dangerous form of skin cancer. It's thought that UV damage may increase the risk of getting skin cancer later in life, so people are advised to avoid being in direct sunlight for long periods at a time.

The graph shows the number of new cases of melanoma found per year in people who spend at least 5 hours of each working day exposed to direct sunlight.

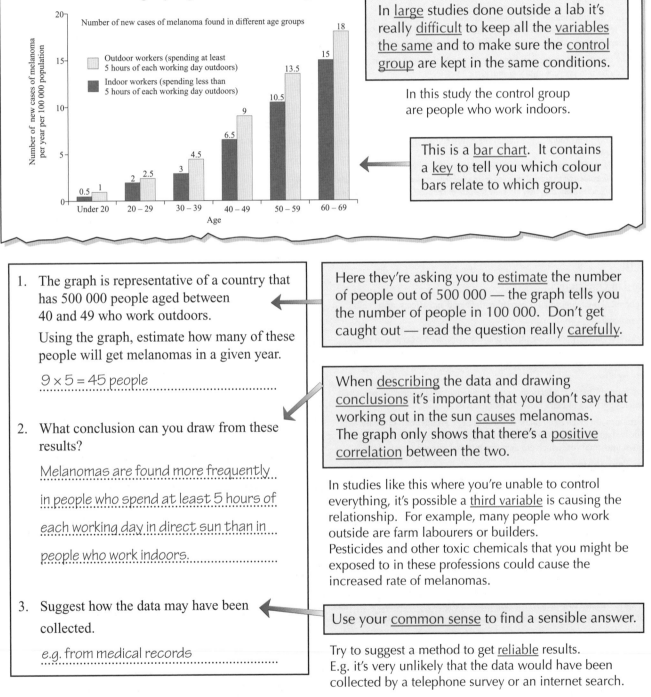

Number of new cases of melanoma found in different age groups

Key:
- Outdoor workers (spending at least 5 hours of each working day outdoors)
- Indoor workers (spending less than 5 hours of each working day outdoors)

In large studies done outside a lab it's really difficult to keep all the variables the same and to make sure the control group are kept in the same conditions.

In this study the control group are people who work indoors.

This is a bar chart. It contains a key to tell you which colour bars relate to which group.

1. The graph is representative of a country that has 500 000 people aged between 40 and 49 who work outdoors.

   Using the graph, estimate how many of these people will get melanomas in a given year.

   9 × 5 = 45 people

Here they're asking you to estimate the number of people out of 500 000 — the graph tells you the number of people in 100 000. Don't get caught out — read the question really carefully.

2. What conclusion can you draw from these results?

   Melanomas are found more frequently in people who spend at least 5 hours of each working day in direct sun than in people who work indoors.

When describing the data and drawing conclusions it's important that you don't say that working out in the sun causes melanomas. The graph only shows that there's a positive correlation between the two.

In studies like this where you're unable to control everything, it's possible a third variable is causing the relationship. For example, many people who work outside are farm labourers or builders. Pesticides and other toxic chemicals that you might be exposed to in these professions could cause the increased rate of melanomas.

3. Suggest how the data may have been collected.

   e.g. from medical records

Use your common sense to find a sensible answer.

Try to suggest a method to get reliable results. E.g. it's very unlikely that the data would have been collected by a telephone survey or an internet search.

A relationship doesn't necessarily imply cause and effect

It's really difficult to prove what causes what in science, especially with all the things you've got to control. The experiments are usually done in a lab first so that you can control as much as possible. Then they're done in the real world to see if the same thing happens, and to find any unexpected results.

Page 13

Warm-Up Questions

1) eyes, ears, nose, tongue, skin

2) It receives information from the sense organs and coordinates responses.

3) as electrical impulses

4) a synapse

5) accommodation

6) The brain can use information from both eyes to judge distances, depth and how fast things are moving.

Exam Questions

1 (a) reflex action *(1 mark)*

(b) (i) B *(1 mark)*

(ii) D *(1 mark)*

(c) When the electrical impulse reaches the end of the neurone, it stimulates the release of a chemical *(1 mark)*. The chemical diffuses across the gap/synapse to activate an electrical impulse in the next neurone *(1 mark)*.

(d) Any one of, they minimise damage to the body (because they are so quick) / they help to prevent injury *(1 mark)*

2 (a) E.g. when the receptors in the eye detect an increase in the level of light, they send impulses to the central nervous system (CNS) along sensory neurones *(1 mark)*. The CNS then sends impulses to the circular muscles along motor neurones *(1 mark)*, which causes the muscles to contract *(1 mark)*. This reduces the size of the pupil, so less light can enter the eye *(1 mark)*.
Exactly the same reflex happens if the light is too dim, except that the CNS sends impulses to the radial muscles instead of the circular muscles. When the radial muscles contract, they increase the size of the pupil, so more light gets in.

(b) It prevents the eye's receptor cells from being damaged by very bright light *(1 mark)*.

Page 19

Warm-Up Questions

1) A chemical messenger that is carried in the blood and affects target cells.

2) the pancreas

3) E.g. hormonal responses are slower than nervous responses / hormonal responses persist for a longer time period than nervous responses / hormonal responses are normally quite widespread, whereas nervous responses are very localised.

4) Any four of, sperm production / voice deepening / enlargement of penis and testicles / growth of extra hair / development of muscles.

5) Hormones are given to a female to stimulate egg production. Eggs are collected and fertilised in a laboratory using the male's sperm. The eggs are grown into embryos, which are then transplanted into the female.

Exam Questions

1 C *(1 mark)*

2 B *(1 mark)*

3 (a) It causes the lining to thicken and grow *(1 mark)*.

(b) It maintains the lining *(1 mark)*.

(c) day 14 *(1 mark)*

4 Any two of, e.g. abdominal pain / vomiting / dehydration / increased risk of cancer *(1 mark for each)*.
There are risks associated with most medical treatments, and IVF is no exception. People who decide to undergo IVF treatment should know and understand the risks, but if it's the only way they can have a child, then perhaps the benefits outweigh those risks.

Page 24

Warm-Up Questions

1) The maintenance of a constant internal environment.

2) Any six of, e.g. carbon dioxide / oxygen / water / salt / ions / temperature / blood glucose levels.

3) In sweat, in breathing out, in urine and in faeces.

4) This is the optimal temperature for most enzymes in the body.

5) Using a glucose-monitoring device — they prick a finger to get a drop of blood, which the handheld machine checks.

Exam Questions

1 E.g. hairs stand on end, which traps a layer of warm air next to the skin *(1 mark)*. Sweat production decreases *(1 mark)*. Vasoconstriction occurs (blood vessels constrict to limit the amount of blood reaching the surface of the skin) *(1 mark)*. Shivering generates heat *(1 mark)*.

2 kidney *(1 mark)*

3 (a) negative feedback *(1 mark)*

(b) (i) pancreas *(1 mark)*

(ii) liver *(1 mark)*

(iii) glycogen *(1 mark)*

(c) (i) E.g. after eating a meal containing carbohydrate/sugar *(1 mark)*.

(ii) cellular metabolism / respiration *(1 mark)*

(iii) vigorous exercise / being diabetic *(1 mark)*

(d) Injection of insulin *(1 mark)* and restriction of simple carbohydrate/sugar intake *(1 mark)*.

Page 25

Revision Summary for Section One

9) (a) Response A

(b) Response B

Page 32

Warm-Up Questions

1) Unbalanced diet, over eating and not enough exercise.

2) E.g. to keep food moving smoothly through the digestive system / to avoid constipation.

3) the liver

4) Cholesterol deposits narrow the lumen of the arteries and can cause blood clots.

5) Any three of, high salt intake / getting older / being overweight / drinking too much alcohol / stress

Exam Questions

1 C *(1 mark)*
The proportion of muscle to fat in the body, amount of exercise, and gender all have an effect on metabolic rate.

2 (a) (i) $81 \div (1.85)^2 = 23.67$ *(1 mark)*
Don't forget you need to change the height from cm to m.

(ii) normal *(1 mark)*

(b) Any one of, e.g. arthritis / diabetes / high blood pressure / heart disease / some kinds of cancer *(1 mark)*.

3 (a) (i) increased blood cholesterol levels *(1 mark)*

(ii) decreased blood cholesterol levels *(1 mark)*

(b) High salt intake may cause high blood pressure *(1 mark)*. High blood pressure increases the risk of blood vessels bursting in the brain *(1 mark)*.

Page 39

Warm-up Questions

1) A substance that alters chemical reactions in the body.

2) E.g. where has the health claim been published? Was the research carried out by a qualified person? Was a large enough sample used? Have the results been backed up by other findings?

3) Any one of, e.g. caffeine, alcohol, nicotine.

4) A dummy treatment that doesn't contain any active drug.

5) E.g. it can take many years to develop and test a drug, many potential drugs are rejected, scientists have to be paid.

Exam Questions

1 (a) B *(1 mark)*

(b) They slow down the activity of the nervous system *(1 mark)*.

2 (a) Computer models, testing on human tissues, testing on live animals, clinical trials on human volunteers (*4 marks*).

(b) Double blind trials involve two groups of patients, one is given the drug, the other is given a placebo (*1 mark*). Neither the patients nor the scientists know which group is given the real drug and which is given the placebo until the results have been gathered (*1 mark*).
This process prevents scientists or patients unconsciously affecting the results (it prevents bias).

3 (a) (i) A physical or psychological need for a drug (*1 mark*).

(ii) The body has become used to having the drug so a higher dose is needed to get the same effect (*1 mark*).

(b) (i) Class A (*1 mark*).
In addition to being the most dangerous, Class A drugs also carry the most severe punishments if you're caught with them.

(ii) E.g. heroin / LSD / ecstasy / cocaine (*1 mark*).

(c) Any one of, e.g. drug abuse can affect the immune system making infections more likely / sharing needles, which helps some infections to spread (*1 mark*).

Page 44

Warm-up Questions

1) Any two of, e.g. the brain / lungs/breathing passages / liver

2) opiates

3) E.g. emphysema, bronchitis

4) Substances that can cause cancer.

5) E.g. because cannabis is illegal.

Exam Questions

1 (a) Tar damages the cilia in the tubes of the lungs and windpipe. It also makes chest infections more likely (*1 mark*).

(b) Carbon monoxide reduces the oxygen carrying capacity of haemoglobin in the blood/red blood cells (*1 mark*).

(c) Nicotine is addictive (*1 mark*).

2 (a) (i) Aspirin inhibits the formation of prostaglandins, the chemicals that cause swelling and sensitise the endings of nerves that register pain (*1 mark*).

(ii) Morphine interferes with the mechanism by which pain-sensing nerve cells transmit impulses. They also act on the brain to stop it sensing the pain (*1 mark*).

(b) Taking an overdose of paracetamol can cause liver damage (*1 mark*).

3 (a) Alcohol reduces the activity of the nervous system, making reactions slower (*1 mark*). It can also lead to impaired judgement, poor balance and coordination and false confidence (*1 mark*).

(b) E.g. damage to brain cells/reduction in brain function / liver disease/ damage / increased risk of stroke/heart attack (*1 mark*).

(c) Any two of, e.g. increased crime/violence / costs to the NHS / costs to economy through lost working days. (*1 mark for each*)

Page 51–52

Warm-Up Questions

1) A disease-causing organism.

2) Viruses replicate by invading your cells and using the cell machinery to produce many copies of themselves. Then they cause the cell to break open, releasing new viruses into your body.

3) Phagocytosis/to engulf and digest microorganisms, produce antibodies, produce antitoxins.

4) They live in or on the host obtaining nourishment from the host and give nothing in return.

5) Unique molecules which are present on the surface of cells/pathogens/ microorganisms.

Exam Questions

1 (a) Active immunity is where the immune system makes its own antibodies after being stimulated by a pathogen or vaccination (*1 mark*).

(b) Passive immunity is where the body uses antibodies made by another organism (it is only temporary) (*1 mark*).

2 A — 3 (*1 mark*)
  B — 4 (*1 mark*)
  C — 2 (*1 mark*)
  D — 1 (*1 mark*)

3 (a) Flu is caused by a virus (*1 mark*) and antibiotics are not effective against viruses (*1 mark*).

(b) Inappropriate use of antibiotics increases the chances of antibiotic-resistant strains of bacteria emerging (*1 mark*).

4 (a) Vaccinations help to prevent the outbreak of a disease in the first place because some people are immune (*1 mark*). If an outbreak of the disease does occur vaccines help to slow down and stop the spread — if people don't catch the disease they cannot pass it on (*1 mark*).

(b) 4, 3, 1, 5, 2 (*1 mark*)

(c) Any one of, e.g. swelling/redness at site of injection / feeling unwell (*1 mark*)

5 A — 3 (*1 mark*)
  B — 4 (*1 mark*)
  C — 2 (*1 mark*)
  D — 1 (*1 mark*)

Page 53

Revision Summary for Section Two

2) Professional runner, builder, waitress, secretary

18)(a) 6 pm

(b) 8 pm

(c) No

Page 58

Warm-Up Questions

1) Keeping the surface area to volume ratio to a minimum reduces heat loss.

2) Bright warning colours to scare predators away, and a poisonous sting.

3) A species is a group of closely related organisms that can breed to produce fertile offspring.

4) Any two of, e.g. fur / give birth to live young / produce milk to feed young.

Exam Questions

1 A — 2 (*1 mark*)
  B — 3 (*1 mark*)
  C — 4 (*1 mark*)
  D — 1 (*1 mark*)

2 Any three of, e.g. has spines instead of leaves to reduce water loss / small surface area compared to volume reduces water loss from evaporation / storing water in its stem / extensive shallow root system to absorb water over a wide area / deep roots to access underground water (*1 mark each*).

3 A — 3 (*1 mark*)
  B — 1 (*1 mark*)
  C — 2 (*1 mark*)

Page 63

Warm-Up Questions

1) A quadrat is a square frame enclosing a known area. It is used to estimate population size (by finding the number of individuals in a quadrat area, and multiplying by the area of the habitat).

2) A natural ecosystem is one where humans don't control the processes going on within it. An artificial ecosystem is one where humans deliberately promote the growth of certain living organisms and get rid of others which threaten their well-being.

3) Any three of, e.g amount of food available / amount of nutrients available / amount of water available / amount of light available / shelter available

4) Mutualism is a relationship between two different species where both species benefit.

Exam Questions

1 B (*1 mark*)

2 A (*1 mark*)

3 (a) D *(1 mark)*.

(b) E.g. there was a decrease in the number of mice, which means less food for the owls *(1 mark)*.

(c) It will probably decrease due to increased competition (between the owl and the other species) for food *(1 mark)*.

Page 69

Warm-Up Questions

1) Fossils provide us with evidence about an animal or plant that lived ages ago. They can tell us about the organism itself, its diet, behaviour, habitat and how long ago it lived.

2) Gaps exist in the fossil record because few organisms turn into fossils when they die. Most decay completely. Many fossils have been destroyed or remain buried.

3) Organisms with the most useful characteristics will survive to reproduce and pass these characteristics on to the next generation.

4) Evolution is the gradual change/adaptation of a population of organisms over time. Natural selection is the process by which evolution can occur.

Exam Questions

1 C *(1 mark)*

2 (a) Fossils *(1 mark)*

(b) Estimating the age of the layer of rock where the fossil was found (e.g. based on known ages of other rocks or fossils nearby) / radioisotope dating (NOT carbon dating) of the rock containing the fossil, or the rock above and below the fossil. *(1 mark)*

(c) Any one of, e.g. dietary information/what kind of food it ate / roughly how old the individual stegosaurus was when it died. *(1 mark)*

(d) Gaps in the fossil record mean that you might not be able to find evidence of a common ancestor. / Fossils of the ancestor may not have formed/survived. *(1 mark)*

3 (a) Any one of, e.g. all organisms produce more offspring than could possibly survive but population numbers tend to remain fairly constant over long periods of time. / Organisms in a species show wide variation in characteristics, some of which are passed on to the next generation. *(1 mark)*

(b) There is variation within a population. Some individuals are better adapted to their environment *(1 mark)*. These individuals will be more likely to survive and reproduce *(1 mark)*, passing on the characteristics to the next generation *(1 mark)*. Over generations, the characteristics that increased survival becomes more common in the population *(1 mark)*. *Remember, individuals in a species are naturally selected for but individuals cannot evolve; only a species as a whole can evolve.*

(c) E.g. he could not explain how characteristics could be inherited / it went against may people's religious beliefs *(1 mark)*.

Page 76

Warm-Up Questions

1) Any four of, e.g. moisture / temperature / mineral content of soil / sunlight / carbon dioxide

2) the nucleus

3) Genes are lengths of DNA that determine what proteins a cell makes, and so control what the cell does. Each gene makes up a short section of a chromosome. Genes control characteristics, such as blood group and eye colour, that offspring inherit from their parents.

4) During sexual reproduction, an individual receives a mixture of genes/chromosomes from both parents. The combination that it receives determines what features it inherits. Since each offspring inherits a different combination of genes, no two are alike (except for identical twins), leading to a large amount of variation between individuals.

5) E.g. a mutation in a bacterium making it resistant to an antibiotic.

Page 76–77

Exam Questions

1 (a) sperm *(1 mark)* and egg *(1 mark)*

(b) 23 *(1 mark)*

(c) 46 *(1 mark)*

(d) half *(1 mark)*

2 (a) Ruth and Mark have (inherited) different eye-colour genes *(1 mark)*

(b) During sexual reproduction, an individual receives a mixture of genes/chromosomes from both parents. *(1 mark)* The combination that it receives determines what features it inherits. *(1 mark)* Since each offspring inherits a different combination of genes, no two are alike (except for identical twins), leading to a large amount of variation between individuals. *(1 mark)*

(c) B *(1 mark)*

3 D *(1 mark)*

4 C *(1 mark)*

5 (a) Uncontrolled division of cells *(1 mark)*.

(b) A change in the genetic material / a gene / DNA *(1 mark)*.

(c) Any two of, e.g. nuclear radiation / X-rays / UV light *(1 mark each)*.

(d) They may cause favourable changes *(1 mark)* which give the organism a survival advantage *(1 mark)*. *Not all mutations cause disease — some can cause favourable changes, some will have no effect at all. This is important for understanding natural selection (later on in this section).*

6 (a) Because they have exactly the same genes *(1 mark)*

(b) Andrew and Peter look slightly different because their environment/upbringing has affect their development/appearance *(1 mark)*. *Almost every aspect of human development is affected by environment, or upbringing. Factors like diet, exercise, and diseases will affect your physical appearance.*

(c) (i) Any one of, e.g. eye colour / gender / natural hair colour / blood group *(1 mark)*.

(ii) Any one of, e.g. language / scars *(1 mark)*

Pages 82–83

Warm-Up Questions

1) Versions of a gene.

2) Faulty alleles.

3) Thick, sticky mucus is produced in the airways, pancreas and gut.

4) e.g haemophilia and colour blindness

5) No — some genes make people more likely to develop breast cancer, but this doesn't mean that they will definitely develop it.

Exam Questions

1 (a)

	parent's alleles	
	H	h
H	HH	Hh
h	Hh	hh

(left axis label: parent's alleles)

(1 mark)

(b) A *(1 mark)*

2 B *(1 mark)*
There are loads of ethical issues concerned with genetic disorders and testing. Make sure you know about the ethical issues surrounding testing a foetus as well as an adult.

3 D *(1 mark)*

4 (a)

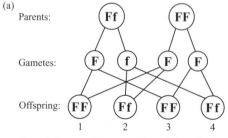

(1 mark for gametes correct, 1 mark for offspring correct)

(b) They will all be unaffected *(1 mark)*.

(c) (i) 1 in 2 / 50% *(1 mark)*

(ii) 2 and 4 *(1 mark)*

(d) E.g. they may not want to risk passing on a genetic disorder to their children / may choose to avoid having children if they are a carrier *(1 mark)*.

Pages 89–90
Warm-Up Questions

1) A clone is an organism that is genetically identical to another.

2) Taking cuttings and tissue culture.

3) Any one of, e.g. hundreds of "ideal" offspring can be produced each year / the prize cow can keep producing eggs all year round

4) Gene splicing is using enzymes to cut an organism's chromosome, and insert a useful gene from another organism into it.

5) Any one of, e.g. creating virus-resistant plants / creating herbicide-resistant plants / creating long-life tomatoes/fruit / creating animals that produce medicines in their milk / curing genetic diseases using gene therapy / adding new nutrients to crops/golden rice

Exam Questions

1 (a) asexual *(1 mark)*

(b) The X-shaped chromosomes split down the middle, forming two identical sets of chromosomes *(1 mark)*. A membrane forms around each set of chromosomes *(1 mark)*. Once the cell has divided, the DNA replicates to form two identical cells, each with a complete set of X-shaped chromosomes *(1 mark)*.

(c) parent *(1 mark)*, bud *(1 mark)*, clone *(1 mark)*

2 D *(1 mark)*

3 (a) There are fewer alleles in a population *(1 mark)*.

(b) E.g. if a population are all closely related and a new disease appears, all the population could be wiped out *(1 mark)*.

4 (a) To produce lots of identical animals with desirable characteristics *(1 mark)*.

(b) Sperm cells are taken from a male and egg cells are taken from a female *(1 mark)*. The sperm is used to fertilise the egg *(1 mark)*. The embryo that develops is split many times (to form clones) *(1 mark)*. The embryos are implanted into surrogate mothers *(1 mark)*.

5 (a) The altering of genes *(1 mark)* in an organism to alter its characteristics *(1 mark)*.

(b) E.g. to cut the gene out of the donor organism's chromosome *(1 mark)*. To cut the DNA of the recipient organism's chromosome *(1 mark)*. To join together the bacterial and human DNA *(1 mark)*.

(c) Any one of, e.g. to give resistance to viruses / to give resistance to herbicides / to produce long-life fruit/vegetables / to give increased yields / to give crops with added nutrients *(1 mark)*.

(d) Any one of, e.g. to produce milk containing human antibodies/proteins / to produce low-cholesterol milk / to produce leaner meat / to give increased yields of wool from sheep *(1 mark)*.

(e) Any two of, e.g. they could affect the numbers of other plants around the crop, reducing biodiversity / they could increase the risk of food allergies / they might not be safe / transplanted genes could transfer to other plants / super-weeds could develop. *(1 mark each)*
Make sure you can explain the pros and cons of genetic engineering because it's a really controversial issue — and it could easily come up in the exam.

6 (a) The nucleus was removed from a sheep egg cell *(1 mark)*. A complete set of chromosomes from an adult body cell (from a sheep) was inserted into the empty egg cell *(1 mark)*. This grew into an embryo which was implanted into a surrogate mother *(1 mark)*.

(b) (i) A cloned embryo that is genetically identical to the sufferer could be produced *(1 mark)* and embryonic stem cells extracted from it (to grow new cells or organs) *(1 mark)*.

(ii) E.g. some people think it's unethical because embryos are destroyed *(1 mark)*.

Page 91
Revision Summary for Section Four

10 E.g.

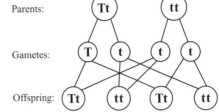

Parents: Tt tt
Gametes: T t t t
Offspring: Tt tt Tt tt

Pages 98–99
Warm-Up Questions

1) Any two of, e.g. modern farming methods have reduced the number of people dying from starvation / modern medicine/vaccination has reduced the numbers dying from disease / clean water is available to more of the world's population / sanitation and basic hygiene have improved for many people.

2) Many people around the world are demanding a better standard of living, so more energy is used to produce the various products that they want. More waste/pollution is also produced by manufacturing these products.
Also accept: people tend to travel more nowadays, e.g. for work and for holidays, which burns a lot of fuel and causes pollution.

3) (i) Any one of, e.g. burning fuels produces carbon dioxide (a greenhouse gas that causes global warming) / sulfur dioxide (causes acid rain).

(ii) Any one of, e.g. household waste is buried in landfill sites / nuclear waste is buried underground / chemicals (e.g. herbicides and pesticides) are used on farmland.

(iii) Any one of, e.g. sewage is released into lakes, rivers and oceans / toxic chemicals from industry can pollute waterways / chemicals used on farmland can be washed into waterways.

4) The greenhouse effect is the process in which certain gases trap reflected heat and prevent it leaving the atmosphere.

5) Carbon dioxide and methane.

6) Any four of, e.g. as the sea gets warmer it expands, which could cause flooding in low-lying areas / lots of cold, fresh water from melted ice entering the sea could disrupt currents, meaning some places (maybe the UK) get colder / there would be changes in the weather — e.g. hurricanes form over water that's warmer than 26 °C, so with more warm water about you could expect more hurricanes / other changes to weather patterns and the climate could mean some areas might become completely uninhabitable / important agricultural areas may no longer be suitable for growing food / higher temperatures melt ice, causing flooding and disrupting ecosystems.
Recent documentaries have shown footage of polar bears swimming for miles as their normal habitat disappears into the sea. But it's not just polar bears that will suffer due to climate change. Species all over the world, including humans, will have to adapt if their climate and habitat change — many could die out altogether.

Exam Questions

1 (a) (i) The concentration stayed about the same *(1 mark)*.

(ii) The concentration rose sharply *(1 mark)*.

(b) Any two of, e.g. deforestation / using cars/planes/other transport / burning fuel in power stations / burning more fuel to heat our homes / industrial processes *(1 mark each)*.

2 (a) Melting ice on land runs into the sea / the sea water becomes warmer and expands *(1 mark)*.

(b) (i) Some places are currently warmed by warm ocean currents, which could be disrupted by cold fresh water from ice melting into the sea *(1 mark)*.

(ii) Hurricanes can only form over water when it is above 26 °C — there is likely to be more water above this temperature as a result of global warming *(1 mark)*.

3 (a) There would be fewer trees to carry out photosynthesis *(1 mark)*, which absorbs/removes the greenhouse gas carbon dioxide from the air *(1 mark)*. Also accept: The trees might be burned/broken down by microorganisms *(1 mark)*, which would release the greenhouse gas carbon dioxide *(1 mark)*.

(b) Using the trees as fuel would contribute more to global warming *(1 mark)*, because combustion releases the carbon in the wood as carbon dioxide *(1 mark)*.

4 (a) The temperature should increase faster in jar 2 *(1 mark)*, because the carbon dioxide in jar 2 will absorb more heat than the air in jar 1 *(1 mark)*.

(b) Jar 1 was acting as a control/used as a comparison *(1 mark)*.

(c) Any one of, e.g. distance from heat lamp / type of container/jar used / starting temperature inside jars *(1 mark)*.

5 (a) The two sets of data show the same pattern/increase at the same time *(1 mark)*.

(b) Any one of, e.g. a relationship between two things doesn't necessarily prove that one causes another / it could be a coincidence / some other factor may have caused both increases *(1 mark)*.

Page 105
Warm-Up Questions

1) Sustainable development is development that meets the needs of today's population without harming the ability of future generations to meet their own needs.

2) Preservation of the natural environment / protecting species by maintaining their habitats and preventing them from being over-hunted or over-harvested.

3) Any three of, e.g. conservation is important to prevent species becoming extinct / it is needed in order to protect the human food supply / conservation maintains biodiversity / an example of the benefits of maintaining biodiversity, such as potential for useful new products, or maintaining the balance of an ecosystem

4) Advantages — any two of, e.g. less waste has to be dumped in landfill sites / fewer new materials have to be extracted, reducing energy use and preventing damage to landscapes / fewer new products have to be manufactured, which uses less energy (and reduces pollution and greenhouse gas emissions) / fewer of the Earth's natural resources are used up.
Disadvantages — any two of, e.g. recycling still uses energy for collecting and processing the waste / some waste materials, e.g. plastics, can be difficult to sort / the equipment needed can be expensive / the quality of recycled material may not be as high as newly produced goods / there's a limit to how many times some things can be recycled.
None of these things are good excuses not to recycle though. Most councils now collect your recycling from you, and the energy used up in dealing with it is almost always less than it would take to make new materials from scratch. It's also a good idea to try and buy stuff made from recycled materials.

Exam Questions

1

Air Pollutant	Source of Pollution	Effect of Pollution
CFCs	old aerosols, fridges, air conditioning systems, polystyrene	ozone depletion
carbon monoxide	burning fossil fuels without sufficient oxygen	prevents blood carrying oxygen
sulfur dioxide	burning fossil fuels (in factories, cars, etc.)	acid rain

(1 mark each)

2 (a) Biodiversity is the variety of different species in an area *(1 mark)*.

(b) Any two of, e.g. species may be able to provide useful products such as medicines / loss of some species may unbalance the ecosystem / we have a responsibility to preserve species for future generations / species are valuable in their own right *(1 mark each)*.

(c) (i) Bacteria in the water increase in numbers and use up oxygen, meaning the water becomes deoxygenated, killing off some of the species *(1 mark)*.

(ii) A few species can tolerate the conditions, so high numbers of these indicate pollution *(1 mark)*. Other species can only live in clean water, so their presence indicates a lack of pollution *(1 mark)*.

3 (a) Between 1955 and 1985 it remained stable/only decreased slightly *(1 mark)*. After 1985, the pH decreased from just below 7.0 to less than 4.0 within twenty years *(1 mark)*.

(b) The lake may have been polluted with acid rain/contaminated with an acidic substance *(1 mark)*.

(c) It would probably kill them *(1 mark)*.

Page 106
Revision Summary for Section Five

11) The fact that one glacier is melting doesn't mean that all glaciers are melting. One glacier melting doesn't mean that the average global temperature is rising. You'd need to collect a lot more data from around the whole world over a long period of time.

16) a) As the world population increases the number of extinct species increases.

b) E.g. more humans means more animals are hunted and more habitats are destroyed to make way for farming, living etc.

20) a) 25

b) 2002

c) 0.5 tonnes

d) 2003

e) Any two of, e.g. conserves finite resources such as metals / reduces landfill / uses less energy, meaning less CO_2 is released.

Pages 115–116
Warm-Up Questions

1) Plant cells have a rigid cell wall, they have a permanent vacuole and they contain chloroplasts.

2) The bases are adenine, thymine, guanine and cytosine. Adenine pairs with thymine and guanine pairs with cytosine.

3) The ribosomes.

4) A catalyst is a substance that increases the speed of a reaction, without being permanently changed or used up in the reaction.

5)

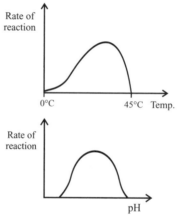

6) The optimum temperature or pH is the temperature or pH at which the enzyme works best.

Exam Questions

1 (a) C *(1 mark)*.

(b) Chlorophyll *(1 mark)*.

(c) It has an elongated shape/a large surface area for absorbing carbon dioxide *(1 mark)*. Palisade cells have a thin shape so that they can be packed in at the top of a leaf where most light falls *(1 mark)*.

2 (a) G—G—C—A—A—A—C—C—C *(1 mark)*.

(b) three *(1 mark)*

(c) a protein/polypeptide *(1 mark)*

3 (a) A group of similar cells that are specialised and work together to perform a function *(1 mark)*.

(b) To control the opening and closing of the stomata *(1 mark)*.

(c) They have thin outer walls and thickened inner walls *(1 mark)*. This makes the cells bend when they're turgid, and so the stoma opens *(1 mark)*.

4 (a) Yes *(1 mark)*, because his DNA profile has the same pattern as the DNA profile from the blood at the crime scene *(1 mark)*.

(b) It is true that usually everyone's DNA is unique *(1 mark)*, but identical twins have the same DNA and so would have identical genetic fingerprints *(1 mark)*.

(a) Accept answers between 38 °C and 40 °C *(1 mark)*.

(b) Enzyme B *(1 mark)*, because it has an unusually high optimum temperature which it would need to work in the hot vent *(1 mark)*.

(c) It would break down the proteins in stains such as blood and grass on clothing *(1 mark)*. It would not be denatured by high-temperature washes *(1 mark)*.

(a) The enzyme has a specific shape which will only fit with one type of substance *(1 mark)*.

(b) In the wrong conditions (e.g. high temperatures), the bonds in the enzyme are broken/the enzyme changes shape, so the substance can no longer fit into it *(1 mark)*.

If you heat a substance you supply it with energy and it moves about more. This helps things to react faster. But if you heat an enzyme too much, it jiggles about such a lot that it ends up breaking some of the bonds that hold it together and it loses its shape. A similar thing happens with pH — the wrong pH disrupts the bonds and the shape is changed.

Page 122

Warm-Up Questions

1) Diffusion is the passive movement of particles from an area of higher concentration to an area of lower concentration.

2) In the lungs/alveoli, in the small intestine/gut/digestive system and at the synapses.

3) Water will move out of the animal cell by osmosis from an area of higher water concentration to an area of lower water concentration.

4) A partially permeable membrane only allows certain substances (e.g. water) to diffuse through it.

Exam Questions

1 (a) Any two of, e.g. the concentration gradient / the distance over which the substances have to move / temperature *(1 mark each)*.

(b) As the blood moves past the alveolus, oxygen diffuses into the blood from the alveolus (from an area of higher concentration to an area of lower concentration) *(1 mark)* and carbon dioxide diffuses out of the blood into the alveolus (from an area of higher concentration to an area of lower concentration) *(1 mark)*.

2 (a) The potato cylinder in tube D *(1 mark)*, because this tube contains the most concentrated sugar solution so this cylinder will have lost the most water by osmosis *(1 mark)*.

(b) Tube A contained distilled water, so some of the water moved by osmosis into the potato cylinder *(1 mark)* from an area of higher water concentration to an area of lower water concentration *(1 mark)*.

Page 123

Revision Summary for Section Six

19 a) pH 1.6

b) This enzyme would be found in the stomach.

Page 126

Warm-Up Questions

1) Respiration is the process of breaking down glucose to release energy, which happens in every cell.

2) glucose + oxygen → carbon dioxide + water (+ energy)

3) glucose → lactic acid (+ energy)

4) Any three of, e.g. the heart rate increases / the breathing rate increases / respiration rate increases / more energy is released in the muscles / anaerobic respiration may begin / the muscles generate more heat / sweating increases.

5) They have a moist lining for gases to dissolve in and very thin walls so that the gases don't have far to diffuse. They also have a very good blood supply and permeable walls.

Exam Questions

1 (a) Any two of, e.g anaerobic respiration doesn't use oxygen and aerobic respiration does / anaerobic respiration produces lactic acid and aerobic respiration produces carbon dioxide and water / aerobic respiration releases more energy *(1 mark each)*.

(b) Both break down glucose *(1 mark)* and both release energy *(1 mark)*.

(c) Aerobic respiration releases more energy/does not result in a painful build-up of lactic acid in the muscles *(1 mark)*. Anaerobic respiration can happen in emergencies when there isn't enough oxygen available *(1 mark)*.

2 (a) During exercise the muscles need more energy from respiration, and this respiration requires oxygen. So the rate of respiration increases and so does the rate of oxygen use *(1 mark)*.

(b)
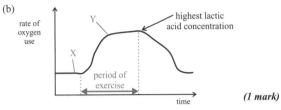
(1 mark)

This isn't a question that involves simply repeating facts you have learned, so don't worry if you found it difficult. You should know that lactic acid builds up when there isn't enough oxygen for aerobic respiration, and then hopefully you can work out that this would happen when oxygen consumption was at its peak (and when the person had been exercising for the longest).

(c) Because there is an oxygen debt/oxygen is needed to break down the lactic acid that has built up *(1 mark)*.

Page 130

Warm-Up Questions

1) Digestion is the breaking down of large food molecules into smaller molecules that can be absorbed into the blood.

2) (i) amylase
(ii) protease
(iii) lipase
Proteases break down proteins, and lipases break down lipids (fats).

3) (i) maltose and simple sugars
(ii) amino acids
(iii) glycerol and fatty acids

4) Bile emulsifies fats and neutralises the hydrochloric acid from the stomach.

Exam Questions

1 (a)
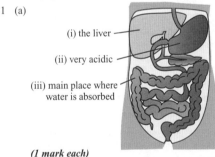

(i) the liver

(ii) very acidic

(iii) main place where water is absorbed

(1 mark each)
The acidic part is the stomach. The large intestine absorbs most of the water.

(b) Any two of, e.g. it's very long to give lots of time for absorption / there are lots of villi to provide a large surface area for absorption / each villus is covered with microvilli to further increase the surface area for absorption / the villi have a thin/single-celled epithelium for good permeability / there are many blood capillaries to absorb the digested food *(1 mark each)*.

2 (a) It stores bile until it is ready to be released *(1 mark)*.

(b) It produces/releases digestive enzymes *(1 mark)*.

(c) It produces bile *(1 mark)*.

3 (a) amylase/carbohydrase *(1 mark)*

(b) Any three of, e.g. temperature / volume of solution / concentration of starch solution / concentration of enzyme solution *(1 mark each)*.

(c) At pH 8 *(1 mark)*, because this is the pH in the part of the gut where this enzyme works/because most enzymes work best at around a neutral pH *(1 mark)*.

Page 136

Warm-Up Questions

1) Any four of, e.g. red blood cells / white blood cells / water / platelets / glucose / amino acids / carbon dioxide / hormones / urea / antibodies / antitoxins.

2) Arteries have thicker walls. Veins have a bigger lumen. Veins contain valves and arteries don't.

3) If you take in too much cholesterol it starts to build up in the arteries, forming plaques in the artery walls. This restricts the flow of the blood to the part of the body that the artery is supplying. Plaques can cause heart attacks if they are in the coronary artery and strokes if they are in an artery in the brain.

4) Mammals basically have two circulatory systems — one connecting the heart to the lungs, and one connecting the heart to the rest of the body.

5) Heart transplants involve major surgery, which can be risky, and require a lifetime of drugs and medical care afterwards. There's a risk that the new heart could be rejected, and the drugs the patient has to take to avoid this suppress the immune system and leave them vulnerable to infections.

Exam Questions

1 (a) Any three of, e.g. they have a biconcave shape giving a large surface area. / They have no nucleus which gives more room for haemaglobin. / They are very flexible which means they can pass through small capillaries. / They contain haemoglobin which reacts with oxygen *(1 mark each)*.

(b) White blood cells *(1 mark)*, which defend the body against infections *(1 mark)*.

2 (a) (i) aorta, vena cava, pulmonary artery, pulmonary vein *(1 mark each)*.

(ii) right atrium *(1 mark)*

(b) (i) four *(1 mark)*

(ii) valves *(1 mark)*

(iii) Valves prevent the blood flowing backwards/in the wrong direction *(1 mark)*.

Page 141

Warm-Up Questions

1) They remove urea from the blood, adjust the blood's ion content and make sure blood contains the right amount of water.

2) It is produced in the liver and removed from the body by the kidneys.

3) Water is lost from the body in sweat, in urine and in the air breathed out.

4) Insulin is produced in the pancreas.

5) Insulin causes the blood glucose level to fall.

Exam Questions

1 (a) X = ureter, Y = bladder, Z = urethra *(1 mark each)*

(b) The blood in the renal vein will contain (any three of): less oxygen, less urea, more carbon dioxide, less water, less salt *(1 mark each)*.

2 (a) Person C *(1 mark)*, because the urine contains glucose *(1 mark)*.

(b) Person A had more protein/amino acids in their diet *(1 mark)*, or they have lost more water in sweat (so all solutes are more concentrated) *(1 mark)*.

3 (a) Any two of, large amounts can be regularly produced / there's less chance of allergic reactions / it is 'human' insulin and therefore more effective. *(1 mark each)*

(b) Advantage: any one of, e.g. it's a permanent cure/there's no need for any more injections / the person can have a more normal diet / the person avoids all of the risks associated with diabetes that isn't properly controlled *(1 mark)*.

Disadvantage: any one of, e.g. there's a possibility of rejection / the person will need to take immunosuppressive drugs / it involves surgery, which always carries some risk *(1 mark)*.

Page 142

Revision Summary for Section Seven

4) a) 60 beats per minute

b) 2 minutes

c) 70 beats per minute

Page 147

Warm-Up Questions

1) Any two of, e.g. height / length / width / circumference.

2) mitosis

3) It gives the athlete an unfair advantage and the growth factors can have harmful side effects.

4) 46

5) 23

Exam Questions

1 (a) meiosis *(1 mark)*

(b) (i) To store the enzymes the sperm needs to penetrate the egg cell at fertilisation *(1 mark)*.

(ii) To provide the energy it needs for movement *(1 mark)*.

(iii) For movement/swimming *(1 mark)*.

2 (a) The dry weight is the weight of an organism when all the water has been removed *(1 mark)*. Wet weight can vary a lot from one day to the next, dry weight doesn't vary as much *(1 mark)*.

(b) To improve the reliability of his results/reduce the chances of the overall pattern being affected by one unusual result *(1 mark)*.

(c) Because measuring the dry mass of the seeds kills them (so they stop growing) *(1 mark)*.

3 (a) (i) Each cell should contain only three chromatids *(1 mark)*, and there should be one of each type *(1 mark)* as shown:

Remember that there are two divisions in meiosis. In the first division, one chromosome from each pair goes into each of two new cells. In the second division, both those cells divide again, with one half of each chromosome going into each of the new cells.

(ii) They contain half the genetic material that the original cell contained *(1 mark)*.

(b) Any three of, e.g. it involves two divisions, instead of one / it halves the chromosome number, rather than keeping it constant / it produces genetically different cells, not genetically identical cells / it produces sex cells/gametes, not body cells. *(1 mark each)*

Page 152

Warm-Up Questions

1) 24 weeks.

2) This used to be the age at which a foetus might survive outside the womb with medical help, although medical advances have meant that babies born earlier than this have now survived.

3) A cell is removed from the embryo and its genes are analysed so that genetic disorders can be detected.

4) Stem cells are undifferentiated cells which have the potential to grow into different types of cell.

Exam Questions

1 (a) Any two of, e.g. the baby is likely to be disabled and so might have a poor quality of life / the disability might cause the child pain and suffering / the child's life might be shortened by the disability / the child's family might find it difficult to cope / caring for the child could cost a lot of money *(1 mark each)*.

(b) Any two of, e.g. the life of a disabled child is just as valuable as any other life / the foetus is a human being and should have rights / aborting this foetus suggests that people with disabilities are 'undesirable', which is wrong *(1 mark each)*.

2 (a) This means that the egg was fertilised outside the body in the laboratory *(1 mark)*.

(b) (i) E.g. to give a better chance of a successful fertilisation / so that embryos with genetic disorders can be discarded *(1 mark)*.

(ii) Rejected embryos have to be destroyed, which means destroying potential human life *(1 mark)*.

(c) Embryos contain early stem cells *(1 mark)*, that can develop into any other type of cell *(1 mark)*.

(a) bone marrow *(1 mark)*

(b) (i) They are both undifferentiated/able to develop into different cell types/ capable of unlimited division *(1 mark)*.

(ii) Embryonic stem cells can develop into any other type of cell, but adult stem cells are more limited *(1 mark)*.

(c) Stem cells could be used to make new nerve cells to replace the faulty cells *(1 mark)*.

Page 159
Warm-Up Questions

1) Auxins are plant hormones that control a plant's growth.

2) Fruit normally only grows on plants that have been pollinated. These fruits contain seeds. But if the right growth hormone is applied to some types of plant, fruit will grow without the plant being pollinated and there will be no seeds.

3) Organisms with the best characteristics are selected and bred with each other. The best of their offspring are then selected and bred. This process is repeated over several generations.

4) A clone is an organism that is genetically identical to another organism.

5) Any two of, e.g. cloning other mammals has resulted in high rates of miscarriage and stillbirth / other cloned mammals have tended to suffer health problems / other cloned mammals have often died prematurely / the person might suffer psychological damage from knowing that they're a clone of somebody else / cloning is a new science and might have consequences that we don't know about yet.

Exam Questions

1 (a) The right side *(1 mark)*.

(b) Auxin from the tip diffuses down into the stem *(1 mark)*, so there is more auxin on the right side *(1 mark)*, and the auxin stimulates more growth there *(1 mark)*.

(c) Because light would change the distribution of the auxin *(1 mark)*.

2 (a) By using selective breeding *(1 mark)* — only the fastest horses are chosen for breeding *(1 mark)*, and so over time this characteristic becomes predominant in the offspring *(1 mark)*.

(b) Any one of, e.g. the horses are inbred, and so may be more prone to genetic disorders. / An inbred population of horses may all be susceptible to the same diseases and could all contract the same disease *(1 mark)*.

3 (a) So that it does not contain Beatrix's genes/So it can receive the genetic information from Brenda *(1 mark)*.

(b) Brenda *(1 mark)*, because it is her genetic information that is being transmitted to the baby *(1 mark)*.
Belinda gave birth to the baby mouse, but the egg cell that was implanted into her uterus came from Beatrix, and the nucleus (where all of the genetic material came from) was from Brenda. The baby mouse is therefore a clone of Brenda.

Pages 167–168
Warm-Up Questions

1) Carbon dioxide, water, (sun)light, chlorophyll.

2) A limiting factor is something that stops photosynthesis from happening any faster.

3) Any four of, e.g. leaves are broad, so there's a large surface exposed to the light / they are thin, so carbon dioxide only has to travel a short distance to the photosynthesising cells / the spongy mesophyll has air spaces in it to allow gases to diffuse more easily and to provide a large surface area for gas exchange / leaves contain chlorophyll to absorb the light energy for photosynthesis / most of the chloroplasts are found near the top of the leaf where the light is strongest / the upper epidermis is transparent so that light can pass through it / the leaves have stomata to let carbon dioxide in / the leaves are supplied by veins to provide water from the roots.

4) Through the stomata.

Exam Questions

1 Making cell walls — cellulose *(1 mark)*
Making enzymes — amino acids *(1 mark)*
Making fruit sweet — sucrose *(1 mark)*
Storing energy — starch *(1 mark)*

2 (a) A = palisade mesophyll layer *(1 mark)*, B = epidermis *(1 mark)*, C = stoma *(1 mark)*.

(b) Any two of, e.g. irregularly shaped cells for a large surface area / air spaces for rapid diffusion / thin permeable cell walls for carbon dioxide uptake / chloroplasts for light absorption *(1 mark each)*

(c) The palisade cells in the palisade mesophyll layer. *(1 mark)*

3 (a) (i) At the higher temperature the molecules/enzymes work more rapidly / there are more collisions and more energetic collisions between reacting molecules, so the rate of photosynthesis is quicker. *(1 mark)*

(ii) At 50 °C the enzymes are denatured/the plant dies. *(1 mark)*

(b) In the experiment the rate was highest at this temperature *(1 mark)*, but the optimum could actually be anywhere between 30 °C and 50 °C (where no measurements were made) *(1 mark)*.

4 (a) By counting the number of bubbles produced/measuring the volume of gas produced, in a given time/at regular intervals *(1 mark)*.

(b) (i) The rate of photosynthesis/number of bubbles/volume of gas *(1 mark)*.

(ii) The light intensity *(1 mark)*.

(c) E.g. carbon dioxide concentration in the water/temperature/the plant being used *(1 mark)*.

5 (a) A label anywhere on the sloping part of the graph, before it levels off *(1 mark)*.

(b) Carbon dioxide concentration/temperature/amount of chlorophyll *(1 mark)*.

6 (a) Chlorophyll *(1 mark)*.

(b) (i)

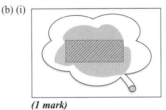

(1 mark)

(ii) Plants need both chlorophyll and light to photosynthesise and produce starch. There is only chlorophyll in the green area of the plant, and light can only reach parts of the leaf not covered by black paper *(1 mark)*.

Page 173
Warm-Up Questions

1) The transpiration stream is the constant flow of water through a plant from roots to leaves caused by the evaporation of water and diffusion of water vapour from the leaves.

2) (a) The roots.

(b) The leaves.

3) Bright light, a warm temperature, lots of air movement/wind, dry.

4) The cell is so short of water that the cytoplasm has shrunk and pulled away from the cell wall.

5) Xylem vessels transport water and phloem vessels transport food substances around a plant.

Exam Questions

1 (a) (i) One of, e.g. repeat the experiment / compare results with the results of others doing the same experiment *(1 mark)*.

(ii) Keep other factors constant *(1 mark)*, such as temperature/humidity/ light intensity/plant used *(1 mark)*.

(b) The results show that the rate of transpiration increases with air movement *(1 mark)*, but the rate of increase is lower at higher air speeds *(1 mark)*.

2 (a) Any two of, xylem vessels have no cytoplasm / they have thicker (or lignified) cell walls / there are no end-walls between cells / they are dead *(1 mark each)*.

(b) Xylem vessels transport water (and minerals) instead of sugars *(1 mark)*. Xylem vessels help to support the plant *(1 mark)*.

3 (a) The lower surfaces have more stomata *(1 mark)*.

(b) The loss of water means that the cells are flaccid and their turgor pressure decreases, making the plant droop *(1 mark)*.

(c) The waterproof cuticle helps to reduce water loss, which is especially important in the hot, dry climates where cacti are found *(1 mark)*.

Page 176

Warm-Up Questions

1) phosphates

2) It has yellow leaves and could be stunted.

3) active transport

4) osmosis

Exam Questions

1 (a) Taking in water and mineral ions *(1 mark)*.

(b) The elongated shape of the root hair gives it a large surface area for absorption *(1 mark)*.

2

Mineral	Function
magnesium	needed for making chlorophyll
phosphates	needed for making DNA and cell membranes and for healthy roots
potassium	**needed for making enzymes for respiration and photosynthesis, and for flowers and fruit**
nitrate	**needed for proteins/growth**

(1 mark each)

3 (a) nitrates *(1 mark)*

(b) potassium *(1 mark)*

(c) phosphates *(1 mark)*

Page 182

Warm-Up Questions

1) A feeding level in a food chain or web.

2) Because material and energy are lost at every stage in a food chain, so it takes a lot of animals to support each carnivore.

3) Plants are the only organisms that are able to make their own food using energy from the Sun. They are at the bottom of every food chain, so even animals at the top depend on them.

4) Biomass is basically the mass of living material at a trophic level or in an area — how much it weighs.

5) E.g. trees/wood and biogas (also accept gasohol).

Exam Questions

1 (a) C *(1 mark)*.

If you think about it, it's quite likely that a woodland ecosystem might be based on a tree. And it's pretty obvious which pyramid has a smaller number of big trees at the bottom with lots of little creatures eating them. So you can use a process of elimination if you leave this part of the question until last.

(b) B *(1 mark)*

(c) A *(1 mark)*

2 (a) (1500 ÷ 15000) × 100 = 10% *(1 mark)*

(b) Any two of, e.g. the small animals use energy for movement which is lost from the food chain as heat via respiration / energy is lost through excretion/egestion in the animals / some of the small animals die without being eaten by the fish / the fish may not eat all parts of the small animals / the fish might not digest all the parts of the animals they eat *(1 mark each)*.

3 (a) Because the fungus produces heat energy as it respires *(1 mark)*. Too much heat will denature its enzymes and too low a temperature will be less efficient *(1 mark)*.

(b) Any two of, e.g. pH / concentration of nutrients / concentration of oxygen / concentration of carbon dioxide/waste products *(1 mark each)*.

(c) Any two of, e.g. production is faster / it's not dependent on the weather / land that's unsuitable for agriculture can be used to produce food / waste materials can be used as 'food' for the fungus *(1 mark each)*.

Page 189

Warm-Up Questions

1) DDT can't be removed from the body so it accumulates in food chains. The top predators, like falcons and otters, can receive enough DDT from animals lower in the chain for the level to be toxic.

2) Hydroponics is where plants are grown without soil — nutrient solutions (water and dissolved fertiliser) are used instead.

3) Growing a cycle of different crops in a field each year stops the pests and diseases of one crop building up. Most cycles include a legume plant to help put nutrients back into the soil.

4) Organic farming requires more land and more labour, so it's more expensive to produce the food. Yields are likely to be lower without artificial fertilisers, pesticides and herbicides, so farmers need to charge a bit more to make a profit. Organic farmers have to pay for their food to be certified organic.

Exam Questions

1 (a) (i) To stop predatory birds from eating the fish *(1 mark)*.

(ii) To stop the fish escaping / to limit their movement so they use less energy / to protect them from predators *(1 mark)*.

(b) Any two of, e.g. controlled feeding programme / using pesticides or fungicides / rearing the young in special tanks *(1 mark each)*.

(c) (i) Disease/pests may spread from the farmed fish to the wild fish *(1 mark)*.

(ii) Pollution by pesticides/fish faeces/leftover food could harm the loch ecosystem *(1 mark)*.

2 (a) To prevent disease (which may be more likely in the warm, crowded conditions) *(1 mark)*.

(b) The disease organisms may develop resistance to the antibiotics, which makes the disease harder to treat *(1 mark)*.

(c) This reduces the energy the cattle lose as heat *(1 mark)*. Keeping them inside means they use less energy because they move less, and using less energy means they'll need less food and so cost less money. *(1 mark)*.

3 (a) Living organisms are used to control a pest *(1 mark)*.

(b) Rabbits were no longer eating the young tree seedlings *(1 mark)*, so they began to invade grassland. Foxes had fewer rabbits to eat, so ate hens instead *(1 mark)*.

Page 194

Warm-Up Questions

1) Detritivores are organisms such as earthworms and woodlice that feed on dead and decaying material and break it into smaller pieces. Saprophytes are organisms such as bacteria and fungi that feed on decaying material by secreting digestive enzymes outside their bodies and then absorbing the digested material.

2) Any three of, e.g. burning fossil fuels / respiration by plants and animals / burning products made from plants and animals / carbon compounds from dead plants and animals being broken down by bacteria.

3) As nitrates

4) Proteins

Exam Questions

1 (a) A = burning/combustion, B = photosynthesis, C = respiration *(1 mark each)*.

(b) (i) There would be less photosynthesis and so more carbon dioxide in the atmosphere/less carbon dioxide removed from the atmosphere *(1 mark)*.

(ii) There would be more carbon dioxide in the air, because burning fossil fuels produces carbon dioxide *(1 mark)*.

(c) photosynthesis *(1 mark)*

convert ammonia to nitrates — nitrifying bacteria *(1 mark)*
convert nitrates to nitrogen gas — denitrifying bacteria *(1 mark)*
convert nitrogen gas to nitrates — nitrogen-fixing bacteria *(1 mark)*
convert proteins to ammonia — decomposing bacteria *(1 mark)*

(a) (i) The legume contains nitrogen-fixing bacteria *(1 mark)*, which convert nitrogen gas into nitrates/ammonia/amino acids *(1 mark)*.

(ii) This decays to release nutrients/nitrates into the soil *(1 mark)*.

(b) This would increase the nitrate content of the soil *(1 mark)*, because the lightning has enough energy to cause a reaction between the nitrogen and oxygen in the air, forming nitrates *(1 mark)*.

Page 195
Revision Summary for Section Nine

3) a) 40 units

   b) Any two of, e.g. temperature / light / water.

Page 200
Warm-Up Questions

1) Active transport involves moving substances from an area of lower concentration to an area of higher concentration — diffusion can only move substances the other way (down a concentration gradient).

   Active transport needs energy from respiration and diffusion does not.

2) Alveoli.

3) The total lung capacity is the total volume of air that can fit in the lungs and the vital capacity is the total amount of **usable** air (the biggest amount that can be breathed in or out).

4) Spirometer.

5) Cilia beat to push mucus (containing trapped dust and microbes) out and away from the lungs.

6) The muscles around the person's airways contract, narrowing the airways and making it hard for the person to breathe.

Exam Questions

1 (a)
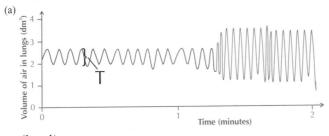

(1 mark)

(b) 12 breaths per minute *(1 mark)*

(c) (i) They breathe more quickly *(1 mark)* and more deeply *(1 mark)*.

(ii) Any one of, e.g. The person is probably exercising / The person may be under stress *(1 mark)*.

2 Answer should be similar to: The diaphragm contracts *(1 mark)*, and the intercostal muscles contract *(1 mark)*. This increases the volume of the thorax *(1 mark)*, and so decreases the pressure in the thorax, drawing air in *(1 mark)*.

Pages 207–208
Warm-Up Questions

1) It carries deoxygenated blood.

2) The sequence of events in one heartbeat — the atria contract, then the ventricles contract.

3) The SAN is the pacemaker, and stimulates the atria to contract. The AVN delays the electrical current, causing the ventricles to contract slightly later than the atria.

4) An ultrasound scan of the heart.

5) E.g. haemophilia.

Exam Questions

1 (a) four *(1 mark)*

(b) A label on any of the tallest peaks on the graph *(1 mark)*.

(c) The heart has missed a beat *(1 mark)*.
That's the flat bit in the middle — you should be seeing nice regular peaks the whole way across.

2 (a) (i) B has 150 more deaths due to CHD per 100 000 of the population per year *(1 mark)*.

(ii) Any one of, e.g. People living in country B may have less healthy diets / may drink more alcohol / smoke more / have more stressful lifestyles / country B may have an older population *(1 mark)*.

(b) Any three of, e.g. Take regular moderate exercise / stop smoking / drink less alcohol / lose weight / eat less fat/saturated fat/cholesterol / avoid stress *(1 mark each)*.

3 (a) An antigen is a substance that can trigger a response from the body's immune system *(1 mark)*.

(b) (i) They can give blood to people of any blood group *(1 mark)*.

(ii) Blood groups B and AB *(1 mark)*.

4 (a) A damaging blood clot forms in the veins *(1 mark)*.

(b) This helps to keep the blood circulating *(1 mark)*, reducing the chances of a clot *(1 mark)*.

(c) Aspirin is a drug that reduces the risk of blood clotting in vessels *(1 mark)*.

5 (a) and (b)   *(1 mark for showing arrows correctly)*

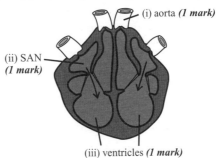

(i) aorta *(1 mark)*

(ii) SAN *(1 mark)*

(iii) ventricles *(1 mark)*

Page 214
Warm-Up Questions

1) Part of the kidney, where the blood is filtered and purified.

2) The pituitary gland.

3) This is a person who donates an organ (e.g. a kidney) or part of an organ (e.g. a piece of their liver) to somebody else while he/she is still alive.

4) Artificial valves avoid some of the problems of rejection that you can get with a transplant.

Exam Questions

1 (a) Glucose is actively reabsorbed back into the blood *(1 mark)*.

(b) The membrane between the blood and the capsule acts as a filter *(1 mark)*, and protein molecules are too big to fit through *(1 mark)*.

2 (a) (i) The urea diffuses out through the dialysis membrane *(1 mark)*, because the concentration of urea in the blood is more than in the dialysis fluid/because the dialysis fluid contains no urea *(1 mark)*.

(ii) The dialysis fluid contains the same concentration of glucose as healthy blood *(1 mark)*, so there is no concentration gradient *(1 mark)*.

(b) Any one of, e.g. She will not have to have dialysis sessions three times every week for hours each time / She can eat a more normal diet / She won't suffer from the high blood pressure associated with kidney disease, which can lead to other health problems *(1 mark)*.

3 (a) Any two of, e.g. Mr Chester's heart may not be healthy enough / He might be too old / There may not be a good tissue match / His heart might be the wrong size *(1 mark each)*.

(b) Any one of, e.g. She might have religious objections / She might prefer her husband to be buried complete *(1 mark)*.

(c) Any one of, e.g. The law could be changed so that organs can be used unless people opt out / The law could be changed so that family members no longer have to give their consent / Advertising campaigns could be used to encourage people to opt in *(1 mark)*.

Page 219

Warm-Up Questions

1) Any two of, e.g. Support / movement / protection of vital organs / making blood cells.

2) An oily fluid that acts as a lubricant at joints.

3) a) Any one of, e.g. knee / elbow.

   b) Any one of, e.g. shoulder / hip.

4) Because muscles can't push, only pull (so two muscles are needed for movement in both directions).

5) They hold the bones together at a joint.

Exam Questions

1 (a) X = cartilage *(1 mark)*, Y = compact bone *(1 mark)*,
       Z = marrow cavity *(1 mark)*.

   (b) It makes the bone lighter in relation to its strength, so it's easier to move it *(1 mark)*.

2 (a) They will provide plenty of calcium (which helps to reduce the effects of osteoporosis) *(1 mark)*.

   (b) Any two of, e.g. It may cause the surrounding tissue to become inflamed and painful / Dislocation is more likely / Blood clots are more likely / There's a risk of infection after surgery / Her legs may not be exactly the same length afterwards / The artificial hip will eventually need replacing *(1 mark each)*.

3 (a) The biceps relaxes/gets longer *(1 mark)* and the triceps contracts/gets shorter *(1 mark)*.

   (b) To reduce friction/rubbing / To act as a shock absorber *(1 mark)*.

   (c) A hinge joint only allows movement backwards and forwards/in one plane, but the ball and socket joint allows movement in all directions/allows rotation *(1 mark)*.

Pages 228–229

Warm-Up Questions

1) Dividing into two of a bacterium (to give two clones).

2) The toxins produced by the microorganisms and/or your immune system's reaction to the infection.

3) Prebiotics are substances that promote the growth of 'good' bacteria in the gut by providing a food supply that only they can use.

4) Either for flavouring or as a preservative.

5) It converts sucrose into glucose and fructose.

Exam Questions

1 (a) X = cell wall *(1 mark)*, Y = DNA/chromosome *(1 mark)*,
       Z = flagellum *(1 mark)*

   (b) (i) Any two of, e.g. has a cell wall / has a cell membrane / has cytoplasm / has DNA *(1 mark each)*.

      (ii) Any two of, e.g. has a different kind of cell wall (not cellulose) / has no nucleus / has no chloroplasts / has no mitochondria / has no vacuole / has a flagellum *(1 mark each)*.

2

Typical method of transmission	Disease
insect bites	E.g. malaria, Lyme's disease
contaminated food/water	E.g. cholera, salmonella
sexual contact	E.g. HIV/AIDS, hepatitis C
droplet infection	E.g. influenza, tuberculosis

(1 mark for each, maximum 1 mark for each method of transmission)

3 (a) (i) Chymosin *(1 mark)*.

      (ii) It's used to clot the milk *(1 mark)*.

   (b) It has to be extracted from a calf's stomach (and she is a vegetarian) *(1 mark)*.

   (c) By using chymosin produced by GM bacteria *(1 mark)*.

4 (a) It caused damage to the sewage system and/or drinking water supplies *(1 mark)*, so the water became contaminated with disease-causing microorganisms *(1 mark)*.

   (b) To kill the cholera bacteria *(1 mark)*.

   (c) Any one of, e.g. isolating infected people / vaccination / repairs to sewage system / repairs to water system / emergency provision of clean water to affected areas *(1 mark)*.

5 (a) They may reduce blood cholesterol *(1 mark)* and so reduce the risk of heart disease *(1 mark)*.

   (b) Sterols are extracted from the soya bean *(1 mark)* and bacteria are used to convert these into stanols *(1 mark)*.

Page 237

Warm-Up Questions

1) Asexually / by budding.

2) Because only anaerobic respiration produces alcohol.

3) To increase the alcohol content/concentration.

4) A mixture of alcohol/ethanol and petrol.

5) Methane.

Exam Questions

1 (a) Any two of, e.g. starting pH / amount of sugar/food provided / volume of culture/container *(1 mark each)*.

   (b) Any one of, e.g. there is less food available / there's a build-up of toxic wastes / the pH has become unfavourable *(1 mark)*.

   (c) The graph should slope upwards more steeply *(1 mark)* but still reach the same maximum *(1 mark)*.

2 (a) It is allowed to germinate so that the starch turns into sugar *(1 mark)* and then it is dried in a kiln *(1 mark)*.

   (b) (i) For flavour *(1 mark)*.
          These are what gives beer its bitter taste.

      (ii) To ferment the sugar into alcohol *(1 mark)*.

   (c) Any one of, e.g. to prevent other microorganisms growing in it / to prevent it spoiling / to kill the yeast and prevent further fermentation *(1 mark)*.

3 (a) Biological waste (e.g. sewage / food scraps / animal dung / remains of plants) *(1 mark)*.

   (b) (i) Because of the unpleasant smell / possibility of harmful bacteria in the waste *(1 mark)*.
          It's really just common sense that something which is busy fermenting poo and rubbish will smell. Don't be afraid to give common sense answers — examiners like to see that you can relate science to real life.

      (ii) So it is convenient for adding animal/plant waste *(1 mark)*.

   (c) Any two of, e.g. it is carbon neutral / it produces less sulfur/nitrogen oxides/acid rain / harmful methane is burned away / it is cheap/readily available / the digested material can be used as a fertiliser / (potentially harmful) waste is disposed of / it saves the damaging effects of mining the coal *(1 mark each)*.

Page 241

Warm-Up Questions

1) Proteins.

2) It breaks down the pectin between plant cell walls / Helps to extract the juice in fruits and vegetables.

3) Any one of, e.g. Attach them to an insoluble material (like silica gel/fibres of collagen/cellulose) / Encapsulate them in alginate beads.

4) The enzyme does not contaminate the product / Enzymes can be reused.

5) To test their blood glucose/sugar concentration.

Exam Questions

1 (a) enzymes *(1 mark)*

   (b) They may contain lipase enzymes *(1 mark)*, which break down fat/grease to fatty acids and glycerol, which can be washed away more easily *(1 mark)*.

   (c) Above this temperature the enzymes may be denatured and stop working *(1 mark)*.

295

(a) (i) 41 °C (accept answers between 40 and 44 °C) *(1 mark)*.

(ii) 63 °C (accept answers between 60 and 66 °C) *(1 mark)*.

(b) The enzyme in solution has been denatured *(1 mark)*, but the immobilised enzyme is more temperature-stable and is working quickly at the higher temperature *(1 mark)*.

(a) Lactase *(1 mark)*,

(b) Lactase breaks down lactose in milk into glucose and galactose that can be absorbed *(1 mark)*. Without the treatment, cats would not be able to digest the lactose *(1 mark)*.

Page 245

Warm-Up Questions

1) An organism that has had its DNA altered, e.g. by having DNA from another organism inserted into its genetic material.

2) A patent allows a company to be the only one permitted to produce their discovery for a set period of time. Also, patents allow companies to charge what they like for their product (e.g. drugs they have developed).

3) Any two of, e.g. Early diagnosis of diseases / Prevention of diseases / Improved understanding of the causes of diseases / Improved efficiency in developing new treatments / Ability to tailor drugs to people's individual needs.

4) To treat/prevent malaria.

Exam Questions

1 (a) It may reduce the need to use environmentally damaging chemical pesticides *(1 mark)*.

(b) (i) Any one of, e.g. They may think that people eating the GM tomatoes could have an unexpected (allergic) reaction to them / They may be concerned that the technology is quite new and could have unforeseen consequences *(1 mark)*.

(ii) Any one of, e.g. Weeds nearby may (pick up the gene and) become resistant to insects / Wildlife in the area may be negatively affected *(1 mark)*.

2 (a) 1. Resistance gene extracted from a wild bean plant. DNA loop removed from bacterium.
2. Resistance gene inserted into bacterial DNA loop.
3. Modified DNA loop re-inserted into bacterium.
4. Bacterium allowed to infect soya plant cells.
5. Modified soya cells grown in a medium containing herbicide.
(1 mark for three correct points, 2 marks for all five)

(b) To check that they have taken up the resistance gene/are resistant *(1 mark)*.

3 (a) Any one of, e.g. More people would be able to afford the drugs / the companies would not be able to make huge profits from people's illness'. *(1 mark)*.

(b) Drug research is expensive *(1 mark)* and so companies would be less likely to invest money in developing new drugs if they are less sure of being able to make it back *(1 mark)*.

Page 246

Revision Summary for Section Eleven

18 a) Biogas is suitable because waste from the goats and cows can be used in the biogas generator.

Advantages: villagers won't have to spend time collecting wood, digested material could be used to fertilise soil, and waste would be disposed of, reducing disease.

Disadvantages: biogas production slows down in cold conditions, so they might need an alternative fuel source in winter.

b) Their conclusion isn't valid. Possible reasons that it isn't: the amounts spread on the ground might have been different, the weather in the two places might have been different, the species of crop might have been different etc.

Pages 254–255

Warm-Up Questions

1) A simple inherited or conditioned behaviour, where a stimulus produces a simple response, e.g. sneezing / salivation / coughing / blinking / moving quickly away from a painful stimulus.

2) By rewarding the dog (with food/praise) when it obeys the command to sit.

3) Any three of, e.g. Can help animals to stay together in a group / Allows an animal to warn others of predators / Can help to avoid unnecessary fighting / Babies can communicate their needs to parents / Allows predators to coordinate their attacks.

4) E.g. by seeing whether the animal can recognise itself in a mirror.

Exam Questions

1 (a) This is when an animal learns to stop responding to a stimulus that isn't beneficial or harmful to it *(1 mark)*.

(b) Learned *(1 mark)*, because the animal's behaviour changes as a result of experience *(1 mark)*.

(c) It prevents the animal wasting energy responding to unimportant stimuli *(1 mark)*.

2 (a) The frequency of pressing lever A increased over time *(1 mark)*, while the frequency of pressing lever B decreased *(1 mark)*.

(b) Operant conditioning/trial and error learning *(1 mark)*.

(c) The frequency with which it pressed lever A would gradually decrease *(1 mark)*.

3 (a) Sounds — because the birds can't see each other very well through the trees *(1 mark)*.

(b) E.g. through smell/chemicals *(1 mark)*, such as pheromones/scent markings *(1 mark)*.

4 (a) Communication without language/through physical gestures or expressions *(1 mark)*.

(b) A — disgust *(1 mark)*, B — saying "no" *(1 mark)*, C — surprise *(1 mark)*.

(c) B is learned, A and C are inherited *(1 mark)*.

5 (a) Inherited *(1 mark)*, because it is performed by different bees all over the world *(1 mark)*.

(b) It helps the bees to find food for the hive more easily *(1 mark)*.

6 (a) It was a control experiment to check that the dogs don't naturally produce saliva at the sound of a bell *(1 mark)*.
Obviously this is pretty unlikely, but an important part of being a scientist is being incredibly fussy and trying to rule out every other possible explanation of the results.

(b) (i) The dogs produce saliva on seeing and smelling the food *(1 mark)* and are learning to associate the sound of the bell with being given food *(1 mark)*.

(ii) The dogs at first continue to produce saliva when the bell is rung *(1 mark)*, but without the food the effect is lost eventually *(1 mark)*.

(c) Classical conditioning is passive learning/learning without trying, whereas operant conditioning is active learning/learning by trial and error *(1 mark)*.

Page 260

Warm-Up Questions

1) An organism that eats meat.

2) To help them judge distance accurately when catching prey.

3) Because plants are low in essential nutrients, so they have to eat a lot of them to get the quantities they need.

4) Mammals and birds.

5) Any one of, e.g. Chimpanzees use twigs to get ants out of holes/honey from beehives/to dig up roots / Woodpecker finches use cactus spines to get grubs out of tree bark / Vultures throw stones at egg shells to break them / Nuthatches use pieces of bark to pry under tree bark and find insects / Crows use hooked twigs to pull grubs from inside tree trunks / White-winged choughs use pieces of mussel shell as hammers to open other mussels.
Crows in Japan have been seen deliberately placing nuts in front of waiting traffic so that the cars drive over the nuts and break them open. The crows then fly down and carry the opened nuts away to eat. Of course, this doesn't strictly count as tool use since the cars are not used as an extension of the birds' bodies. But it's pretty clever.

ANSWERS

Exam Questions

1 B *(1 mark)*
What the thrush is doing doesn't count because it is not using the stone as an extension of its body.

2 (a) (i) Any one of, e.g. The wildebeest has eyes at the sides of its head so it can see all around it and spot predators / It has large ears so that it can hear a predator approaching *(1 mark)*.

   (ii) It has sharp horns *(1 mark)*.

   (b) Any one of, e.g. At any time, some members of the group will not be feeding but will be looking around (so they can spot predators) / Each individual wildebeest has a good chance of the predator picking a different target in its herd *(1 mark)*.
   This can be a hard idea to explain, but if a wildebeest is alone and encounters a predator it will be the only target. If it's in a group, there's likely to be somebody else younger, older, sicker or weaker who is an easier target.

3 (a) (i) The pecking of the chick *(1 mark)*.

   (ii) The red spot on the parent's beak *(1 mark)*.

   (b) (i) Determined by genes rather than experience/innate *(1 mark)*.

   (ii) So that it can start feeding as soon as it hatches — if it had to wait to learn the behaviour by trial and error, it might starve first *(1 mark)*.

Page 265

Warm-Up Questions

1) Any one of, e.g. birds (or a named example) / whales / crickets / frogs.

2) Any two of, e.g. releasing chemicals / displaying aggression / courtship displays (or named example, e.g. dancing, posturing) / building a nest / providing gifts.

3) Any two of, e.g. By protecting them from predators / Providing a shelter / Teaching them skills.

4) Any two of, e.g. More of the young survive / Young can be less developed when they are born, which is less risky than a longer pregnancy for the mother / More of the parental genes are passed on to future generations.

Exam Questions

1 (a) Staying with just one mate *(1 mark)*.

   (b) Any two of, e.g. It ensures the animals are of the same species, not two similar ones / It ensures that both animals are ready to mate / It helps the animals (usually the female) to choose a strong and fertile mate *(1 mark each)*.

2 (a) (i) Two of the fertilised eggs need to survive for the population size to stay constant *(1 mark)*, so:
   $(2 \div 200) \times 100 = 1\%$ (or 1/100) *(1 mark)*
   This was tricky so don't worry if you slipped up. You'll know now if you get something similar in the exam — for a population to stay the same size, each animal has to replace itself, so a particular pair need to produce an average of two surviving offspring over their lifetimes.

   (ii) herring *(1 mark)*

   (b) The blackbird *(1 mark)*, because the number of eggs is lowest and so good parental care is needed to ensure a good survival rate *(1 mark)*.

3 (a) Any one of, e.g. To reduce the competition for food/mates in his area / To show potential mates that he is strong and fit enough to defend a territory from other males *(1 mark)*.

   (b) E.g. it might attract females/show them he is fertile/ready to mate *(1 mark)*.

Page 272

Warm-Up Questions

1) Animals that feed on detritus (partly broken down bits of plant or animal tissue).

2) Advantage: Any one of, e.g. There is a plentiful supply of water / There are generally no sudden temperature changes / The water provides support / Waste materials are easily dispersed.

   Disadvantage: Any one of, e.g. More energy is required in order to move about / Animals have to constantly regulate the amount of water in their bodies / It is harder to get oxygen.

3) Through simple lungs and also through the skin.

4) Any one of, e.g. They are highly folded to give a large surface area for gas exchange / They have a good blood supply.

Exam Questions

1 (a) They decompose dead matter into ammonium compounds *(1 mark)*.

   (b) They convert ammonium compounds into nitrates *(1 mark)*.

2 (a) The cells of the animal are likely to contain a higher solute concentration than the surrounding water *(1 mark)*. Without water regulation, water molecules would enter the cells, causing them to swell and burst *(1 mark)*.

   (b) The cells of the animal are likely to contain a lower solute concentration than the surrounding water *(1 mark)*. Without water regulation, water molecules would leave the cells, causing them to shrivel and die *(1 mark)*.
   Remember, water particles always move to try and even up the concentration on the two sides of the membrane.

   (c) The contractile vacuole stores the water that diffuses into the amoeba by osmosis *(1 mark)*. It is regularly emptied to get rid excess water *(1 mark)*.

3 (a) May *(1 mark)*

   (b) (i) Any one of, e.g. the water is warmer / there is more light *(1 mark)*.

   (ii) The plankton are growing and reproducing very quickly in the summer, so they take up a lot of phosphate (an essential nutrient) *(1 mark)*.

   (c) This should be a point soon after the peak in the phytoplankton population — accept anywhere from June to September *(1 mark)*.

Page 277

Warm-Up Questions

1) About 200 000 years ago.

2) To help them when hunting, or to guard camps/settlements.

3) Any two of, e.g. Leather for shoes / Skins for fur coats / Wool for woolly clothes.

4) Any one of, e.g. Animals can be used to produce antibodies for vaccines / They can be genetically modified so that they secrete drugs in their milk / They can provide organs for transplants.

5) Because intensive farming can be cruel to animals — they have to live in cramped, unnatural conditions, can't go outside, may be more susceptible to injury and disease, etc.

Exam Questions

1 D — *Australopithecus afarensis* *(1 mark)*.

2 (a) Any one of, e.g. By riding them / Using them to transport food, tools and other belongings / Using them to help with farm work / As a source of food *(1 mark)*.

   (b) Any one of, e.g.
   Dogs *(1 mark)*, for hunting / companionship / protection *(1 mark)*.
   Cattle *(1 mark)*, for meat / milk / ploughing *(1 mark)*.
   Sheep *(1 mark)*, for meat / milk / clothing *(1 mark)*.
   Goats *(1 mark)*, for meat / milk / clothing *(1 mark)*.

3 (a) Any one of, e.g. To check that it is safe to use / To see if it works / To find out more about possible side effects *(1 mark)*.

   (b) Any two of, e.g. It causes the animals to suffer / It is wrong to exploit animals for human benefit / It is unfair to use animals as they can't agree to the tests — human volunteers should be used instead / A slimming treatment is an unnecessary luxury / Animals tests are not a good guide to the drug's effects on humans *(1 mark each)*.

   (c) Some drugs are life-saving and/or may be used in treating sick animals, but others (like Slimmo) are not *(1 mark)*.

Index

Index

Index